Statistics for textiles
and
apparel management

Statistics for textiles
and
apparel management

J. Hayavadana

WOODHEAD PUBLISHING INDIA PVT LTD
New Delhi ● Cambridge ● Oxford ● Philadelphia

Published by Woodhead Publishing India Pvt. Ltd.
Woodhead Publishing India Pvt. Ltd., G-2, Vardaan House, 7/28, Ansari Road
Daryaganj, New Delhi – 110002, India
www.woodheadpublishingindia.com

Woodhead Publishing Limited, 80 High Street, Sawston, Cambridge,
CB22 3HJ UK

Woodhead Publishing USA 1518 Walnut Street, Suite1100, Philadelphia

www.woodheadpublishing.com

First published 2012, Woodhead Publishing India Pvt. Ltd.
© Woodhead Publishing India Pvt. Ltd., 2012

Woodhead Publishing India Pvt. Ltd. ISBN: 978-93-80308-04-3
Woodhead Publishing Ltd. ISBN: 978-0-85709-002-7

Typeset by Sunshine Graphics, New Delhi
Printed and bound by Sanat Printers, Kundli.

Contents

Foreword

The role played by statistical techniques in any production system can never be underestimated.

As a matter of fact, in textile production both online and offline quality control techniques are used, and it is needless to say that the apparel industry will be very much benefited by the capability studies, which are purely based on statistical concepts.

Statistical evaluation of the process carried out help us in evaluating the process and eventually increasing the efficiency of the process by alteration of the conditions.

Keeping in view the need for a comprehensive approach to infuse zeal to learn, this book is written in a lucid manner by Prof. J. Hayavadana, Head Textile Technology, University College of Technology (Autonomous), Osmania University, Hyderabad.

The book essentially caters to the need of the students at all levels of textile education. Concepts have been derived from the basics. One specialty of the book is that the topics have been dealt with examples at appropriate stages, and concepts have been demonstrated with worked out examples.

It is imperative that the understanding of any subject is essentially dependent on the person studying but access to study material should be simple on explanation and act as a guide to full of information. The book incorporates both these requirements.

The book is divided in to 11 chapters and in each chapter examples from spinning, weaving and apparel production are covered.

I am sure that this book would be a source of knowledge, and my overall evaluation of the book is positive. I assure that students, staff and technologists working in the industry would find this book very useful.

Dr. P. S. Sampath Kumaran
Retd. Deputy Director
Indian Institute of Chemical Technology
Hyderabad

Preface

I am pleased to release my first book titled "Statistics for Textiles and Apparel Management" to my textile fraternity. Indeed it is a common experience of a student to feel shortage of textile books as compared to other fields and it is a fact also. Statistics is such an important subject without which the business world would have perished. Any product development or production without quality control is like a lifeless object. Textile production is not an exception and any research concludes its results using statistical techniques.

It was my long cherished dream to write a book on statistical methods for textile production and it took nearly 6 years to finalise the topics and book.

The book primarily caters the need to learn basics of statistics in textile production. The book is organized in 11 chapters with examples at each point of discussion. I hope that book will leave up to the expectations of textile world. Any help in the form of suggestions or guidelines, etc., in improving the quality of the book is highly appreciable and will be suitably acknowledged.

Introduction to statistics in textiles

1.1 Introduction

Statistics is not a new discipline but as old as human society itself. It is not exaggerative if mentioned that no part of technology or social sciences, life sciences, sports or medical sciences, etc., is completed if statistical methods are not used in understanding various concepts. Statistics has been in use since the existence of life on earth. In olden days statistics was regarded as the "Science of Statecraft", but today it is defined as a tool for scientific management, where the decisions are based on the use of statistical tools irrespective of the type of the business activity practiced. Any research study is incomplete if statistics is not applied. 'Statistics' in its connotation is a system of methods or techniques employed for making decisions in the case of uncertainty. Statistics is used for the collection, analysis and interpretation of data in order to provide a basis for making correct decisions. Statistics can be used either in numerical data from or as statistical methods. Statistical methods include all those devices that are used in collection and simplification of large numerical data in such a way that the data is analyzed and understood without difficulty. In short, statistics finds use wherever a mass of quantitative data needs simplification and analysis for meaningful interpretation. Experimental methods are differentiated from statistical methods as the former include the study of various parameters at selected levels. For example, effect of drafting systems with ranges of draft, drafting elements, drafting roller pressures, etc., on yarn quality. But statistical methods are applied to study the effect of the parameters on yarn quality in understanding their significant effect.

The very word 'Statistics' is said to have been derived from Latin word 'Status' or the Italian word 'Statista' or the German word 'Startistik' or the French word 'Statistique' means a political state. In olden days the scope of statistics was limited to only collection of social data which may be governmental or economical for many years. The word 'Statistics' was associated mainly with the analysis of facts and figures to the economic, demographic and political situations prevailing in a country.

Statistics is defined as follows:

It is the aggregate of facts affected to a marked extent by multiplicity of causes numerically expressed, enumerated or estimated according to the reasonable standards of accuracy, collected in a systematic manner for a pre-determined purpose and placed in relation to each other.

Boddington defines statistics as the science of "estimates and probabilities".

Lovitt defines statistics as "the science that deals with the collection, classification and tabulation of numerical facts as the basis for explanation, description and comparison of phenomena".

Statistics is used in the form of statistical methods, applied statistics, descriptive applied statistics and scientific applied statistics. The word "statistics" means numerical statement of data collected from various sources; use of scientific methods to analyze the collected data for quick, accurate and easy interpretation; a measure to evaluate the data collected.

The above facts can be very well understood if examples from textile/apparel field are considered:

1. The production of a synthetic fibre (staple fibre) or filament (partially oriented yarn) or twisted yarn or finished fabric from a firm (here statistics is referred for analyzing the data collected).
2. Consider two yarns are produced from the same mixing but spun on the same or different frames. The objective is to find whether the two yarns produced on the same frame are differing or the frames are differing. This can be very well understood by analyzing the data and using a suitable statistical tool like significance testing (here statistics is used to represent the statistical methods).
3. Consider analysis of plain fabric samples with observations of threads per cm, crimps (warp × weft) and count (warp × weft) to assess the nature of clothes as warp faced, light weight, medium weight or heavy weight, close set, open set, etc. (here statistics is used to analyze the set of observations).

The word "statistics" is used as plural and singular. In its plural form it refers to the numerical data collected in a systematic manner with some definite objective. In singular form, it means the science of statistics or the subject itself including the methods, principles with collection, analysis and interpretation of numerical data under consideration. Statistics is defined in many ways. One of the simple ways is to define statistics as a "science of collecting, presenting, analyzing and interpretation of numerical data under consideration". A number of definitions are made available in the statistics books and the reader is instructed to refer in case of need. However, in modern days, statistics is viewed not only as mere devise for collecting the numerical data but also as means of developing techniques for their analysis and interpretation and thus drawing interferences on scientific basis. To understand this one can consider production of several types of garments produced by typical apparel units to select the best group of readymade garments using multivariate analysis technique with or without the help of SPSS.

1.2 Salient features of statistics

Statistics is a multifacinated subject applicable to all types of production/ testing/manufacturing processes.

1. The data collected can be expressed as primary or secondary data.
2. In the research data, the present shift can be calculated helping in understanding the effect of change made in the substrate (e.g., the changes in bending – length/drape). Crease recovery angle from control to finished/changed state can be understood by computing percent shift. Positive or negative value of shift is interpreted according to the property under consideration).
3. The data helps in understanding about the population.
4. In textile production, statistics forms the basis for process settings and process control.
5. Statistics is the aggregate of facts.
6. Statistical data is expressed numerically and thus has a potential for further editing, retrieving or processing.

1.3 Functions of statistics

1. The techniques of statistics examine the relationship between the variables (e.g., relation between thickness and air permeability; rigidity and drape; load and elongation; threads/inch and cover factor, etc.).
2. The method of statistics aims in simplifying the complex data (for e.g., consider the selection of polyester dress materials of two groups, low and high twisted, and these samples be heat set at various temperatures in stenter in tant and black form. Subsequently scored or weight reduced with a number of parameters like material to liquor ratio, caustic%, etc, leading to a great or larger sample size. Let these fabrics be tested for 16 mechanical properties of KES-F and FAST. It is necessary for an experimenter to select best fabric in terms of THV or TAV. The statistical data is analyzed systematically for results).
3. Statistics aims at comparison of two different processes (for e.g., comparing the efficiency and properties of conventional and enzyme-scoured fabrics).

4. It presents the experimental data in a simple form.
5. It helps in decision-making process as the techniques are used in forecasting and planning.
6. Statistics also help in designing, framing policies for different types of management in government or business organizations.
7. Variability in any process can very well be analyzed or studied by using statistical tools.

1.4   Applications of statistical tools in various processing stages of textile production

1.4.1   Fibre production

Measures of central tendency like process average gives an idea about average staple length of fibre produced in a continuous or batch wise process. Coefficient of variation (CV) of the process signifies about the process control. On the other hand, analysis of time series is helpful in estimating the future production based on the past records.

Measures of dispersion such as standard deviation and CV are useful in comparing the performance of two or more fibre-producing units or processes. Significance tests can also be applied to investigate whether significant difference exists between the batches for means or standard deviations. Analysis of variance can be applied for studying the effect of parameters of fibre production and methods of polymer dissolving.

1.4.2   Textile testing of fibres, yarns and fabrics

Results analysis in textile testing without the applications of statistical tools will be meaningless. In other words every experiment in textile testing include the use of statistical tools like average calculation, computation of SD, CV and application of tests of significance (t-test, z-test and f-test) or analysis of variance (one way, two way or design of experiments). Populations can be very well studied by normal or binomial or Poisson's distributions. Random sampling errors are used in studying about the population mean and SD at 95% and 99% level of confidence. Application geometric mean for finding out the overall flexural rigidity or G_o has an important role in fabric selection for garment manufacture.

A special mention is made in determination of fibre length by bear sorter where all the measures of central tendency and dispersion (mean length, modal length quartile deviation, etc., in the form of frequency distribution) are computed to understand about the cotton sample under consideration for testing its potential in yarn manufacture. On the other hand ball sledge sorter uses weight distribution from which mean and

SD are computed. In the case of cotton fibres, the development of cell wall thickening commonly referred as "Maturity" concept can be very well determined using normal distribution and confidence intervals. Several properties are tested for different packages produced from the same material or from the same frame by applying significance tests. Effect of instruments and variables for different types of samples can be very well studied by using ANOVA. All the fabric properties tested on a single instrument or different instrument can be understood by using design of experiments. In one of the research applications, which include the testing of low stress mechanical properties for nearly 1000 fabrics are studied by 'Principle Bi component analysis or Bi plot'. Measures of dispersion like coefficient of variation and percentage mean deviation are very much used in evenness measurement.

1.4.3   Yarn production

There are several stages involved in the cotton yarn production. When fibres are mixed and processed through blow room, within and between lap variations are studied by computing mean, SD and CV lap rejection, and production control are studied by $\bar{p}$ and $\bar{x}$ charts. Average measure is used to find the hank of silver in carding, draw frame, combing and average hank of roving in roving frame and average count at ring frame. Generally the spinning mill use 'average count' as the count specification if it is producing 4–5 counts. On the other hand the weaving section uses 'resultant count' which is nothing but the harmonic mean of the counts produced. Control charts are extensively used in each and every process of yarn production (for example, the process control with respect to thin places, neps, etc.). Application of probability distributions like Poisson, Weibull and binomial for various problems in spinning is found very much advantageous to understand the end breakage concept. In ring spinning section several ring bobbins are collected and tested for CSP and difference between the bobbins and within the bobbins is studied using 'range' method. In cone winding section the process control can be checked either by using control chart for averages or chart for number defectives.

1.4.4   Fabric production

Design of experiments such as latin square design or randomized block design can be used to identify the effect of different size ingredients on wrap breakages on different looms in fabric formation. Most of the suiting fabric constructions involve the use of double yarn which is nothing but the harmonic mean of different counts. Poisson's and normal distribution can be applied for loom shed for warp breakages. Using statistical techniques the interference loss can also be studied in loom shed. Various weaving parameters such as loom speed, reed and pick can be correlated with corresponding fabric properties and are interpreted in terms of loom parameters. Control charts are used to study the control of process/product quality in fabric production also. For example, selection of defective cones in a pirn winding from a lot (fixed population) or in a production shift n $\bar{p}$ and $\bar{p}$ charts are used. The width of the cloth and its control can be understood by $\bar{x}$ and defectives per unit length and their control is understood by $\bar{c}$ charts. The testing process includes determination of average tensile strength (and single thread strength also) and the corresponding CV%.

1.4.5   Chemical processing and garment production

The scope of statistics is unlimited. For example the effect of n number washes (identical conditions) on m fabrics on a particular fabric property can be easily found by either tests of significance or analysis of variance. Similarly the effect of different detergents on fabric types can be investigated by two-way analysis of variance. Similarly different types of fabrics and the effect of sewing conditions can be studied by ANOVA.

In garment production the control of measurements and its distribution can be well understood by control and polar charts.

1.5   Scope of statistical techniques in textile production

The scope of statistics in analyzing the performance of machines or equipments is mentioned below.

1.5.1   Measures of central tendency and frequency distribution

Study of average pick spacing, average count in two or more spinning mills, average weft insertion rate in shuttles looms, less than or more than ogives for computing the number of end breaks in weaving and ring spinning, cumulative frequency of fibre length and fabric GSM, fineness by torsion balance measurement, number of defective rolls of fabric, bivariate frequency distribution of single thread strength or tensile strength and elongation plotting of idle time and down time of spindles in ring frame, yarn clearing and tensioning in cone winding, frequency distribution of linear density of yarns, end breaks in winding, warping, etc.

Use of mean in wettability of fabrics, felting of wool test, fibre length distribution in different bales, permanganate values (in ppm) of a dye effluent factory, distribution showing time taken for doffing and donning in ring frame, and winding, warping and sizing processes; calculation of mean length of garments in garment unit. Geometric mean is used in one of the incentive wage payment system, and weighted mean is used in fibre length distribution. Mean is also used to know the mean yarn tpi in a mill producing wide range of twisted yarns.

1.5.2   Use of standard error, confidence intervals

Standard error is used for sample mean and population and hence the limits are known.

Standard error and CV also give an idea about the number of tests to be carried out to keep the error at a known level.

The concept is also useful to known the limits of moisture content of yarn sample. The same explanation also holds good in case of linear density, extension at break, etc.

1.5.3   Statistical distributions

Normal, Poisson's and binomial distributions are applied in most of the testing cases like water proof or rain coat, to find the average number of coats that are expected to be water proof or probability of coats failing in the test or machine break downs, end breaks in weaving, end breaks in ring spinning, etc. When a roll of fabrics is checked for defects, by using these probability distributions, it is possible to know whether the price will contain more than one defect or no defects.

1.5.4   Correlation and regression

Correlation between fibre maturity and micronaire values can be found by Karl Pearson's co-efficient. Correlation is applied for determining the correlation between:

(i)   Dye up take and fibre structure.
(ii)   Drafting roller pressure and imperfections.
(iii) Bleaching (whiteness index) and dye up take.

Regression analysis is applied in different situations. Some of the examples are the following:

(i)   Relation between processing tension and modules of tire cord yarns.
(ii)   Shrink-resist finish and percent area shrinkage.

(iii) Relation between loop length and course/unit length in plain knitted fabrics.
(iv) Thickness and bending rigidity of yarn and fabrics.
 (v) Fabric drape vs fabric bending length.
(vi) Relation between the relative viscosity of dye liquor and dye up take on the fabric.

1.5.5 Application of other statistical techniques to textile problems

Following are the some of the statistical methods applied to study the textile problems.

(1) Factor analysis
(2) Cluster analysis
(3) Duncan multiple range test
(4) Multiple regressional analysis
(5) Principle component analysis
(6) Weibull distribution (Applied to study yarn or fabric fatigue mechanism and end breaks at ring spinning)

Factor and cluster analysis

To understand better application of these techniques consider the following problem. Let there be 6 groups of fabrics identical in geometric properties be subjected to various chemical treatments like sourcing, bleaching, mercerizing etc. Let at least 3–4 levels of parameters be selected in each of these processes. Following the treatment, fabrics were subjected to handle measurement. Factor analysis provides the investigator about the idea of factors most responsible for the change in the fabric properties following treatment. Similarly cluster analysis lists those properties which influence the fabric behaviour when considered as 2 clusters or 3 clusters and so on.

Duncan's multiple range test

This test is applied only when the ANOVA confirms about the existence of significant differences among or between the treatments or both. To understand this test, consider a study in which a nominal count say 30 spun with 3 levels of simplex drafts and 3 levels of drafts at ring frame i.e., in total there will be 9 combinations. Let the samples be subjected to measurement of yarn properties like CSP, CCSP, U%, single thread strength CV%, imperfections count, etc. ANOVA can be carried out to investigate the effect of treatments on the property under consideration. If ANOVA confirms the significant difference, range factor q is computed and compared to actual range and if calculated q value is greater than the actual, the values are subjected to ranking. The ranks are given depending on the variable nature. Finally the ranks are multiplied by the weight factors fixed for the parameter based on the end use. The combination which possesses highest value can be concluded as significant combination.

Multiple regressional analysis

This technique is useful to a case study as considered in serial number 1 and 2. In THV measurement a fabric is subjected to various deformations like tensile, shear, bending, compression, and surface etc. Primary hand values are computed from these deformations using regressional analysis.

Principle component analysis (PCA)

This is also known as Biplot and could be applied where the population size is large. For example, consider about 700 fabric samples selected for THV measurement. Those fabrics may include different substrates differing in geometry and treatment. PCA gives the distribution of fabric samples in clusters across the 4 quadrants depending on the nature of the fabric and the properties measured.

1.6   Limitations of statistics

Although statistics is indispensable to almost all stages in textile/apparel production, but some limitations restrict its scope and utility. Following are some of the limitations:

(1) *Statistics does not study qualitative phenomena.* As statistics is a science dealing with a set of large/small numerical data, it can be applied to those studies only which can be measured quantitatively. Thus, statements like "production of 2/20s honey comb towels has increased considerably during the last decade" or "the cost of living in Tirupur is very high as compared to Coimbatore" do not constitute statistics. In other words, statistics is not suitable in the study of qualitative phenomena such as beauty, rich, honesty, etc. However, they can be assigned some weightage based on their significance and can be processed further. For example, the intelligence of a group can be better understood on the basis of intelligence quotient.

(2) *Statistics does not study individuals.* A single or isolated figure can't be regarded as statistics unless it is a part of the aggregate of facts related to a particular field. Statistical methods do not consider an

object or person or an event in isolation. For example, the production of a synthetic fibre by a manufacturing unit for a particular year does not serve any purpose or does not yield any information, unless we are given the same information for different years or similar companies.

(3) *Statistical laws are not exact.* The statistical laws are not as perfect as laws of physics or chemistry, since statistics laws are probabilistic in nature; inferences based on them are only approximate and are not like the inferences based on mathematical or scientific laws.

(4) *Statistical results are true only in case of average.*

(5) *Statistics is collected with a given purpose and so it can't be applied to any other situation.*

(6) *Statistics relations may not result in cause and effect relationship.*

(7) *Statistics are liable to be misused.* According to characteristics, it must be used only be experts and not by unskilled or dishonest workers. For example, the figures may be changed or manipulated or moulded by politicians or antisocial elements for personal or selfish motives. Statistics neither proves nor disproves anything. If statistics is used by unskilled workers, the interpretation of results may prove to be disastrous.

(8) *Statistics does not reveal the entire story.*

Treatment of data and construction of frequency distribution

2.1 Introduction

In practice there are number of methods available for collecting the data for a specific purpose. In doing so, the first step is to organise the data for better understanding. The organisation of figures should be in such a form that their significance, purpose, etc., may be appreciated well through comparison with masses of similar origin, so that the data may be processed further to reveal some information. This is possible through a systematic classification process and subsequently tabulation of data. Following this the data need to be arranged in a form for an easy composition, further to understand the concept. The data collected from any method are raw, voluminous, huge and uncompressible. Classification and tabulation present the data in a more comprehensive and condensed form highlighting important characteristics of the data collected. Generally in classification, items having common characteristics are grouped together prior to the tabulation. In other words, classification refers to the grouping of data into homogeneous classes and categories. In classification process the data are arranged into sequences and groups according to their common characteristics or separating them into different related parts.

Following are the objectives of classification:

1. To condense the mass data
2. To enable grasp of data
3. To prepare the data for tabulation
4. To study the relationships
5. To facilitate the comparison

However, some basic rules are followed for a good classification; these are listed below:

1. *Exhaustive*: Classification must be exhaustive in which each and every data must be belonging to one of the classes. Description like 'residual class', 'rest', 'other classes' should be avoided.
2. *Mutually exclusive*: The classes should not overlap.

3. *Suitability*: Classification should confirm to the object of inquiry.
4. *Stability*: The basic principle of classification should be retained throughout the study.
5. *Homogeneity*: Items included in each class must be homogenised.
6. *Flexibility*: A good classification is the one which is flexible.

2.2   Statistical series

The quantitative classification of the data include 'variable', which is defined as the parameter that can be expressed through measurement. For example, micronaire value of cotton, count of warp and weft, count strength product, etc. The variable normally assumes a range of values within certain limits. Variables may be 'discrete' or 'continuous' in nature. A discrete variable is characterised by jumps and gaps between the values. For example, end breakages in ring spinning, warp breaks in loom, warp breaks in warping, etc., i.e., discrete variable takes integral values depending on the type of variable under study. On the other hand continuous variables are those which can take all possible values (integral as well as fractional) in a given specified range. For example, the CSP of leas, new count in leap, GSM of fabrics, count of yarn, fibre length, etc.

Similarly, it is necessary to consider the measures of series in statistics. It can be defined as quantitative values. A series, as used statistically, may also be defined as things and attributes of things arranged according to some logical order. Various types of series are expressed in a chart as follows:

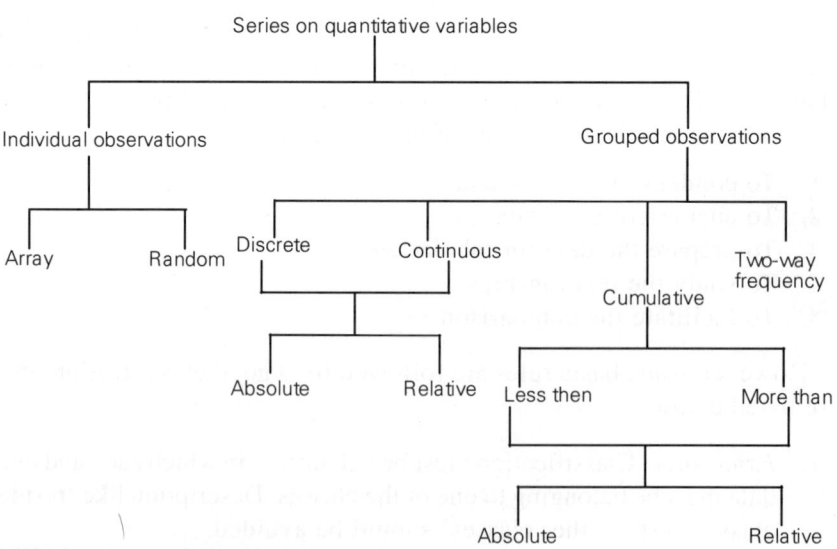

2.1 Series on quantitative variables.

2.3   Classification and tabulation

2.3.1   Data, types and collection

Data are the information collected through various means (censuses or surveys) in a routine/systematic manner. Data are referred as 'raw' when the information collected/ recorded can't be used directly or immediately. In other words, it is necessary to convert the raw data into suitable form so as to understand about the process for which the information is straight.

Data may be primary or secondary. Primary data are collected by a particular person or organisation from the primary source. Secondary data are collected by some other person or organisation for their own but also get it for their use. In other words, data can be primary for one person and secondary for the other.

2.4   Methods of collecting primary data

Following are the methods of collecting primary data:

1. *Direct personal observation*: In this method the investigator collects the data personally. Accuracy or errors depend on several factors.
2. *Indirect oral investigation*: The investigator collects the data indirectly. The third person is contacted for the information. We normally observe this in the form of enquiry commissions or committees appointed by the government.
3. *From correspondents/local sources*: Agents are appointed to collect the data. The accuracy depends on the network of person.
4. *By questionnaires.*

2.5   Methods of collecting secondary data

Secondary data are collected through Internet, periodicals, newspapers, trade journals, R&D institutes, research papers, UGC, central/state letters, national or international institutions.

2.6   Classification of data

The primary data are a raw data and need conversion/modification or classification so as to process further. The process of arranging the things in a group of classes according to their common characteristics and affinities is called 'classification of data'. The basis of classification may be any one of the bases given below:

1. Qualitative
2. Quantitative (numerical size based)

3. Temporal or chronological or historical
4. Geographical

2.7   Tabulation

This is the last stage in the compilation. After the data have been collected and classified, it is necessary to arrange them in proper tables with rows and columns. Tabulation is defined as a scientific process used in setting out the collected data in an understandable form. Even though there are no hard and fast rules for constructing a table, it is necessary to prepare the table to get maximum benefits from least efforts. Following are the guidelines:

1. A rough draft of table should be prepared first
2. Figures to be placed/arranged nearer to each other
3. Heading of the table should be self-explanatory
4. Number the rows and columns for better readability
5. Giving the footnotes is necessary

2.7.1   Examples on tabulation

Example (1): In a co-operative spinning mill, data were collected of graduate disciplines in textile technology and comprised both men and women, respectively. In 1990 the total number of workers was 2000, out of which 1400 were diploma cadre, 100 were women; however in all there were 600 women working in the mill. In 1995 number of diploma cadre was increased to 1700, out of which 250 were women, but the number of graduates falls to 500 of which 50 were men. In 2000, out of 800 women, 650 were diploma cadre, whereas the total number of diploma was 2200. The number of men and women graduates was equal. Represent the above information in tabular form and calculate the percentage increase in the number of graduate workers in 2000 as compared to 1990.

Percentage increase in graduation in 2000 as compared to 1990 =

$$= \left(\frac{2200 - 1400}{1400} \right) \times 100 = 57.14\%$$

Table 2.1 Table showing worker details according to education and sex (1990–2000)

Year	Diploma		Total	Graduation		Total	Grand total
	Men	Women	(a)	Men	Women	(b)	(a + b)
1990	1300	100	1400	100	500	600	2000
1995	1450	250	1700	50	450	500	2200
2000	1550	650	2200	150	150	300	2500
Total	**4300**	**1000**	**5300**	**300**	**1100**	**1400**	**6700**

Example (2): Out of total number of 2807 women who were interviewed for employment in a textile unit, 912 were from textile areas and the rest from non-textile areas. Amongst the married women, who belonged to textile areas, 347 were having some work experience and 173 did not have work experience, while in for non-textile areas the corresponding figures were 199 and 670, respectively. The total number of women having no experience was 1841 of whom 311 resided in textile areas; of the total number of women 1418 were unmarried, and the number of women having experience in the textiles and non-textile areas was 254 and 166, respectively. Information is tabulated below.

Table 2.2 Distribution of workers according to marital status, experience

	Textile			Non-textile			Total		
	Expe-rience	No expe-rience	Total	Expe-rience	No expe-rience	Total	Expe-rience	No expe-rience	Total
Married	347	173	520	199	670	869	546	843	1389
Unmarried	257	138	392	166	860	1026	420	998	1418
Total	**601**	**311**	**912**	**365**	**1530**	**1895**	**966**	**1841**	**2807**

Example (3): In 1995 out of total 4000 workers in a textile factory, 3300 were members of a trade union. The number of women workers was 500 out of which 400 did not belong to the union. In 1994, the number of workers in the union was 3450 out of which 3200 were men. The number of workers not belonging to the union was 3450 out of which 3200 were men. The number of workers not belonging to the union was 760 out of which 300 were women. Tabulate the information.

Table 2.3 Distribution of workers by sex and membership (1944–95)

	1994			1995		
	Men	Women	Total	Men	Women	Total
Members of union	3200	250	3450	3200	100	3300
Non-members	430	330	760	300	400	700
Total	**3630**	**580**	**4210**	**3500**	**500**	**4000**

2.8   Problems for practice

1. Out of the total number of 1798 women, who were interviewed for employment in a textile factory, 512 were from textile areas and the rest were from non-textile areas. Amongst the married women who belonged to textile areas, 247 were experienced and 73 were inexperienced. While in non-textile areas the corresponding figures were 40 and 520. The total number of inexperience women was 1341,

out of which 111 resides in textile areas; of the total number of women 918 were unmarried; and the number of experienced women in the textile and non-textile areas was 154 and 16, respectively. Tabulate the information.

2. In 1985, out of 1750 workers of a textile factory, 1200 workers were the members of trade union. The number of women employed was 200 of which 175 did not belong to the union. In 1990, the number of union workers increased to 1510 out of which 1290 were men. On the other hand, the number of non-union workers fell down to 208 out of which 180 were men. In 1995, there were 1800 employees on the payroll, who belong to a trade union and 50 who did not. Of all the employees in 1995, 300 were women of whom only 8 did not belong to trade union.

2.9   Construction of frequency distribution

Statistical data are collected in order to understand easily and accordingly conclusion can be drawn. When data are presented in tables or charts in order to bring out their salient features, it is called the presentation of data.

In other words, the method to condense the data in a tabular form to study their salient features is known as presentation of data.

The collected data is converted into frequency distribution table having columns like variant, tally mark and frequency. Following are some of the terms related to the construction of frequency distribution:

1. *Raw data*: It's a statistical data in original form before any statistical techniques are applied to characteristic the data.

2. *Variate*: It's a character which varies from one individual to another. They may be qualitative or quantitative. Variables may be continuous or discrete in nature. A continuous variable is capable of assuming any value within certain range or interval.

   For example, the moisture region of textile fibres can be expressed not only in the integral part but also in fractions.

   A discrete variable can assume only integral values and is capable of finding out exact measurement, or in other words discrete variables are those which assume only a finite set of value. Discrete variables are also called as discontinuous variables. When continuous variables are arranged in series, it is known as continuous series and similarly the discrete series.

3. *Frequency*: The number of times an observation occurs in the given data is called as frequency.

4. *Frequency distribution*: It is the arrangement of the given data in the

form of table showing frequency with a variable. In other words, frequency distribution of a variable x is the order set (x, f), where 'f' is the frequency.

5. *Class*: The given information is divided into groups which are bounded by limits. The end value of a class is called as class limits. The smaller one is known as 'lower limit' and the other one is 'upper limit'.

   For example, picks/inch in 20 fabrics were recorded as primary data or raw data as follows:

   28, 38, 48, 18, 44, 58, 54, 64, 74, 22, 32, 18, 33, 23, 25, 29, 28, 35, 39, 42

   For the array mentioned above, the class limits may be 0–10, 10–20, 20–30, 30–40, 40–50, 50–60, 60–70, 70–80.

6. *Class interval (CI)*: The difference between lower limit (L) and upper limit (U) of a class is known as class interval, i.e. $I = U - L$. In other words the range of class is CI. Referring to above, it may be stated that there are 8 class intervals which are arranged. However, there are some guidelines for forming a definite number of class intervals.

   The class intervals may be constructed in inclusive or exclusive ways. These are further explained as follows:

   (a) *Inclusive method*: When the CI is so fixed that the upper limit of the class is included in that class, it is known as inclusive method. For example, the loom spades are recorded as
        130–139, 140–149, 150–159 rpm
        It is clear that all CI under inclusive methods form discontinuous series.

   (b) *Exclusive method*: When the class interval is so fixed that the upper limit of one CI is a lower limit of the next CI. The common point of two classes is included in the higher class. For example, fabric GSM 10–15, 15–20, 20–25, etc., a value like 15 is included in 15–20 class rather than 10–15 class.

7. *Class limit*: They are upper and lower limits of a class.

   Correction factor is necessary to convert an inclusive CI as an exclusive or continuous CI. For this purpose, a correction factor is calculated and subtracted from the lower limit and added to upper limit. In other words, Real Class boundaries are formed.

   Correction factor = ½ × difference between upper and lower limits. Real Class boundaries are also known as actual or true class limits.

   For example: 11–20, 21–30 will be with true class limits as 10.5–20.5, 20.5–30.5, etc.

8. *Range*: It is the difference between the largest and smallest number in the given data. Range is useful in calculating the number of CI.

9. *Class mark/midpoint/ mid value*: The central value of a CI is called as class mark. It is nothing but the arithmetic mean of lower and upper limit of the same class.

$$\text{Mid-value or class mark} = \frac{\text{Lower class limit} + \text{Upper class limit}}{2}$$

$$\text{Class mark} = \frac{\text{True upper class limit} + \text{True lower class limit}}{2}$$

10. *Class magnitude or class width*: It is the difference between upper class bounding and lower class bounding of the class.

2.10   Formulae to calculate the number of CI

Various approaches are available to calculate the number of CI. However, one can have larger or smaller number of CI by choosing the class limits; i.e., if the class width chosen is smaller, more no. of CI is obtained and vice-versa.

Following are the most popular method used to find the number of CI.

1. No. of CI = $\dfrac{\text{Range}}{\text{Classwidth}}$

2. Seruggers formulae

    No. of CI = (1 + 3.3 log n)

    where 'n' is number of observation considered.

3. No. of CI = 0.45 × no. of observation × ¼

2.11   Numerical examples on construction of frequency distribution

Discrete series

Example (1): Read the following passage and construct a frequency distribution based on letter count.

To understand the nature of fabric, low-stress mechanical properties are measured which give total hand value (THV). The maximum limit for THV is 5. Any fabric whose THV is nearer to 5, it is being considered as best. From the 5 modes of deformation, primary hand values are computes which has range 1–10.

Solution: The above text can be converted into a frequency distribution based on letter count and neglecting punctuation marks and numbers.

Table 2.4

Letters	Tally	Frequency
1	–	0
2	卌 IIII	9
3	卌 卌 I	11
4	卌	5
5	卌 卌 I	11
6	IIII	4
7	II	2
8	II	2
9	–	0
10	IIII	4
11	I	1
		4.9

In this example, each word is counted in terms of letters and noted by a tally bar (Tally is a method to keep count in blocks of five; tally bars are straight bars used in Tally). Each item falling in the particular class is represented by a stroke (vertical bar) called as tally bar in a class; the fifth item is marked by a horizontal or slanted line across the tally bars.

Example (2): In a spinning mill the cones produced on a winding machine were tested for count by Beesey balance. The resultant counts recorded were 15, 16, 15, 18, 16, 17, 15, 18, 18, 20, 22, 20, 18, 24, 14, 15, 18. Construct a frequency distribution.

Table 2.5 Frequency distribution of resultant count

Variate	Tallay	Frequency
14	I	1
15	IIII	2
16	II	1
17	I	5
18	卌	5
19	–	0
20	II	2
21	–	0
22	I	1
23	–	0
24	I	1
		17

2.11.1 Problems for practice

1. For the following distribution, construct the frequency distribution. Table shows the number of major defects in readymade garments.

Table 2.6

Lot	1 0 2	2 0 1	3 1 1	4 0 2	5 0 1
Defects	3 0 1 2	2 3 0 2	1 1 0 2	0 0 3 3	2 2 0 1

2. A study was undertaken to examine the status of blow room process in a spinning mill. In this regard the number laps produced per shift was recorded for a period of 5 days. Construct the frequency distribution.

Table 2.7

Days	1	2	3	4	5
	85	78	76	68	72
	69	86	92	88	92
	82	87	96	69	96
	96	92	98	79	98
Number of laps	95	86	89	89	62
	82	88	87	84	83
	79	92	94	98	78
	88	92	98	82	88
	72	73	76	78	85
	86	87	88	92	94

2.11.2 Special cases on discrete series

1. Referring to problem, (a) calculate the number of words with 6 letters or more; (b) calculate the proportion of words with 5 letters or less; (c) the percentage of words with number of letters between 2 and 8 (i.e., more than 2 and less than 8).

Solution:

(a) Number of words with 6 letters or more
$$4 + 2 + 2 + 4 + 1 = 13$$

(b) Proposition of words with 5 letters or less is given by

$$\frac{49-13}{49} \times 100 = 73\% \text{ or } 0.73$$

(c) The percentage of words with number of letters between 2 and 8 is given by

$$\frac{11+5+11+4+2+2+4+1}{49} \times 100 = 82\%$$

Following are the steps to construct a continuous frequency distribution table:

1. Find the range from the data given.
2. Decide the number of classes to be formed (generally it will be 5–15).
3. Workout no. of CI from range and class width or using Strugger's formulae.
4. Select each data one at a time and place the data into the respective class by tally mark. Exhaust all the items in the data given.
5. Count tally marks and write down the frequency.
6. Give a suitable title to the frequency distribution table.

From the above method one can calculate frequency density and relative frequency.

Frequency density is defined as the ratio of frequency of a class under consideration and class width. Sometimes if it is necessary to express the frequency of a class as a fraction or percentage of total frequency, relative frequency is computed.

Relative frequency is the class frequency expression as a rate of total frequency.

R.F. = Class frequency/ total frequency

The sum of all the relative frequencies will be 1.00 or 100%. R.F. is used to compare two or more distributions or two or more classes of the same frequency distribution.

2.11.3 Examples

Example 1. The number of laps rejected per week in a blow room were recorded as follows

20, 11, 11, 37, 15, 40, 31, 29, 8, 27, 13, 7, 29, 25, 37, 42, 30, 10, 9, 27, 25, 18, 29, 47, 17, 11, 32, 41, 6, 29, 15, 13, 39, 21, 40, 10, 15, 3, 4

Solution: Minimum no. of laps rejected = 2

Maximum no. of laps rejected = 47
Therefore, range = 47 – 2 = 45
Suppose if the proposed class width is 9, then 45/9 = 5 are formed
(RF – relative frequency, FD – frequency density)

Table 2.8

CI	Tally	f	R.f.	F.D.
0–9	JHf II	7	–	–
10–19	JHf JHf II	12	–	–
20–29	JHf IIII	9	–	–
30–39	JHf II	7	–	–
40–49	JHf	5	–	–

Example 2. In a fabric analysis lab students of a B.Tech (textile technology) class obtain GSM as follows:

Table 2.9

126	131	113	82	75	204	81	84	118	104
78	90	115	110	98	106	99	107	84	76
119	93	187	139	129	130	68	195	123	125
110	80	107	111	141	136	123	90	186	82
100	109	128	115	107	115	111	92	86	70

Form a frequency distribution with equal class width of 20 such that the mid-point of first class is 70.

Solution: Class width = 20, mid-point = 70, maximum value = 204

Let 'a' be the mid-point of a class and 'h' be the class width then lower limit of class $a - \dfrac{h}{2}$, upper limit $a + \dfrac{h}{2}$.

Therefore, lower limit of first class $= a - \dfrac{h}{2} = 70 - \dfrac{20}{2} = 60$

Upper limit of first class $\qquad = a + \dfrac{h}{2} = 70 + \dfrac{20}{2} = 80$

Therefore, first CI is 60–80 and similarly other CIs are 80–100 and 100–120.

Table 2.10

GSM	Tally	f
60–80	JHf	5
80–100	JHf JHf III	13
100–120	JHf JHf JHf II	17
120–140	JHf JHf	10

(Contd.)

GSM	Tally	f
140–160	I	1
160–180	–	0
180–200	III	3
200–220	I	1
		Σf = 50

Note: The student is instructed to compare RF and FD for this problem.

Example 3. The class marks of a frequency distribution are 6, 10, 14, 18, 22, 26, and 30. Find the class size and class intervals.

Solution: Class mark is class mid-point and class size is class width. We know that

class size = Difference between two successive class marks
$$= 10 - 6$$
$$= 4$$

Let the lower limit of the first CI be 'a', and hence its upper limit is a + 4, i.e.

$$\frac{a + (a+4)}{2} = 6, \, 2a + 4 = 12, \, 2a = 8, \, a = 4$$

Therefore, the first class interval is 4–8.

Let the lower limit of the last CI be 'b' and its upper limit is b + 4.

Therefore, $\dfrac{b + (b+4)}{2} = 30$ or b = 28

Therefore, the last CI is 28–32. Hence the required CI are 4–8, 8–12, 12–16, 16–20, 20–24, 28–32.

Example 4. The mid-points of a distribution are 26, 31, 36, 41, 46, 51, 56, 61, 66, and 71. Find true class limits.

Solution: We note that the class marks are uniformly placed, so the class size is difference between two class marks.

Therefore, class size = 31 − 26 = 5

Let 'a' be the class mark of a class interval of width or size 'h' then

lower limit of the CI is $a - \dfrac{h}{2}$ and upper limit is $a + \dfrac{h}{2}$, respectively.

Therefore, lower limit of first CI = $26 - \dfrac{5}{2} = 23.5$

Upper limit of first CI = $26 + \dfrac{5}{2} = 28.5$

First CI is 23.5–28.5 and thus CI are as follows 23.5–28.5, 33.5–38.5, 38.5–43.5, 43.5–48.5, 48.5–53.5.

As these are the CI formed by exclusive method, the limits are true class limits.

Example 5. Production in meters/shift of 350 advanced shutless looms is as follows. Find the percentage of looms having more than 760 meters, between 650 and 850 meters and less than 530 meters.

Table 2.11

Production (m)	300–400	400–800	500–600	600–700	700–800	800–900	900–1000
No. of looms	6	18	73	165	62	22	4

Solution: First let us assume that data are normally distributed. Calculate the required number of looms by interpolation.

(A)   No. of looms producing more than 760 metres.

$$4 + 22 + \left(\frac{62}{100} \times 40 \right) = 26 + 24.8 = 50.8 \text{ or } 51 \text{ or } 15\%$$

(B)   No. of looms with production between 650 and 850 meters.

No. of looms with 650 meters

$$4 + 22 + 62 + \left(\frac{165}{100} \times 50 \right) = 171 \text{ looms}$$

No. of looms with 850 metres $= 4 + \left(\frac{22}{100} \times 50 \right) = 15$.

Therefore, the no. of looms with production between 650 and 850 is 171 – 15 = 156 and the percentage is $\frac{156}{350} \times 100 = 44.57\%$.

(C)   Less than 530 meters

$$6 + 18 + \frac{73}{100} \times 30 = 46 \text{ or } 13.14\%$$

2.11.4   Problem for practice

A readymade garment unit appoints 110 sales promoters for sales campaign. At the end of each fixed period the sales are analysed. The data are as follows:

Table 2.12

Sales (Lakhs)	No. of salesman	Sales (Lakhs)	No. of salesman
50–55	4	75–80	18
55–60	7	80–85	12
60–65	20	90 and above	5
70–75	22	–	–

Three categories of salesman are identified: those who make up sales (a) less than 68 lakhs, (b) more than 68 lakhs but less than 86 lakhs, (c) more than 86 lakhs. The first category of salesmen are given training and for the third group, an efficacy of 2.5% of sales are planned. Calculate necessary statistics.

2.11.5 Practical difficulties while forming frequency distribution

During the construction of frequency distribution, one finds some problems as mention below:

1. The number CI should not be too small or too large. As mentioned earlier 5–15 is most preferable. But in some cases it becomes inevitable to have open-ended class intervals even though it is not desired.
2. Using formulae to calculate number of CI, sometimes it is necessary to form classes with unequal width.
3. One should be careful in recording the tally mark and it's counting as frequency.

Measures of central tendency

3.1 Introduction

One of the most important objectives of statistical analysis is to get one single value that describes the characteristic of the entire mass of data. Such a value is called "central value" or an "average" or "the expected value". The word average is very frequently used in day-to-day conversation. For example, we often talk about average boy in the class, average of height of a person, life of an Indian, strike rate of a batsman, etc. In statistics, mean is defined as "an attempt to find one single figure to describe whole of figures" or "a typical value that is sometimes employed to represent all the individual values in a series or a variable".

From the above definitions it can be said that average is a single value that represents a group of values. Such a value is of great significance because it depicts the characteristic of the whole group. Since an average represents the entire data, its value lies somewhere in between the two extremes, i.e., the largest and the smallest items. For this reason an average is frequently referred to as "measure of central tendency".

3.2 Objectives of averaging

1. To get a single value that describes the characteristic of the entire group.
    If we consider a central value by condensing the mass of data, it will enable us to get a bird's-eye view of the entire data. Thus, one value represents thousands, lakhs and even millions of values. For example, it is impossible to remember the individual incomes of millions of people of India; even if it is done it will be useful to some extent. But if the total National Income is divided by the total population, we get one single value that represents the entire population.
2. To facilitate comparison.
    By calculating average we can compare two phenomena either at a time or over a period of time. For example, comparison of results can be made between different colleges. This will conclude which is

the best college. On the other hand, we can compare the results of the same college over a period of time. This will help the officials to take right decisions at right time.

3.2.1   Requisites of a good average

Since the average is the single representing mass, it is desirable that such a value satisfies the following properties:

1. *Easy to understand* – As the statistical methods are designed to simplify complexity, it is desirable that an average should be easily understandable, otherwise its use will be limited.
2. *Simple to compute* – The average should also be easy to compute.
3. *It should be based on all items* – The average should depend upon each and every item of the series so that if an item is dropped the average should also get altered.
   For example, the arithmetic mean of 10, 20, 30, 40 and 50 is

$$\frac{10 + 20 + 30 + 40 + 50}{5} = 30$$

   If we drop an item say 50, the arithmetic mean will be 25.
4. *Mean/average should not be affected by any outside factor.*
5. *Rigidly defined* – An average will have one and only one value. It should be defined by algebraic formula so that anybody who calculates should get the same answer. The average should not depend on bias or personal judgment.
6. *Capable of further algebraic treatment* – The average calculated should be easily subjectable to further algebraic treatment or statistical analysis. For example, we are given averages of two counts of different other spun from various mills. It should be subjectable to further treatment to calculate average or resultant count.

3.2.3   Types of averages (means)

Following are the important types of averages:

1. Arithmetic mean
   (a)   Simple
   (b)   Weighted
2. Median
3. Mode
4. Geometric mean
5. Harmonic mean

3.2.3.1 *Merits and demerits of arithmetic mean*

Merits are as follows:

1. Mean is rigidly defined.
2. It is based on all items in the given distribution.
3. It is least affected by fluctuations in the sample.
4. It is easily understandable and simple in calculation.
5. It can be subjected to algebraic treatment.

Demerits are as follows:

1. It is greatly affected by the extreme items, and its usefulness as a "summary as a whole" may be considerably reduced.
2. When the distribution has open class, its computation is based on assumption and therefore may not be valid.
3. It can be determined by inspection as in the case of mode or median.

3.2.3.2 *Properties of arithmetic mean*

The mean possess several properties which make it very useful. Some of them are described below:

1. *Mean acting as "centre of gravity"*

Mean of a distribution parallels the physical idea of a centre of gravity or balance point of ideal objects arranged in a straight line. For example, imagine an ideal board having zero weight. Along this board are arranged stacks of objects at various positions. The objects have uniform weight and differ from each other by their position on the board. Let the board provided with markings.

Now at what point the fulcrum could be placed? The "push" of objects on one side of the board is exactly equal to the push exerted by the other side. This can be found from the mean of the positions of the various objects.

$$M = \frac{3+3+9+11\times3+16\times2+19+21}{10} = 12$$

2. *Deviations in one direction of the mean exactly are equal to the deviations in other direction.*

Deviations from the mean

Score (X)	Deviations (x)	Squares of deviations (x^2)
6	2	4
5	1	1
4	0	0

(Contd.)

Score (X)	Deviations (x)	Squares of deviations (x²)
3	−1	1
2	−2	4
$\sum X = 20$	$\sum X = 0$	$\sum x^2 = 10$

$$\overline{X} = 20 / 5 = 4$$

From the above table we can say that the deviations of mean in upward and direction are exactly equal. This confirms that always the sum of deviations about the mean in any distribution is always zero. It can also be shown that the sum of deviations taken from any other arbitrary value will not be zero.

3. *The principle of least squares*

The sum of the squared deviations of all the scores about the mean is less than the sum of the squared deviations about any other value. This is called the principle of least squares. For example, referring to the above table the sum of the squared deviations about the mean is 10. If however, 3 and 6 are taken as arbitrary values of the mean, the $\sum x^2$ becomes 15 and 30, respectively. Thus we can say that when mean is 4 the value $\sum x^2$ is 10 which is less than 15 and 30. From this we can say that, the essential property of mean is that it is closer to the individual scores over the entire group than any other single value. This concept is used in regression and prediction.

4. *Effect of a constant on a mean*

Case (i) :   if a constant is added to each score of a distribution, the value of mean will increase by the value of that constant.

Case (ii) :   if a constant is subtracted each score of a distribution will lead to a decrease in the mean equal to that constant.

Case (iii) :   the multiplication and division will also lead to a result equal to the product of mean and the constant.

Below is an example showing effect of a constant on a mean.

Original each score	Adding 2 to each score score	Subtracting 2 from each score	Multiplying each score by 2	Dividing score by 2
4	6	2	8	2
5	7	3	10	2.5
6	8	4	12	3
7	9	5	14	3.5
8	10	6	16	4
$\sum = 30$	40	20	60	1.5
M = 6	8	4	12	3.0
Effect	(6 + 2)	(6 − 2)	(6 × 2)	(6 ÷ 2)

5. *Combination of mean*

Arithmetic mean and number of items of two or more means of related groups can be computed to get a combined average. This can be obtained by using the below formula.

$$\overline{X_{12}} = \frac{N_1\overline{X_1} + N_2\overline{X_2}}{N_1 + N_2}$$

Where

$\overline{X_{12}}$ = combined mean of two groups

$\overline{X_1}$ = }

$\overline{X_2}$ = } mean of 1st and 2nd group

N_1 and N_2 are number of items of 1st and 2nd groups.

3.2.4 Properties of geometric mean

1. The product of the values of series will remain unchanged when the value of GM is substituted for each individual value. For example, if GM of 2, 4, 8 is 4, then $2 \times 4 \times 8 = 64 = 4 \times 4 \times 4$.
2. The sum of the deviations of the logarithms of the original observations above or below the logarithm of the GM is equal.

3.2.4.1 *Uses of geometric mean*

1. GM is used to find the average percent increase in sales, production, population or other economic or business series. For example, from 1986 to 1988 prices were increased by 5%, 10% and 18%, respectively. The average annual increase is not $\frac{5+10+18}{3} = 11\%$ as given by arithmetic mean but 10.9% as given by GM.
2. GM is theoretically considered to be the best average in the conservation of index number.

3.2.4.2 *Merits and demerits of GM*

Merits are as follows:

1. Since it is less affected by the extreme values, it is a more typical average than AM.
2. Since it gives equal weight to equal ratios of change, it is particularly adopted, when ratios of change are used.
3. It is capable of algebraic treatment.
4. It is rigidly defined.

Demerits are as follows:

1. Its computation is relatively difficult.
2. It cannot be calculated when one of the values is zero.
3. It is not widely popular average.

3.3 Calculation of 'simple' arithmetic mean – individual observations – case (i)

The process for calculating arithmetic mean is very simple in the case of individual observations.

Procedure:

1. Add all the observations to get ΣX
   Where $\Sigma X = X_1 + X_2 + X_3 + X_4 + \ldots \ldots X_n = \Sigma X$
2. Divide ΣX by the number of observations.

Example: Following table will give monthly used set lengths in a sizing in a factory compute the arithmetic mean.

Set length in sizing: 1780, 1760, 1690, 1750, 1840, 1920, 1100, 1810, 1050, 1950

$N = 10$, $\Sigma X = 16,650$ $\overline{X} = 16,650 / 10 = 1,665$

3.3.1 Short-cut method

Arithmetic mean is also obtained by "arbitrary origin". Deviations are taken from this arbitrary origin.

Formula:

$$\overline{X} = A + \Sigma d / Nd = (X - A), \text{ where A – assumed mean}$$

Procedure:

1. Select an assumed mean.
2. Take deviations of items from the assumed mean and denote these by letter 'd'.
3. Calculate Σd.
4. Find $\overline{X}$ using the formula.

Example: Referring to the above example calculate arithmetic mean by short-cut method.

Take assumed mean as 1800.

Sorts	Set length (X)	(X – 1800)	Sorts	Set length	(X – 1800)
1	1780	– 20	7	1100	– 700
2	1760	– 40	8	1810	+10
3	1690	– 110	9	1050	– 750
4	1750	– 50	10	1950	+150
5	1840	+40			
6	1920	+120			

$$\sum d = -1350$$

$$\overline{X} = A + \sum d/N = 1800 - 1350/10 = 1665$$

3.3.2   Discrete series

In discrete series we have two methods:

Direct method:

$$\overline{X} = \sum fX / N \text{ (where } N = \sum f)$$

Procedure:

1. Obtain the product fX and $\sum fX$
2. Divide by N is $\sum f$.

Example: From the following data of the tpi of 60 yarns produced in a mill. Calculate the arithmetic mean.

(X) tpi	20	30	40	50	60	70
(f) Number of yarns	8	12	20	10	6	4

$N = \sum f = 60$

Solution:

f(x)   160   360   800   500   360   280 $\sum f(X) = 2460$

$$\overline{X} = \sum fX / N = 2460 / 60 = 41$$

Short-cut method:

Select an assumed mean as 40.

(X – 40) = d	–20	–10	0	+10	+20	+30	
f d =	–160	–120	0	+100	+120	+120	$\sum fd = 60$

$$\overline{X} = A + \frac{\sum fd}{N} = 10 + \frac{60}{60} + 41$$

3.3.3   Correcting incorrect values

Example: The GSM of 100 fabrics were found as 40. Later on it was discovered that an observation of 53 was misread as 83. Find the correct mean corresponding to the correct score.

$$N = 100 \qquad \overline{X} = 40$$

$$\therefore \Sigma X = N \quad \overline{X} = 40 \times 100 = 4000$$

But this is not correct Σx.

Correct Σx = Incorrect Σx – wrong item + correct item

$$= 4000 - 83 + 53 = 3970$$

$$\text{Correct } \overline{X} = \frac{\text{Correct } \Sigma x}{N} = \frac{3970}{100} = 39.7$$

3.4   Calculation of mean

Mean is calculated (grouped or ungrouped) by different methods.

Example: Calculate the mean for the following set of observations.

$$\text{(i) } 30, \ 35, \ 40, \ 25, \ 40 = \frac{30 + 35 + 40 + 25 + 40}{5} = 34$$

3.4.1 Calculation of mean by "long method"

$$\overline{X} = \Sigma fx \ / \ x, \text{ where } x = \text{mid-point of each CI}$$

Steps:

1. From the given frequency distribution, calculate the mid-point of each class interval and call them X.
2. Multiply the given frequencies of each class by the mid-points to get "fX".
3. Calculate ΣfX.
4. Divide the Σfx by n to get mean.

Example: A cotton gave the following results, when tested on ball's sorter.

Length in 1/8^2	Percentage frequency
2	0
3	2

(Contd.)

Length in 1/8²	Percentage frequency
4	5
5	10
6	18
7	30
8	24
9	11
	100

Normal CI 1/8″	Mid-point (x)	Frequency (f)	fx
1.5–2.5	2	0	0
2.5–3.5	3	2	6
3.5–4.5	4	5	20
4.5–5.5	5	10	50
5.5–6.5	6	18	108
6.5–7.5	7	30	210
7.5–8.5	8	24	192
8.5–9.5	9	11	99
		$\Sigma f = 1004$	685

Mean $\overline{X}$ = $\Sigma fx/n$ = 685/100 = 6.85;
Mean length 6.85/8 = 0.85

Example: The micronaire (Mc) value of 4 cottons used in 40ˢ mixing is

Cotton	No. of bales	Mc Value
H – 4	2	3.9
S – 4	5	3.5
Mcu – 5	9	3.2
Isc – 67	4	3.7
20		

Find the average micronaire value of the mixing.

No. of bales (x)	Frequency (f)	(fx)
2	3.9	7.8
5	3.5	17.5
9	3.2	28.8
4	3.7	14.8
20		68.9

Example: Calculate the average Lea-count from the following data.

Class interval of Lea-count	Frequency
10.2–11.1	4
11.2–12.1	15
12.2–13.1	26
13.1–14.1	19
14.2–15.1	6
	70

Class interval	Exact class interval	Mid-point	Frequency (fx)
10.2–11.1	10.15–11.15	10.65	42.6
11.2–12.1	11.15–12.15	11.65	174.75
12.2–13.1	12.15–13.15	12.65	328.90
13.2–14.1	13.15–14.15	13.65	259.35
14.1–15.1	14.15–15.15	14.65	87.90

$$\bar{x} = \frac{\Sigma fx}{n} = 12.26$$

Example: Calculate the mean from the following data:

Class interval of Lea strength	Frequency
161–162	05
163–164	20
165–166	35
167–168	60
169–170	15
171–172	05

Class interval	Mid-point	Frequency	fx
161–162	161.5	05	807.5
163–164	163.5	20	3270.0
165–166	165.5	35	5792.50
167–168	167.5	60	10050.00
169–170	169.5	15	2542.50
171–172	171.5	05	857.50
			140

$$\bar{x} = \frac{\Sigma fx}{n} = 166.42$$

Example: Find mean from the following data

Class interval of Lea strength	Frequency
20–24	10
25–29	19
30–34	32
35–39	17
40–44	12

Class interval	Mid-point (x)	Frequency (f)	fx
20–24	22	10	220
25–29	27	19	513
30–34	32	32	1024
35–39	37	17	629
40–44	42	12	504
		90	2890

$$\overline{x} = \frac{\Sigma fx}{n} = \frac{2890}{90} = 2890/90 = 32.11$$

Example: Find mean from the following data:

Nep count	Frequency
22–23	07
24–25	18
26–27	50
28–29	20
30–31	05

Class interval	Mid-point (x)	Frequency (f)	fx
22–23	22.5	07	157.5
24–25	24.5	18	441.0
26–27	26.5	50	1325.0
28–29	28.5	20	570.0
30–31	30.5	05	152.5
		100	

$$\overline{x} = \frac{\Sigma fx}{n} = \frac{2646}{100} = 26.46$$

Example: The table below shows the frequency distribution of 100 count test results. Find mean.

Mid-point of class (x)	Class frequency (f)	fx
60	1	60
62	0	00
64	3	192
66	6	396
68	12	816
70	18	1260
72	23	1656
74	16	1184
76	12	912
78	4	312
80	3	240
82	2	164
		100

$$\overline{x} = \frac{\Sigma fx}{n} = \frac{7192}{100} = 71.92$$

3.4.2   Calculation of mean by short-cut method or assumed mean method

Steps:

1. Tabulate the results into a frequency distribution and mid-point for each class is found out (x).
2. From the set of obtained mid-points assume any one mid-point as "arbitrary" point. (Take the mid-point of an interval somewhere near the center of the frequency distribution/centre of CIs, if possible the interval should contain largest frequency (A)).
3. Calculate the deviations of mid-points (x) from A in units of CI.

$$\left\{ d' = \frac{\text{Mid-point } (x) - \text{Assumed mean (A)}}{\text{Size of CI}} \right\}$$

(Note: keep the signs intact)

4. Calculate the product fd' and hence $\Sigma fd'$ (Note: The signs of fd' above 'A' may be '+ve' and below '-ve' or vice-versa while calculating Σ one should keep signs intact)
5. Calculate the mean $\overline{X}$ using the formulae

$$\overline{X} = A + \left\{ \frac{\Sigma fd'}{\Sigma f} \right\} c \qquad \text{where, } d' = \left\{ \frac{X - A}{CI} \right\}$$

Example: Calculate the mean by "short-cut method" from the following frequency distribution

Class interval	Mid-point (x)	Frequency (f)	Deviations from AM in CI units	fd′
5–9	7	9	−4	−36
10–14	12	5	−3	−15
15–19	17	7	−2	−14
20–24	22	8	−1	−8
25–29	27	8	0	0
30–34	32	6	1	+6
35–39	37	2	2	+4
40–44	42	3	3	+9
45–49	47	2	4	+8

As 25–29 CI is the centre of frequency distributions, assume 27 as arbitary point.

Mean $\bar{X} = 27 + \left(\dfrac{-46}{50}\right) \times 5 = 22.4$

Example: Calculate the mean from the following frequency distribution by assumed mean method.

Class (GSM)	f
0–8	8
8–16	7
16–24	16
24–32	24
32–40	15
40–48	7
	77

Class interval	Mid-point (x)	Frequency (f)	d′	fd′
0–8	4	8	−3	−24
8–16	12	7	−2	−14
16–24	20	16	−1	−16
24–32	28	24	0	0
32–40	36	15	1	15
40–48	44	7	2	14
				−25

$A = 28$ 　 $\bar{X} = A + (\Sigma fd' / \Sigma f)\, C$
$= 28 + (-25/77) \times 8 = 25.40$

Example: Calculate the mean from the following data.

Class interval of Lea strength	Frequency
161–162	5
163–164	20
165–166	35
167–168	60
169–170	15
171–172	05

CI	Real class boundary	Mid-point	Frequency	(X – A / CI)	fd'
161–162	160.5–162.5	161.5	5	–3	–15
163–164	162.5–164.5	163.5	20	–2	–20
165–166	164.5–166.5	165.5	35	–1	–35
167–168	166.5–168.5	167.5	60	0	0
169–170	168.5–170.5	169.5	15	+1	+15
171–172	170.5–172.5	171.5	05	+2	+10
			140		$\Sigma fd' = -50$

$$\bar{X} = A + \left(\frac{\Sigma fd'}{\Sigma f}\right) \times C$$

$$= 167 - \left(\frac{50}{40}\right) \times 2$$

$$= 167.5 - 0.7142 = 166.68$$

Example: Find the mean from the following data

Class interval of lea strength	Frequency
20–24	10
25–29	19
30–34	32
35–39	17
40–44	12

A = 32, CI = 5

CI	Real-class boundary	Mid-point	Frequency	d' = (X – A /CI)	fd'
20–24	19.5–24.5	22	10	–2	–20
25–29	24.5–29.5	27	19	–1	–19
30–34	29.5–34.5	32	32	0	0
35–39	34.5–39.5	37	17	+1	+17
40–44	39.5–44.5	42	12	+2	+24
			100		$\Sigma fd' = +2$

$$\overline{X} = \left(\frac{\Sigma fd'}{\Sigma f}\right) \times CI$$

$$= 32 + (2/100) \times 5 = 32.1$$

Example: Find the mean from the following data

Nep count	Frequency
22–23	07
24–25	18
26–27	50
28–29	20
30–31	05
X = 26.5	C = 2

CI	Real-class boundary	Mid-point	Frequency	d' = (X – A)/CI	fd'
22–23	21.5–23.5	22.5	07	– 2	–14
24–25	23.5–25.5	24.5	18	– 1	–18
26–27	25.5–27.5	26.5	50	0	0
28–29	27.5–29.5	28.5	20	+1	+20
30–31	29.5–31.5	30.5	05	+2	+10
			$\Sigma f = 100$		$\Sigma d' = -2$

$$\overline{X} = A + \left(\frac{\Sigma fd'}{\Sigma f}\right) \times C$$

$$= 26.5 \left(\frac{-2}{100}\right) \times 2 = 26.5 - 0.04 = 26.46$$

Example: Compute the average of the following distribution

Class (picks/inch)	f
0–9	32
10–19	65
20–29	100
30–39	184
40–49	288
50–59	167
60–69	98
70–79	46
80–89	20
	1000

Class	Mid-point (x)	Frequency (f)	d'	fd'
0–9	4.5	32	–4	–128
10–19	14.5	65	–3	–195

Class	Mid-point (x)	Frequency (f)	d'	fd'
20–29	24.5	100	−2	−200
30–39	34.5	184	−1	−184
40–49	44.5	288	0	0
50–59	54.5	167	1	167
60–69	64.5	98	2	196
70–79	74.5	46	3	138
80–89	84.5	20	4	80
		$\sum f = 1000$		−126

$$\overline{X} = A + \left(\frac{\Sigma fd'}{\Sigma f}\right) \times C$$

$$= 44.5 + \left(\frac{-126}{1000}\right) \times 10 = 43.24$$

3.5   Mathematical property of median

The sum of the deviations of the items from median, ignoring signs is the least. The deviations from 8 ignoring signs are 4, 2, 0, 2, 4 and the total is 12. This total is smaller than the one obtained if deviations are taken from any other value.

Merits:

1. Especially useful in the case of open-end classes, since only the position and not the values of items must be known. Median calculation is also recommended if the distribution has unequal classes, since it is easier to compute the mean.
2. Extreme values do not affect the median as strong as they do the mean.
3. In markedly skewed distributions such as income distributions or price distributions where the arithmetic mean would be distorted by extreme values, the median is especially useful.
4. It is most useful data where qualitative data is considered, i.e., where ranks are given or there are other types of items that are not measured or not counted but are scored.
5. Value of the median can be determined graphically, but mean cannot be.

Limitations:

1. For calculating median it is necessary to arrange the data. Other averages do not need any re-arrangement.

2. Since it is a positional average, its values are not determined by each and every observation.
3. It is not capable of algebraic treatment. For example, we cannot get combined median of two classes.
4. It is not familiar as arithmetic mean.
5. It is erratic if the number of items is small.

Merits:

1. Since it is the most typical value, it is the most descriptive average.
2. It is most usual item and thus representative of the series.
3. Like median mode is not unduly affected by extreme values
4. Its value can be easily determined even in open-end class.
5. It can be used to describe qualitative phenomenon.
6. Value of the mode can be determined graphically.

Limitations:

1. It is incapable of further mathematical treatment.
2. In small number of items mode may not exist.
3. Mode cannot be determined always.
4. Value of mode is not based on each and every item of the series.
5. It is not rigidly defined. Different formulae give different answer.

3.6   Different types of mean and their importance

1. *Geometric mean*

Geometric mean of 'n' positive number is the 'nth' root of their product. The geometric mean is

$$G = n\sqrt{x_1, x_2, x_3, \ldots x_n}$$

Example: Find the geometric mean of (3 and 12); (1/3, 1, 8, 1)
G1 = 2 3 × 12 = 6
G2 = 3 1/3 × 1 × 81 = 3

Importance:

It is normally used to average ratio, rates of change, economic indexes. It is rarely used in textiles.

2. *Harmonic mean*

It is defined as the reciprocal of the arithmetic mean of the reciprocals of the observations.

The isothermic mean of 'n' number $x_1, x_2, x_3, \ldots\ldots x_n$ is 'n' divided by the sum of the reciprocals of 'n' number. Namely

$$H = \cfrac{n}{\cfrac{1}{X_1} + \cfrac{1}{X_2} + \ldots\ldots\ldots \cfrac{1}{X_n}} = \cfrac{n}{\sum\limits_{1}^{n}\left(\cfrac{1}{X}\right)}$$

Practical utility of harmonic mean

1. It is extensively employed in estimation of resultant count of yarn (indirect system)

   Example: Find the resultant count of 20^s and 40^s

   $$H = \cfrac{2}{\cfrac{1}{20} + \cfrac{1}{40}} = \cfrac{2}{\cfrac{2+1}{40}} = \cfrac{2}{26.66}$$

   i.e., 13.33^s

2. It is used in calculating the overall micronaire value when cottons of different fibre fineness are mixed together.

3. It is used in calculating the ratings for the abrasion resistance of fabrics.

   $$D = \cfrac{2}{\cfrac{1}{B} + \cfrac{1}{P}}$$

Similarly, figure of merit

$$= \cfrac{3}{\cfrac{1}{B} + \cfrac{1}{P} + \cfrac{1}{F}}$$

3. *Weighted mean*

Weighted arithmetic average is calculated by first calculating the product of each item in the given series by its weight. Then the total of the product is divided by the total of the weights.

$$\text{Weighted mean } \overline{X}_w = \frac{W_1X_1 + W_2X_2 \ldots\ldots\ldots\ldots W_nX_n}{W_1 + W_2 + \ldots\ldots W_n} = \frac{\sum WX}{\sum W}$$

Practical utility of weighted mean

This mean is used in calculating the fiber length.

Example: Calculate the weighted mean of the monthly income of a company employees.

Employee cadre	No. of employees (W)	Monthly income (X)	WX
Supervisor	3	300	900
Asst. supervisor	6	150	900
Foreman	10	100	1000
Workers	20	60	1200
	39 $= \Sigma$W		4000 $= \Sigma$WX

$\overline{X}_w = 4000/39 = $ Rs. 102.5

4. *Combined mean*

Grand mean $\overline{\overline{X}} = \dfrac{n_1\overline{X_1} + n_2\overline{X_2} + \ldots\ldots\ldots\ldots n_K\overline{X_K}}{n_1 + n_2 + n_3 + \ldots\ldots n_K} = \dfrac{\Sigma n\overline{X}}{\Sigma n}$

Example: The following table shows the AM of 3 sub-groups A, B, C of weaving sections. Calculate the AM of the whole group.

Sub-group	No. of men working n_1	Average wages $\overline{X}_w$
A	80	61
B	100	70
C	120	80

$\overline{X} = (80 \times 61 + 100 \times 70 + 120 \times 80) / (80 + 100 + 120) =$

$= 21480/300 = $ Rs. 71.6

5. *Weighted arithmetic mean*

Example:

$\overline{X} = \Sigma WX / \Sigma W$ in individual case.

$\overline{X}_w = \Sigma W(fx) / \Sigma W$ in discrete/continuous case.

Example: Comment on the performance of the students of the 3 universities given below using simple and weighted averages.

University	X			Y			Z		
	No. of pass % students in hundreds			No. of pass % students in hundreds			No. of pass % students in hundreds		
Course of study ↓	X	W	WX	X	W	WX	X	W	WX
B.Tech in silk tech	71	3	213	82	2	164	81	2	162
MMFT	83	4	332	76	3	228	76	3.5	266
Spinning	73	5	365	73	6	438	74	4.5	333
Textile science	74	2	148	76	7	532	58	2.0	116
Garment technology	65	3	195	65	3	195	70	7.0	490
Fashion design	66	3	198	60	7	420	73	2.0	146
	ΣX	ΣW	ΣWX	ΣX	ΣW	ΣWX	ΣX	ΣW	ΣWX
	432	20	1451	432	28	1977	432	21	1513

6. *Simple and weighted means*

X $\bar{X} = \Sigma X / N = 432/6 = 72$ $\bar{X}_w = \Sigma WX / \Sigma W = 1451/20 = 72.55$

Y $\bar{X} = \Sigma X / N = 432/6 = 72$ $\bar{X}_w = \Sigma WX / \Sigma W = 1977/28 = 70.61$

Z $\bar{X} = \Sigma X / N = 432/6 = 72$ $\bar{X}_w = \Sigma WX / \Sigma W = 1513/21 = 72.05$

We find the arithmetic mean is same for all universities. But this will be a wrong conclusion on comparing weighted arithmetic mean. We can say that $\bar{X}$ of X university is high. Hence the students of this university have done well.

3.7   Properties of arithmetic mean

Example: In a certain cloth examination the average GSM of all fabrics in mill A is 68.4 and fabrics in mill B is 71.2. If the average of both mills combined is 70. Find the ratio of the number of fabrics in mill A to B.

Solution: Let us assume that the number of fabrics in Mill A is 'X' and mill B is 'Y'.

$$\bar{X}_{12} = 70, \ \bar{X}_1 = 68.4, \ \bar{X}_2 = 71.2$$

$$\bar{X}_{12} = \frac{N_1 \bar{X}_1 + N_2 \bar{X}_2}{N_1 + N_2},$$

$$70 = \frac{68.4X + 71.2Y}{X + Y}$$

$$70 (X + Y) = 68.4X + 71.2Y$$
$$-68.4X + 70X + 70Y - 71.2Y = 0$$
$$1.6X = 1.2Y$$
$$X/Y = 3/4$$

Hence, for every 3 fabrics in mill A there are 4 fabrics in mill B.

3.7.1 Calculation of arithmetic mean in case of open-end classes

We know that open-end classes are those in which the lower limit of first class and upper limit of last class is known. In such case determination of arithmetic mean is very difficult unless we make an assumption about the unknown limits. The assumption mainly depends on the CI following the first class and preceding the last class.

Example:

Count	No. of mills	Assumed new distribution	
Below 10	4	0 – 10	4
10–20	6	10 – 20	6
20–30	10	20 – 30	10
30–40	15	30 – 40	15
40–50	8	40 – 50	8
Above 50	7	50 – 60	7

Here, CI are uniform, the appropriate assumption based on the CI of first class and CI of the class preceding the last class will be as follows: known CI width = 10,

First class = 0–10
Last class = 50–60

Example: Consider the following distribution

Count	Number of mills	Modified CI
Below 10	4	0–10
10–30	6	–
30–60	10	–
60–100	7	–
Above 100	3	100–150

It can be seen that the CI for second class is 20, third class is 30, fourth class is 40. Therefore, for fifth class it will be 50, i.e., 100–150 and similarly for first class 0–10.

3.7.2 Some illustrative examples on "assumed mean method"

Example: Calculate the arithmetic mean from the following series:
5 men get less than Rs. 5
12 men get less than Rs. 10
22 men get less than Rs. 15
30 men get less than Rs. 20

36 men get less than Rs. 25
40 men get less than Rs. 30

Solution: We are given cumulative frequencies (totaling 40). Therefore, first simple frequency table is constructed.

Income	Mid-point	f	d' = (X – 12.5/CI)	fd'
0–5	2.5	5	–2	–10
5–10	7.5	7	–1	–7
10–15	**12.5**	10	0	0
15–20	17.5	8	+1	+8
20–25	22.5	6	+2	+12
25–30	27.5	4	+3	+12
		$\sum f = 40$		$\sum fd' = +15$

$$\overline{X} = A + (\sum fd' / \sum f)\ CI = 12.5 + (15/40) \times 5 = 14.375$$

Example: Missing frequency
Find the missing frequency if mean is 28 of the data given below.

Profits/lots	0–20	10–20	20–30	30–40	40–50	50–60
No. of lots	12	18	27	?	17	6

Let the missing frequency be X

Class	Mid-point (X)	F	d' = (X – 35)/CI	fd'
0–10	5	12	–3	–36
10–20	15	18	–2	–36
20–30	25	27	–1	–27
30–40	35	X	0	0
40–50	45	17	+1	+17
50–60	55	6	+2	+12
		80+X		$-70 = \sum fd'$

$$\overline{X} = A + (\sum fd' / \sum f)\ X\ CI$$
$$28 = 35 - (700 / (80 + X))\quad X = 20$$

Example: From the following compute the mean count of all yarns of 50 mills.

Count processed	No. of yarns	Average of yarns produced in a mill
More than 35	7	200
30–35	10	250
25–30	15	300
20–25	9	200
15–20	5	150
Less than 15	4	100

Solution: Given data may be written in ascending order.

Class interval	No. of mills	Average no. of yarns/mill	Total no. of yarns	Mid-point (X)	d' = (X − A)/CI	fd'
10–15	4	100	400	12.5	−3	−1200
15–20	5	150	750	17.5	−2	−1500
20–25	9	200	1800	22.5	−1	−1800
25–30	15	300	4500	27.5	0	0
30–35	10	250	2500	32.5	+1	+2500
35–40	7	200	1400	37.5	+2	+2800
			11, 350 = N			+800 = $\sum$fd'

$$\overline{X} = A + (\sum fd' / \sum f) \times CI = 27.5 + (800/11350) \times 5 = 27.5 + 0.35 = 27.85$$

Example: In winding department of a preparation shed piece rate of system is followed. Bonus is also given to a worker on the basis of individual output.

The rate of bonus payable is as follows:

Output units	Bonus (Rs.)
70–74	40
75–79	45
80–84	50
85–89	60
90–94	70
95–99	80
100–104	100

The individual output of a batch of 50 workers is as follows:

94	83	78	76	88	86	93	80	91	82
89	97	92	84	92	80	85	83	98	103
87	88	88	81	95	86	99	81	87	90
84	97	80	75	93	101	82	82	89	72
85	83	75	72	83	98	77	87	71	80

Calculate: (i) average bonus per worker, (ii) average output/worker.

Class	Frequency/tally	F	Bonus X	Mid-point (x)	d' = (X − 87)/5	fd'	fx
70–74	111	3	40	72	−3	−9	120
75–79	1111	5	45	77	−2	−10	225
80–84	111111111111	15	50	82	−1	−15	750
85–89	1111111111	12	60	87	0	0	720
90–94	111111	7	70	92	+1	+7	490
95–99	11111	6	80	97	+2	+12	480
100–104	11	2	100	102	+3	+6	200
		50 = $\sum$f				−9 = $\sum$fd	2985 = $\sum$fx

Average bonus paid/worker = (2985/50) ($\Sigma fx/N$) = 59.7
Average output/worker X = A + ($\Sigma fd'$ / Σf) × CI = 87 – (9/50) × 5 = 86.1 units.

Example: The following is the age distribution of 2000 persons working in a composite mill.

Age group	No. of persons
15 but less than 20	80
20 but less than 25	250
25 but less than 30	300
30 but less than 35	325
35 but less than 40	287
40 but less than 45	220
45 but less than 50	268
50 but less than 55	150
55 but less than 60	75
60 but less than 65	25
65 but less than 70	20

Because of heavy losses management decided to bring down the strength to 40% of the present number according to the following scheme.

(i)   To retrench the first 10% from lower group.
(ii) To absorb the next 40% in branches.
(iii) To make 10% from the highest age group to retire prematurely.

What will be the age limits of persons retained in the mill and of those transferred to other sections? Also calculate the average age of those retained.

(i)   The number of persons to be retrenched from the lower group = (2000 × 10)/100 = 200.
      But already 80 persons are from 15–20 and rest (200–80) = 120 will be (200 – 80) = 120 from 20–25 age group to be retrenched.
(ii) The persons to be absorbed in other branches = (2000 × 40)/100 = 800.

They belong to the following groups.

Age group	No. of persons
20–25 (250–120)	130
25–30	300
30–35	325
35–40 (287–242)	45
	800

Those who are retire are (2000 × 10) / 100 = 200 in all and belong to highest age group. Their age groups are as follows:

Age group	No. of persons
65–70	20
60–65	25
55–60	75
50–55 (150–170)	80
	200

Hence the age groups of those who is to be retained in the mill are 40 of 2000 to complete 1000 (40 × 2000)/100 = 800.

Age group	No. of persons
35–40	242
40–45	220
45–50	268
50–55	70
800	is remaining

Calculation of average age of those retained.

Age-group	Mid-point	f	$(m - 47.5) / 5$, i.e., d'	fd'
35–40	37.5	242	−2	−484
40–45	42.5	220	−1	−220
45–50	47.5	268	0	0
50–55	52.5	70	+1	+70
		800 = N		$\Sigma fd' = -634$

$$\overline{X} = A + (\Sigma fd/N) \times i =$$
$$= 47.5 - (634/800) \times 5 =$$
$$= 47.5 - 3.96 = 43.54 \text{ years}$$

3.7.3 Illustrative examples in "discrete and individual" cases

Example: A computer has 50 resistors, 10 have failed and their average life is 2.5. In total the life of resistors were 281. Find the average life of those who have not failed.

Solution: N = 50, Failed = 10; Mean life of resistors = 2.5

Total life of failed resistors = 2.5 × 10 = 25; Total resistors not failed = 281 – 25 = 256

Average life of resistor which has not failed = 256/40 = 6.4

Example: In a spun silk factory there are 100 skilled, 250 semi-skilled and 150 unskilled workers. To weave a unit length of 5.5 m in 3 days by a skilled worker, 4 days by semi-skilled and 5 days by unskilled worker. After training of 2 years the semi-skilled workers are expected to become skilled workers and the unskilled workers become semi-skilled workers. Would you say that 2 years of training was justifiable?

Solution: Average time/worker before training is given by

$$\frac{(100 \times 3) + (250 \times 4) + (150 \times 5)}{100 + 250 + 150} = \frac{2050}{500} = 4.1h$$

Now after training, the composition of workers is as follows:
Skilled worker = 100 + 250 = 350
Semi-skilled worker = 150
Unskilled worker = nil
Average time/worker after training is [(350 × 3) + (150 × 4)] / 500 = 3.3 h.
Therefore, training is justifiable.

3.7.4   Geometric mean – calculations

For individual case, GM = Antilog (Σlog X / N)
Discrete series, GM = Antilog (Σf log X / N)
Continuous series, GM = Antilog (Σf log m/N)

Example: Calculate the GM of the following data:
125, 1462, 38, 7, 0.22, 0.08, 12.75, 0.5

X	log X
125	2.0969
1462	3.1650
38	1.5798
7	0.8451
0.22	1.3424
0.08	2.9031
12.75	1.1055
0.5	1.6990
	Σlog X = 6.7368

GM = Antilog (Σlog X/N) = 6.952

Case (ii): Discrete series, continuous series

Calculate the GM of the following series.

Marks:	4–8	8–12	12–16	16–20	20–24	24–28	28–32	32–36	36–40
Frequency:	6	10	18	30	15	12	10	6	2

Class	Mid-point	F	log m	F × log m
4–8	6	6	0.7782	4.6692
8–12	10	10	1.0000	10.0000
12–16	14	18	1.1461	20.6298
16–20	18	30	1.2553	37.6790
20–24	22	15	1.3424	20.1360
24–28	26	12	1.4150	16.9800
28–32	30	10	1.4771	14.7710
32–36	34	6	1.5315	9.1890
36–40	38	2	1.5798	3.1596
				137.1936

GM = AL (Σf log m / N) = 20.45

Example: The price of PVA increased by 5% from 1985 to 1986, 8% from 1986 to 1987 and 77% from 1987 to 1988. The average increase from 1986 to 1988 is quoted as 26% and not 30%. Explain and verify the result.

Example: The appropriate mean here is GM and not AM.

%Rise	Price at the end of the year taking preceding year 100(X)	logX
5	105	2.0212
8	108	2.0334
77	177	2.2480

GM = AL (Σlog X / N) = 126.2

The average increase from 1986 to 1988 = 126.2 − 100 = 26%

Verification:

When the average rise is 30%

Year	Rate of change	Total change	Price at the end of year
1st	30% 100	30	130
2nd	30% 130	39	169
3rd	30% 169	50.7	219.7

When the average rise is 26%

Year	Rate of change	Total change	Price at the end of year
1st	26% on 100	26	126.00
2nd	26% on 126	32.76	158.76
3rd	26% on 158.76	41.27	200.02

When 5%, 8% and 77% the changed price at the end of each year

Year	Rate of change	Total change	Price at the end of year
1st	5% on 100	5.00	105.00
2nd	8% on 105.00	8.40	113.40
3rd	77% on 113.40	87.318	200.00

The above calculations make it clear that in the second and third cases the price at the 3rd year is same. Therefore 26% increase is acceptable.

3.8 Weighted geometric mean

Like weighted arithmetic mean, weighted GM is given by

$$GM = \text{Antilog}\left[\frac{\Sigma(\log XW)}{\Sigma W}\right]$$

Example: Find the weighted geometric mean from the following:

Group	Index no.	Weights
Food	260	46
Fuel and lighting	180	10
Clothing	220	8
House rent	230	20
Education	120	12
Misc.	200	4

Group	Index no.	Weights (W)	log X	W × log X
Food	260	46	2.4150	111.09
Fuel and lighting	180	10	2.2553	22.5530
Clothing	220	8	2.3424	18.7392
House rent	230	20	2.3617	47.2340
Education	120	12	2.0792	24.9504
Misc.	200	4	2.3010	9.2040
		$100 = \Sigma W$		$233.7706 = \Sigma W \times \log X$

$$GM = AL\left[\frac{\Sigma W \log X}{\Sigma W}\right] = 217.6$$

Example: The weighted geometric mean of 4 members 8, 25, 17 and 30 is 15.3. If the weights of the first three members are 5, 3, and 4, respectively, find the weight of the fourth number.

Solution: Let the weight of the fourth number be W_1

X	W	log X	W log X
8	5	0.9031	4.5155
27	3	1.3979	4.1937
17	4	1.2304	4.9216
30	W_1	1.4771	$1.4771W_1$

$\Sigma W = 12 + W \qquad \Sigma W\, Wg\, X = 13.6308 + 1.4771\, W_1$

$\log GM_w = [\Sigma W \log X / \Sigma W]$

$\log 15.3 = (13.6308 + 1.4771W_1) / (12 + W_1)$

$1.1847 (12 + W_1) = 13.6308 + 1.4771W_1$

$W_1 = 2.003$ The weight of fourth number is 2

Example: Find the average rate of increase in % utilisation of travelers in a R/F section. Which in the first month was 20%, second month was 30% and in the third month was by 40%?

Month	%Rise	Proportion of travelers at the end of each month taking the number in preceding month as 100	log X
1st	20%	120	2.0792
2nd	30%	130	2.1139
3rd	40%	140	2.1461
			Σlog X = 6.3392

$GM = AL (\Sigma \log X/N) = 129.7$

Thus, the average rate of increase in utilisation of traveler is = 129.7 – 100 = 29.7% per month.

Example: The geometric mean of 10 observations was calculated as 28.6. It was later discovered that one of the observations was recorded as 23.4 instead of 32.4. Apply appropriate correction and calculate the correct geometric mean.

GM of 'n' observations is given by

$GM = (X_1, X_2, X_3, \ldots \ldots \ldots X_n)^{1/n}$

$GM^n = X_1 X_2 X_3 \ldots \ldots$ [(GM)^n × correct item] / [wrong item]

Here $(GM)^n = (28.6)^n$

$$\therefore \text{Correct GM} = \left[\frac{(28.6)^{10} \times 32.4}{23.4} \right]^{1/10}$$

Log GM = 1/10 [10 × log 28.6 + log 28.6 + log 32.4 + log 23.4] =

$\qquad$ = 1/10 [10 × 1.4564 + 1.5105 – 1.3692] =

$\qquad$ = 1/10 [14.564 + 1.5105 – 1.3692] = 1.47053

GM = 29.54

On weighted average:

Example: Satish started from a place 'X' to a village Y which is at a distance of 6 km. He first traveled by his car at 40 km and covered 4 km. Car stopped because of engine fail. He then took a rickshaw at a speed of 10 km/h after travelling a distance of 1.5 km he left rickshaw and covered the remaining distance on foot at a speed of 4 km/h. Find the average speed per hour of Mr. Satish and verify the calculations.

Solution:

Speed (X)	Distance (W)	W/X
40	4 km	0.1
10	1.5 km	0.15
4	0.5 km	0.125
$\sum W = 6$		$\sum (W/X) = 0.375$

Average speed = $\sum W$ / $\sum (W/X)$ = 6/0.375 = 16 km/h

Verification:

The correctness of the answer can be verified by calculating the time taken

Mode of conveyance	Distance	speed	Time taken
Car	4 km	40 km/h	6 min
Rickshaw	1.5 km	10 km/h	9 min
On foot	0.5 km	4 km/h	7.5 min
Total distance = 6 km		Total time taken = 22.5 min	

In 22.5 minutes 6 km is cover

In 60 minutes, $\dfrac{6 \times 60}{22.5} = 60 = 16$ km

Hence the speed is 16 km/h.

Example: A train runs 25 miles at a speed of 30 km/h and then 50 km at a speed of 40 km/h. Then due to repairs the tracks rail travels at a speed of 10 km/h and finally covers the remaining of 24 km at a speed of 24 km/h. What is the average speed?

Train takes 25 km @ 30 km/h taking = 50 min.
Train takes 50 km @ 40 km/h = 75 min.
Train takes 6 min @ 10 km/h = 1 km.
Time taken in covering 24 km @ 24 km/h = 60 min.

Speed (W)	Time (X)	WX
30	50	1500
40	75	3000
10	6	60
24	60	1440
191 = $\sum W$		6000 = WX

Average speed $\sum WX / \sum W = 6000 / 191 = 31.4$ km/h

3.9   Harmonic mean

Example: Find the harmonic mean from the following 2574, 475, 75, 5, 0.8, 0.08, 0.005, 0.0009

X	(1/X)	X	(1/X)
2574	0.0004	0.8	1.2500
475	0.0021	0.08	12.5000
75	0.0133	0.005	200.0000
5	0.2000	0.0009	1111.1111
			1325.0769 = $\sum(1/X)$

HM = $N/\sum(1/X)$ = 8/1325.0769 = 0.006

Example: From the following data compute the value of HM.

Marks	10	20	25	40	50
No. of students	20	30	50	15	5

Solution:

Marks (X)	f	(f/X)
10	20	2.00
20	30	1.5
25	50	2.0
40	15	0.375
50	5	0.1
	120 = N	5.97 = $\sum(f/X)$

HM = $N/\sum(f/X)$ = 120/5.9 = 20

Example: An airplane covers for 4 sides of a square at speeds of 1000, 2000, 3000 and 4000 km/h, respectively. What is the average speed of the plane in its flight around the square?

Solution: If we compute AM, we get

$$\overline{X} = \frac{1000 + 2000 + 3000 + 4000}{4} = \frac{10,000}{4} = 2500 \text{ km/h}$$

However, this is not correct answer.

$$HM = \cfrac{1}{\cfrac{1}{1000} + \cfrac{1}{2000} + \cfrac{1}{3000} + \cfrac{1}{4000}} = \cfrac{4}{\cfrac{12 + 6 + 4 + 3}{12,000}} = \cfrac{4}{\cfrac{25}{12,000}} = 1,920 \text{ km}$$

Verification:

Suppose one side of a square is 1000 km, i.e., it covers 1000 km at average speed 1000, 2000, 3000, 4000 km/h, respectively. From this we can calculate the time taken in covering the entire distance, i.e., in 125 minutes it covers 4000 km.

In 60 min it covers (4000 / 125) × 60 = 1920 km

Distance (km)	Speed (km/h)	Time taken (min)
1000	1000	60
1000	2000	30
1000	3000	20
1000	4000	15
		125

3.10   Problems on missing frequency

i) Discrete data

From the following data calculate the missing value when its mean is 115.86.

Wages (Rs.):	110	112	113	117	(X)	125	128	130
No. of workers:	25	17	13	15	14	08	06	02

Wages (X)	f	f(X)
110	25	2750
112	17	1904
113	13	1469
117	15	1755
X	14	14X
125	08	1000
128	06	768
130	02	260
	N = 100	9906 + 14X = $\sum$f X

$\bar{X} = \sum f X / N = (9906 + 14X)/100 \qquad X = 120$

ii) Continuous data

Example: Find the missing frequency from the following data:

Marks: 0–10   10–20   20–30   30–40   40–50   50–60
No. of students: 5   15   20   –   20   10

Given mean is 24

Solution: Let the missing frequency is X.

Marks	f	Mid-point (m)	fm
0–10	5	5	25
10–20	15	15	225
20–30	20	25	500
30–40	X	35	35X
40–50	20	45	900
50–60	10	55	550
$70 + X = \sum f$			$\sum fm = 2200 + 35X$

$$\overline{X} = \sum fm/N; \quad 34 = \frac{2200 + 35X}{70 + X} = 180 = X.$$

3.11 Median

The median, symbolized by Md, is the point that divides the distribution into two parts such that an exactly equal number of scores fall above and below the point. It means that 50% of the scores will be above the median and the remaining 50% below it. If all the individuals are arranged in order of size, the median is the value of the middle individual. If the number of individuals is odd and half way between the two middle individuals, the number is even.

When the number of values 'n' is odd, the middle-most value $\frac{(n+1)^{th}}{2}$

in the arrangement will be the unique median. On the other hand, if 'n' is even, the median is the average of $n/2^{nd}$ and $(n/2 + 1)^{st}$ values of the given observation.

Computation of "median" varies in different circumstances, viz., (i) ungrouped data (ii) grouped data

3.11.1 Ungrouped data (Without duplication of number)

(i) When there is an odd number of scores in the distribution:

If in a distribution, there exists odd number of scores (but no duplication of the score near the median), the median is the middle score. The given scores have to be arranged in an ascending order or descending order.

Example: Consider a distribution 4, 6, 7, 8, 10.

Arranging the scores in ascending order 4, 6, 7, 8, 10.

Median is given by $\dfrac{(n+1)^{th}}{2}$ term. If n = 5, (5+1)/2 = 3rd term, i.e., **7**

which is the middle value and divides the distribution into two equal halves.

(ii) When there is even number of scores in the distribution:

i.e. n = 6.45, which implies n = 6

$$\text{Median} = \dfrac{\dfrac{n}{2} + \left(\dfrac{n}{2} + 1\right)}{2} = \dfrac{3 + (3+1)}{2} \text{ terms}$$

This convention applies even if the scores near the median are not adjacent.

Example: In a series of scores 4, 5, 6, 10, 11, 14

$$\text{Median} = \left(\dfrac{3 + (3+1) \text{ terms}}{2}\right) = \left(\dfrac{6 + 10}{2}\right) = 8$$

(iii) When there is a duplication of scores near the median

When more than one instance of a score value falling near the median exists, the median is obtained by "interpolation".

Even number (solved by interpolation and formulae)

Example: Find the median of 4, 5, 6, 6, 6, 7, 7, 8
The distribution can be represented as

Class interval	f	
3.5–4.5	1	|these two are below the median class therefore 4 of the
4.5–5.5	1	|8 observations will fall below the median class.
5.5–6.5	3	→ Median class
6.5–7.5	2	| But out of 4 already score is existing remaining 2 of
7.5–8.5	1	| the 3 scores are within median class.

1. *Interpolation* – Below the median class there are 2 scores and two of the 3 scores are existing between 5.5 to 6.5., i.e. 2/3 or 0.67 of the one unit interval is added to its lower limit. Therefore, 5.5 + 0.67 = 6.17
Median = 6.17

2. *Formula –*

$$Md = L + \left[\frac{\frac{N}{2} - F_b}{F_w} \right] i$$

L = Lower limit of the interval containing median

N = Total number of scores (frequency)

F_b = Number of scores falling below the lower limit of the median class

F_w = Number of scores within the median class

i   = Class size

Here L = 5.5; N = 8; F_b = 2; F_w = 3; i = 1

$$Md = 5.5 + \frac{(4-2) \times 1}{3} = 5.5 + (2/3) = 6.17$$

Odd Number

Example: Find median of 4, 5, 6, 6, 6, 7, 7, 8, 8

The given distribution can be represented as

Class interval	f	
3.5–4.5	1	
4.5–5.5	1	
5.5–6.5	3	→ median class
6.5–7.5	2	
7.5–8.5	2	

Here out of 9 scores 4½ must be below the median and 4½ should be above the median. But in 4½, already 2 scores fall below the lower limit of median class and therefore remaining 2½ of the 3 scores will be within the median class. Therefore, 2½ of the 3 scores of one unit interval are added to its lower limit.

i.e., 2½ / 3 = 0.83 of one unit interval must fall below the median.

∴ The median = 5.5 + 0.83 = 6.33

Formula

L = 5.5; F_b = 2; N = 9; F_w = 3; C=1

$$Md = 5.5 + \left[\frac{\frac{9}{2} - 2}{3} \right] \times 1 = 5.5 + \frac{5}{6} = 6.33$$

3.11.2 Grouped data

"Median" from a frequency distribution:

Formula

$$Md = L + \left[\frac{\dfrac{N}{2} - F_a}{F_w} \right] \times i$$

L = Lower limit of median class
F_a = Cumulative frequency above the median class
F_w = Frequency of the median class
i = Class size
N = Total scores (Σf)

Steps:

1. From the data (if necessary) calculate the exact limits.
2. Cumulate the frequency.
3. Determine N/2, one-half the number of cases.
4. Identify the class interval by referring to the cumulative frequency in which N/2 value lies.
5. Interpolate to find a value on the scale below which and above which ½ of the total number of cases falls. This is the median.

Illustrative examples:

Example: Calculate the mean and median from the following data.

Weight (in g/sq m²)	No. of sorts
410–419	14
420–429	20
430–439	42
440–449	54
450–459	45
460–469	18
470–479	7

Weight	f	c. f
409.5–419.5	14	14
419.5–429.5	20	34
429.5–439.5	42	76
439.5–449.5	**54**	**130**
449.5–459.5	45	175
459.5–460.5	18	193
460.5–479.5	7	200
	200 = N	

Median = N/2 item = 200 / 2 =100

∴ Median class is 439.5–449.5

$$Md = L + \left(\dfrac{\dfrac{N}{2} - cf}{f}\right) \times i = 439.5 + \left\{\dfrac{100 - 76}{54}\right\} \times 10 = 443.94$$

Example: Calculate the median from the following data:

Value	Frequency	Value	Frequency
Less than 10	4	Less than 50	96
20	16	60	112
30		40	120
40	76	80	125

Solution: Given is a cumulative frequency

Value	f	cf	value	f	cf
0–10	4	4	40–50	20	96
10–20	12	16	50–60	16	112
20–30	24	40	60–70	8	120
30–40	36	76	70–80	5	125

$\Sigma f = 125$ Median class = 125/2 = 62.5

$$Md = L + \left\{\dfrac{\dfrac{N}{2} - f_a}{f_m}\right\} \times i = 30 + \left\{\dfrac{62.5 - 40}{36}\right\} \times 10 = 36.25$$

Example: Compute the median from the following data.

Mid value	f	Mid value	f
115	6	165	60
125	25	175	38
135	48	185	22
145	72	195	3
155	116		

Here mid-points are given below:

Class interval	f	cf	Class interval	f	cf
110–120	6	6	160–170	60	32
120–130	25	31	170–180	38	365
130–140	48	79	180–190	22	387
140–150	72	151	190–200	3	390
150–160	116	267			

Median class = 390/2 = 195thL = 150
Note: When CIs are not equal same formula is used.

Example: A cotton gave the following results when tested on balls sorter.

Length in 1/8″	Percentage frequency
2	0
3	2
4	5
5	10
6	18
7	30
8	24
9	11
	100

N / 2 = 50

Class interval	Frequency	Cumulative frequency	
1.5–2.5	0	0	
2.5–3.5	2	2	
3.5–4.5	5	7	
4.5–5.5	10	17	
5.5–6.5	18	35	
6.5–7.5	30	65	Median class
7.5–8.5	24	89	
8.5–9.5	11	100	
	100 = N		

L = 6.5; N = 100; F_a = 35; F_w = 30; C = 1.

$$Md = 6.5 + \left[\frac{50-35}{30}\right] \times 1 = 6.5 + \frac{15}{30} = 7$$

Median length = 7 / 8″

2. Find the mode from the following distribution:

CI	f	Answer	CI	f	cf	
1	8		0.5–1.5	8	8	
2	10		1.5–2.5	10	18	
3	11		2.5–3.5	11	29	
4	16		3.5–4.5	16	45	
5	20		4.5–5.5	20	65	median class
6	25		5.5–6.5	25	90	
7	15		6.5–7.5	15	105	
8	9		7.5–8.5	9	114	
9	6		8.5–9.5	6	120	
	120			120		

N/2 = 60

$$\text{Median} = 4.5 + \left[\frac{60-45}{20} \right] \times 1 = 4.5 + 0.75 = 5.25$$

Note: If instead of CI 'X' is given, it is the mid-point. Hence in such case directly we can write 5 as median without using former.

Example: Find the median from the following distribution

Class interval	f
20–30	3
30–40	5
40–50	20
50–60	10
60–70	5

Class interval	f	c. f	
20–30	3	3	
30–40	5	8	
40–50	20	28	median class
50–60	10	38	
60–70	5	43	
	43		

N/2 = 43/2 = 21.5

$$\text{Md} = 40 + \left[\frac{21.5-80}{20} \right] \times 10 = 40 + \left[\frac{13.75}{20} \right] \times 10 = \text{Rs. } 46.75$$

Example: Find the median from the following distribution

Class interval	f	Exact class interval	f	c f
5–9	9	4.5–9.5	9	9
10–14	5	9.5–14.5	5	14
15–19	7	14.5–19.5	7	21
20–24	8	19.5–24.5	8	29 median class
25–29	8	24.5–29.5	8	37
30–34	6	29.5–34.5	6	43
35–39	2	34.5–39.5	2	45
40–44	3	39.5–44.5	3	48
45–49	2	44.5–49.5	2	50
	50		N/2 = 50/2 = 25	

$$\text{Md} = 19.5 + \left[\frac{25-21}{8} \right] \times 5 = 22$$

Example: Calculate the median for the following data:

Mid-point	Class frequency	Cumulative frequency
60	1	1
62	0	1
64	3	4
66	6	10
68	12	22
70	18	40
72	23	63 median class
74	16	79
76	12	91
78	4	95
80	3	98
82	2	100
N = 100		∴Median = 72

Example: Find the median from the following data:

Class interval of Lea strength	f	Exact limits	f	cf
161–162	5	160.5–162.5	5	5
163–164	20	162.5–164.5	20	25
165–166	35	164.5–166.5	35	60
167–168	60	166.5–168.5	60	120
169–170	15	168.5–170.5	15	135
171–172	05	170.5–172.5	05	140
			140	

N/2 = 140/2 = 70

$$\text{Md} = 166.5 + \left[\frac{70-60}{60}\right] = 166.5 + \frac{1}{3} = 166.83$$

3.12   Mode

Mode is the most frequently occurring value. Mode calculation depends on grouped and ungrouped data.

Ungrouped data:

Example: Calculate the mode in the following cases.

i) 5, 5, 10, 10, 10, 11, 11, 11, 13, 13, 13, 13, 14, 14, 15, 15
    Here the mode is 13 because it repeats 4 times.
ii) 5, 5, 10, 10, 12, 12, 12, 13, 13, 13, 14, 14, 15, 15
    Here 12, 13 have largest frequency but both are repeating thrice
    Therefore, the mode is (12 + 13)/2 = 12.5 (Bimodal case)

iii)   7, 7, 8, 8, 10, 10, 11, 11, 13, 13, 16, 16

Here all are occurring with a frequency of 2. Therefore mode is indeterminate.

3.12.1 Calculation of mode from a frequency distribution

When scores are grouped in the frequency distribution, mode is the mid-point of the class interval with the largest frequency.

Example:

Score	f	
		Here '9' is the highest frequency.
35–39	3	∴ Mode is the mid-point of class 15–19
30–34	4	(15 + 19)/2 = 17
25–29	6	This "mode" obtained is called as "Crude"; it is
20–24	7	approximately equal to true mode.
15–19	9	Modal class
10–14	6	
5–9	5	
	40	

Example: Calculate the mode in the following distribution.

Mid-point	f	
1	4	
2	9	
3	16	
4	25	Mode is 4
5	22	
6	15	
7	7	

In case of continuous frequency distribution

$$\text{Mode} = L + \frac{f_1 - f_0}{2f_1 - f_0 - f_2}(CI)$$

Where, L = lower limit of modal group

f_1 = frequency of modal group

f_0 = frequency of the group above the modal class

f_2 = frequency of the group below the modal class

Example: Find the mode of the following distribution.

Class interval	f	L = 40
0–10	5	$f_1 = 28$
10–20	8	$f_0 = 12$
20–30	T	$f_2 = 20$
30–40	12	

40–50	28	Modal class
50–60	20	
60–70	10	
70–80	10	

$$\text{Mode} = 40 + \frac{28-12}{56-12-20} \times 10 = 40 + \frac{20}{3} = 40.66$$

Example: A cotton gave the following results when tested on the ball sorter.

Length in 1/8″	Frequency
2	0
3	2
4	5
5	10
6	18
7	30
8	24
9	11
	100

Class interval	Frequency	
1.5–2.5	0	
2.5–3.5	2	
3.5–4.5	5	
4.5–5.5	10	
5.5–6.5	18	
6.5–7.5	30	Modal class
7.5–8.5	24	
8.5–9.5	11	
	100	

$$\text{Mode} = 6.5 + \frac{30-18}{60-18-24} \times 1 = 6.5 + 0.66 = 7.16$$

Modal length = 0.89"

Example: Find mode from the following distribution.

Class interval	f	Exact class interval	f	
161–162	05	160.5–162.5	05	
163–164	20	162.5–164.5	20	
165–166	35	164.5–166.5	35	
167–168	60	166.5–168.5	60	Modal class
169–170	15	168.5–170.5	15	
171–172	05	170.5–172.5	05	

$$\text{Mode} = 166.5 \times \frac{60-35}{120-35-15} \times 2 = 167.21$$

Example: Calculate the mode from the following data:

Mid-point of the class	Class frequency	
60	1	
62	0	
64	3	
66	6	
68	12	
70	18	
72	23	Mode is = 72
74	16	
76	12	
78	4	
80	3	
82	2	

Example: Find mode from the following distribution.

Class interval	Least count frequency	Exact CI	Frequency
10.2–11.1	4	10.15–11.15	4
11.2–12.1	15	11.15–12.15	15
12.2–13.1	26	12.15–13.15	26
13.2–14.1	19	13.15–14.15	19
14.2–15.1	6	14.15–15.15	6

$$\text{Mode} = L + \frac{f_1 - f_0}{2f_1 - f_0 - f_2} \times CI = 12.15 + \frac{26 - 15}{52 - 15 - 19} \times 1 = 12.76$$

Example: Find the mode from the following data:

Class interval	f	Exact limits	f	
20–24	10	19.5–24.5	10	
25–29	19	24.5–29.5	19	
30–34	32	29.5–34.5	32	Modal class
35–39	17	34.5–39.5	17	
40–44	12	39.5–44.5	12	

$$\text{Mode} = 29.5 + \frac{32 - 19}{64 - 19 - 17} \times 5 = 31.82$$

Example: Calculate the mode of the following data:

Class interval nep count	f	Exact CI	f
22–23	07	21.5–23.5	07
24–25	18	23.5–25.5	18
26–27	50	25.5–27.5	50
28–29	20	27.5–29.5	20
30–31	05	29.5–31.5	05

$$\text{Mode} = 25.5 + \frac{50 - 18}{100 - 18 - 20} \times 2 = 26.53$$

3.13   Measures of variability

Following are the important measures of dispersion or variability.

1. Range
2. Mean deviation or average deviation
3. Varience
4. Standard deviation
5. Semi-inter quartile range

3.13.1 Range

Range is the difference between highest and lowest values observed.

Range = $X_{max} - X_{min}$

Technically, range is defined as the difference between the upper real limit of largest score minus the lower real limit of the smallest score.

Example:
(i) Strength of fabric A in kg.
     120, 118, 124, 122, 116   Range = 124 – 116 = 8 kg $\bar{X}$ = 120
(ii) Strength of fabric B in kg
     108, 106, 140, 124, 122   Range = 140 – 106 = 34 kg $\bar{X}$ =120

Both the sets of results are having 120 kg strength as mean. But when it is observed, we can say that fabric B is having more variable strength values than fabric A.

3.13.2 Mean range

$\bar{W}_n$ is the mean of the ranges of a number of samples each of size 'n' individuals.

Example: The following shows the method of calculating the mean range from 5 sets of 4 values.

24	21	18	23	Range	6	
16	23	17	20	Range	7	
24	19	14	21	Range	10	
14	17	22	18	Range	8	$\bar{X}$ of 16 readings 19.55
21	20	22	17	Range	5	
				Total 36		

∴ Mean range $\bar{W}_n$ = 36/5=7.2

3.13.3 Percentage mean range

Percentage of the mean $\overline{X}$ $PMR = \dfrac{\overline{W_n} \times 100}{\overline{X}}$

Referring to the above example

$PMR = \dfrac{72 \times 100}{19.55} = 36.8\%$

3.13.4 Inter-quartile range or quartile deviation (Q)

3.13.4.1 *Semi-inter quartile range*

Quartiles divide the area under normal curve into quarters.

Semi-inter quartile range $= (Q_3 - Q_1)/2$

Q_3 = upper quartile Q_2 = median Q_1 = lower quartile

A quarter of the population has values above the upper quartile Q_2, and a quarter has values below the lower quartile Q_1. The inter-quartile range is the difference between the upper and lower quartile range values. It will be appreciated that 50% of the population values lie between these two quartiles. The three quartiles Q_1, Q_2, Q_3 are such values which are 25% of value less than or equal to Q_1, 50% of the values are less than or equal to Q_2 and 75% of the values are less than equal to Q_3.

For calculating quartiles Q_1, we usually count n/4 of the items starting with the smallest values, and for Q_3 we usually count 3n/4 of the item starting with the smallest value.

3.13.4.2 *Coefficient of quartile variation*

It is a measure of relative variation and is given by the ratio of the semi-inter quartile range to the Q_1 and Q_3 multiplied by 100.

$\dfrac{Q_3 - Q_1}{Q_3 + Q_1} \times 100$

Deviation – Deviation is the difference between each value and the arithmetic mean.

Example:
A set of values are 24, 21, 20, 23. Calculate deviation.

X	$(X - \overline{X}) = d$	
24	2	
21	−1	$\overline{X} = 88/4 = 22$
20	−2	
23	1	
88		

3.13.4.3 *Mean deviation*

It is defined as the modulus values of the deviations from the mean divided by the total number of the values considered.

Hence, mean deviation $= \dfrac{\text{Sum of the mean deviations from the mean}}{\text{Total no. of observations}}$

Mean deviations $= \dfrac{\sum \left| X - \overline{X} \right|}{N}$ where, n = Number of observations

$\overline{X}$ = Arithmetic mean
X = Observed value

Mean deviation is not common by use in statistical work, since this is not amenable to mathematical treatment. But in textiles it plays an important role in the measurement of yarn irregularity with yarn evenness testers.

Example: Calculation of mean deviation.

Value X	Deviation from mean $(X - \overline{X})$	
27	2	
22	−3	
24	−1	Mean deviation = 38/10 = 3.8
29	4	Percentage mean deviation = (3.8 × 100)/25 = 15.2%
31	6	
21	−4	
23	−2	
20	−5	Higher the PMD higher will be the dispersion or scatter or variation
32	7	
21	−4	
250	$\sum |X - \overline{X}| = 38$	

$\overline{X} = 250/10 = 25$

3.13.5 Standard deviation

It is very important measure of dispersion and is most useful and therefore widely used.

Definition

It is simply defined as room-mean-square deviation

$$\sigma = \sqrt{\dfrac{\left(X - \overline{X} \right)^2}{n-1}}$$

$$\sigma = \sqrt{\frac{n(\sum x^2) - (\sum x)^2}{n(n-1)}}$$

Note: Use N − 1 when N<30 and use N when N>30 in formulae.

Example: Lea strength in lbs of the yarn tested for 6 leas are as follows: 6, 12, 9, 10, 9, 8

$$\sigma = \sqrt{\frac{(X - \overline{X})^2}{n-1}}$$

I. *Calculate SD of samples.*

X	(X − X̄)	(X − X̄)²	
6	−3	9	σ = √21/5 = 2.04
12	3	9	
9	0	0	
10	1	1	
9	0	0	
8	−1	1	
51	21		

$\overline{X} = 54/6 = 9$

II. *SD can also be calculated by the following formula.*

$$\sigma = \sqrt{\frac{n(\sum x^2) - (\sum x)^2}{n(n-1)}}$$

X	X²	
6	36	
12	144	
9	81	
10	100	
9	81	
8	64	
54	506	σ = 2.0

3.13.6 Variance

Variance is the square of standard deviation $V = \sigma^2$ or $\sigma = \sqrt{V}$

3.13.6.1 *Coefficient of variation*

It is defined as the standard deviation expressed as percentage of mean.
In the above example, mean = 9, σ = 2

CV % = 22.22%

Variance has the useful property of being additive. This means that if each of the factors introduces a certain amount of variation in the product, the total variance is the sum of the independent variance.

Using symbol σ^2 for variance this additive property may be indicated as follows:

$$\sigma^2_T = \sigma^2_1 + \sigma^2_2 + ... \sigma^2_n$$

Example: Due to improper drafting, thin and thick place will resist the variance at 3 drafting zones – 0.8, 1.2 and 3, respectively. What is the total variance of the yarn?
V = 1.2 + 0.8 + 3 = 5

If the distribution is reasonably normal one then

SD = 1.25 × mean deviation

Example: If the mean deviation and mean for a lea strength data for 2 set of yarns having normal distribution are 1.6 and 43, 2 and 45, respectively, then which yarn is more uniform?

1st yarn   σ = 1.25 × 1.6 = 2
                      CV% = 2/43 × 100 = 4.65%
2nd yarn   σ = 1.25 × 2 = 2.5
                      CV% = 2.5/45 × 100 = 5.5%

The 1st set of yarn is more uniform when compared to 2nd set of yarn.

3.14   Deviation score method

Steps:

 (i)   Calculate mean
 (ii) Calculate deviation of each score from the mean.
 (iii) Square each deviation
 (iv) Sum up the squared deviations
 (v)   Substitute in formulae

I. Score	(X– X)	(X– X)²	II. Raw score method		
10	+2	4	Score	X²	
7	–1	1	10	100	
9	+1	1	7	49	
6	–2	4	9	81	
8	0	0	6	36	
			8	64	
5 = N 40		10	40	330	X̄ = 8

$$SD = \sqrt{\frac{\Sigma(x-\bar{x})^2}{N-1}} = 1.58$$

$$\sigma = \sqrt{\frac{n(\Sigma x^2)-(\Sigma x)^2}{n(n-1)}}$$

$$CV = \frac{SD \times 100}{\bar{X}} = 19.75\%$$

Example: Following are the number of imperfections observed in 50 standard bales of cloth. If the standards for SD and CV are 0.5% and 8%, would you say that process of weaving was out of control? How many of observations are falling above 2 and below 3?

```
2 0 4    4 1 4    0 3    2 0
0 1 1    1 0 1    2 4    1 1
1 5 2    2 5 3    4 0    4 0
0 0 3    1 4 2    1 2    0 0
3 1 3    2 0 5    6 3    2 4
```

Determine SD and mean (consider class size as 1).

Class X	Tally	Frequency (f)	Cumulative frequency	fx	(x – x̄)	(x – x̄)²	f(x – x̄)²
0	1111111111	12	12	0	–2	4	48
1	111111111	11	23	11	–1	1	11
2	11111111	9	32	18	0	0	0
3	11111	6	38	18	1	1	6
4	1111111	8	46	32	2	4	32
5	111	3	49	15	3	9	27
6	1	1	50	6	4	16	16
		50		100			140

Mean = $\bar{X}$ = $\Sigma f x / \Sigma f$ = 100/50 = 2

$$SD = \sqrt{\frac{\Sigma f(X-\bar{X})^2}{N}} = 1.6$$

(i)   Proportions of observations will fall below 3.

$$\frac{\text{Comulative frequency upto 3}}{\text{Total number of observation}} \times 100 = \frac{38}{50} \times 100 = 76\%$$

(ii) Proportions of observations falling above 2

$$\frac{\text{Number of observations from 3 to 6}}{\text{Total number of observations}} \times 100 = \frac{15}{50} \times 100 = 36\%$$

3.14.1 Grouped data

Steps:

1.   Write down the class intervals and frequencies.
2.   Find out the mid-point of each interval.
3.   Calculate the mean by the formulae $\Sigma fx / \Sigma f$ where x is the mid-point of each class.
4.   Calculate the deviations from mean (mid-point mean) for each score (x).
5.   Find f(x) where x $(X - \overline{X})$
6.   Find f(x) x (x)
7.   Find Σfx^2
8.   Substitute in the formulae

Calculate SD, CV and variance from the following data.

Calculation of mean:

CI	Mid-point	Frequency (f)	f x	$(X - \overline{X})$	f(x)	f(x)^2
45–49	47	2	94	24.6	49.2	1210.32
40–44	42	3	126	19.6	58.8	1152.48
35–39	37	2	94	14.6	29.2	426.23
30–34	32	6	192	9.6	57.6	552.96
25–29	27	8	216	4.6	36.8	169.28
20–24	22	8	176	–0.4	–3.2	1.28
15–19	17	7	119	–5.4	–37.8	204.12
10–14	12	5	60	–10.4	–52.0	540.80
5–9	7	9	63	–15.4	–138.6	2134.44
		50	1120			

$$\overline{X} = \Sigma fx / N = 1120/50 = 22.4$$

$$\sigma = \sqrt{\frac{\Sigma f(x^2)}{N}} = \sqrt{\frac{6392}{50}} = 11.31$$

$$CV = 11.31/22.4 \times 100 = 50.49$$

3.15   Short-cut method (assumed mean method)

Step deviation method to calculate SD, CV and variance.

Steps:

1. Arrange the scores and frequencies.
2. Find out the mid-points of all the class intervals.
3. Select one of the mid-point as assumed mean. This point should be close to the middle of the distribution as far as possible and should have the largest fs.
4. Deviations from mid-point are calculated (x'). It is a mechanical process. Assign 0 to the class interval in which the assumed mean lies. Go on assigning $-1, -2, -3$, above the zero to the CI (If CI is arranged in ascending order, i.e. regular) and below $+1, +2, +3$, etc., or vice-versa if CI is arranged in descending order.
5. Get the product f x' and sum up to get $\Sigma f x'$.
6. Multiply f x' and x' to get fx^{12} and sum up to get Σfx^{12}.
7. Find out the value of C which is $\Sigma f x' / N$.
8. Substitute these values in the formula.

$$\sigma = i\sqrt{\frac{\Sigma fx^{12} - C^2}{N}}$$

Example:

CI	Mid-point	Frequency	x'	fx'	fx'^2
5–9	7	9	–4	–36	144
10–14	12	5	–3	–15	045
15–19	17	7	–2	–14	028
20–24	22	8	–1	–8	008
25–29	27	8	0	0	000
30–34	32	6	1	6	006
35–39	37	2	2	4	008
40–44	42	3	3	9	027
45–49	47	2	4	8	032
		50		$-46 = \Sigma f x'$	298

$C = \Sigma f x' / N = 0.92$

$$\sigma = \sqrt{\frac{\Sigma fx^{12} - C^2}{N}} = 12.22$$

Example: Calculate SD, CV for the following grouped distribution. A = Assumed mean = 23.

S. no.	CI	Frequency	Mid-point	x'	fx'	x'²	fx'²
1	59–60	2	59.5	–6	–12	36	72
2	61–62	0	61.5	–5	0	25	0
3	63–64	3	63.5	–4	–12	16	48
4	65–66	6	65.5	–3	–18	9	54
5	67–68	11	67.5	–2	–22	4	44
6	69–70	18	69.5	–1	–18	1	18
7	71–72	23	71.5	0	0	0	0
8	73–74	16	73.5	1	16	1	16
9	75–76	12	75.5	2	24	4	48
10	77–78	4	77.5	3	12	9	36
11	79–80	3	79.5	4	12	16	48
12	81–82	2	81.5	5	10	25	50
		100		–8			434

$C = \Sigma f\ x'/N = 0.08$

$$\sigma = 1\sqrt{\frac{434 + 0.0064}{100}} = 2.08$$

Example: Calculate the mean and standard deviation for the following:

CI	Mid-point	f	x'	fx'	x'²	fx'²
36.2–36.4	36.3	6	–0.3	–1.8	0.09	0.54
36.5–36.7	36.6	12	–1.5	–18	–2.25	27.00
36.8–37.0	36.9	18	0	0	0	0.00
37.1–37.3	37.2	14	1.5	21.0	2.25	31.50
37.4–37.6	37.5	05	0.3	1.5	0.09	0.45
		55		2.7		59.49

$A = 36.9 \qquad C = \Sigma f\ x'/N = 0.04$

$$\sigma = 0.2\sqrt{\frac{59.49 - 0.0016}{55}} = 0.20$$

$A = C + (0.06 \times 0.2) = 36.9 + 0.012$

$CV = 0.59\%$

CI	Mid-point	f	f x	$(X - \bar{X})$	$(X - \bar{X})^2$	$f(X - \bar{X})^2$
36.2–36.4	36.3	6	217.8	–0.6	0.36	2.16
36.5–36.7	36.6	12	439.2	–0.3	0.09	1.08
36.8–37.0	36.9	18	664.2	0	0	0.00
37.1–37.3	37.2	14	520.8	0.3	0.09	1.26
37.4–37.6	37.5	05	187.5	0.6	0.36	1.80

$\bar{X} = \Sigma f\ x/\Sigma f = 36.9 \quad \sigma = 0.3 \quad CV = 0.3 \times 100/36.9 = 0.8\%$

Example: Calculate standard deviation.

CI	Mid-point	Frequency	x'	fx'	fx'²
20–24	22	10	–2	–20	40
25–29	27	19	–1	–19	19
30–34	32	32	0	0	00
35–39	37	17	1	17	17
40–44	42	12	2	24	48
		90		41	124

$A = 32$ $C = \Sigma fx' / N = 3/90 = 0.03$ mean $= 32 + (0.03 \times 5) = 32.15$

$$\sigma = 5\sqrt{\frac{124 - 0.0009}{90}} = 5.86$$

$CV = (5.86/32) \times 100 = 18.31\%$

Example: Calculate the mean and standard deviation of the following frequency distribution.

Marks	No. of students	Marks	No. of students
0–10	5	40–50	50
10–20	12	50–60	37
20–30	30	60–70	21
30–40	45		

Marks	Mid-point	f	d	fd	fd²
0–10	5	5	–3	–15	45
10–20	15	12	–2	–24	48
20–30	25	30	–1	–30	30
30–40	35	45	0	0	00
40–50	45	50	1	50	50
50–60	55	37	2	74	148
60–70	65	21	3	63	189
		$200 = \Sigma f$		$118 = \Sigma fd$	$510 = \Sigma fd^2$

$A = 35$

$$\overline{X} = A + \frac{\Sigma fd}{\Sigma f} \times i = 35 + \frac{118}{200} \times 10 = 40.9$$

$$SD = \sqrt{\frac{\Sigma fd^2}{N} - \left(\frac{\Sigma fd}{N}\right)^2} \times 10 = \sqrt{2.55 - 0.3481} \times 10 = 14.839$$

Example: Following data refers to the marks secured by 400 students in an examination.

Marks	No. of students	Marks	No. of students
35–40	25	70–75	15
40–45	50	75–80	12
45–50	110	80–85	08
50–55	34	85–90	07
55–60	40	90–95	03
60–65	60	95–100	01
65–70	10	$\Sigma f = 375$	

Find mean, median, mode and standard deviation.

If the above distribution is assumed to be normal, what percentage of students will score between 64 and 74 marks?

Class	Mid-point	f	D	fd	Cum f	fd^2
35–40	37.5	25	–2	–50	25	100
40–45	42.5	50	–1	–50	75	50
45–50	47.5	110	0	0	185	0
50–55	52.5	34	1	34	219	34
55–60	57.5	40	2	80	259	160
60–65	62.5	60	3	180	319	540
65–70	67.5	10	4	40	329	540
70–75	72.5	15	5	75	344	160
75–80	77.5	12	6	72	356	375
80–85	82.5	08	7	56	364	432
85–90	87.5	07	8	56	371	392
90–95	92.5	03	9	27	374	448
95–100	97.5	01	10	10	375	100
		$375 = \Sigma f$		$530 = \Sigma fd$		$3034 = \Sigma fd^2$

$$Md = L + \frac{\left(\dfrac{N}{2} - f_a\right)}{f_w} \times ci = 50 + \frac{(187.5 - 185)}{34} \times 5 = 50.36$$

A = 47.5   C = 5

Where X – Observed value

$$\overline{X} = A + \left(\frac{\Sigma fd}{\Sigma f}\right) \times C = 47.5 + \frac{530}{375} \times 5 = 54.56$$

$$SD = \sqrt{\frac{\Sigma fd^2}{N} - \left(\frac{\Sigma fd}{N}\right)^2} \times C = \sqrt{\frac{3074}{375} - \left(\frac{530}{375}\right)^2} \times 5 = 12.35$$

$$Z_1 = \frac{X_1 - \overline{X}}{\sigma} = 0.76$$

From area under the curve tables, area upto Z_1 = 0.7764.

$Z_2 = Y_2 - \bar{X}$ = 1.57   Area upto Z_2 = 0.9418

Area between 64 and 74 = 0.9418 - 0.7764 = 0.1654 or 16.54%

3.16   Mathematical properties of standard deviation

Standard deviation has some very important mathematical properties which considerably enhance its utility in statistical work.

1. Combined statistical deviation.
    Similar to computation of combined mean, combined standard deviation of two or three groups can be calculated. Combined standard deviation is given by

$$\sigma_{12} = \sqrt{\frac{N_1\sigma^2_1 + N_2\sigma^2_2 + N_1d^2_1 + N_2d^2_2}{N_1 + N_2}}$$

Where s_{12} = combined standard deviation
s_1 = standard deviation of 1st group
s_2 = standard deviation of 2nd group
$d_1 = ('X_1 - 'X_{12})$ $d_2 = ('X_2 - 'X_{12})$

2. Standard deviation of 'n' natural numbers.

$$\sigma = \sqrt{\frac{1}{12}(N^2 - 1)}$$

{Natural number N = 1 to 10}

3. The sum of the squares of the deviations of items in the series from their arithmetic mean is minimum. In other words, the sum of the squares of the deviations of items of any series from a value other than arithmetic mean would always be greater. This is why standard deviation is always computed from the arithmetic mean.

4. The standard deviation enables us to determine with a great deal of accuracy, where the values of a frequency distribution are located with the help of Cheby cheff's theorem. No matter what the shape of distribution is, at least 75% of the values will fall within $\pm$ 2 SD from mean of the distribution and at least 89% of the values will lie within $\pm$ 3 SD from the mean. With the help of normal curve we can measure even with greater precision the number of items that fall within specific ranges.

    For a symmetrical distribution the following relationships hold good.

    Mean $\pm$ 1 σ covers 68.27% of items

    Mean $\pm$ 2 σ covers 95.45% of items

    Mean $\pm$ 3 σ covers 99.73% of items

3.16.1 Relation between measures of dispersion

In normal distribution there is a fixed relationship between the 3 most commonly used measures of dispersion. Quartile deviation is the smallest, mean deviation next and SD is largest.

QD = 2 / 3 σ and MD = 4 / 5 σ

Co-efficient of standard deviation = SD / Mean

3.17 Correcting incorrect values of mean and standard deviation

Example: Mean and standard deviation of a set of 100 fibre length observations were worked out as 40 and 5, respectively. Find the correct mean and variance.

Solution: $\bar{X} = \Sigma N/N$ or $N\bar{X} = \Sigma X$, N = 100, $\bar{X}$ = 40, ΣX = 100 × 40 = 4000

But this is not the correct ΣX, because an item has been taken as 50 instead of 40.

Correct ΣX = 4000 – 50 + 40 = 3990
Correct mean = 3990 /N = 3990/100 = 39.90

Correct variance

$$\text{variance} = \frac{\Sigma X^2}{N} - \overline{(X)^2}$$

Variance = σ^2 = 25, N = 100

$$25 = (\Sigma X^2 / 100) - (40)^2$$
$$\Sigma X^2 = 2500 + 160000 = 162500$$
$$\text{Correct } \Sigma X^2 = 162500 - 2500 + 1600 = 161600$$

Correct variance = (correct ΣX^2 / N) – (correct $\bar{X}$)²
$$= (161600/100) - (39.9)^2 = 23.99$$

Example: In a silk factory the number of employees, wage/employee and variance of wage/employee is as follows:

Number of employees = 100,
Average wage per employee /week = Rs. 85/-
Variance of wages per employee/week = 16

Suppose the wages of an employee were wrongly noted as Rs. 120/- instead of Rs. 100/-, calculate the correct variance.

$\bar{X} = \Sigma X / N$ $N\bar{X} = \Sigma X$ ΣX = 100 × 85 = 8500

Correct $åX = 8500 - 120 + 100 = 8480$

$$\overline{X} = 8480/100 = 84.8$$
$$\Sigma X^2 = 724100$$
Correct $\Sigma X^2 = 724100 - (120)^2 + (100)^2 = 719700$
$$(719700/100) - (84.8)^2 = 5.96$$

Example: The mean of 5 observations of micronaire value is 4.4 and the variance is 8.24. If the three of the 5 observations are 1, 2 and 6, find the other two.

$$\overline{X} = \Sigma X / N, \quad \Sigma X = N X, \quad N = 5, \quad X = 4.4 \quad \Sigma X = 5 \times 4.4 = 22$$

Let the two missing items be x_1 and x_2

$$1 + 2 + 6 + x_1 + x_2 = 22$$
$$x_1 + x_2 = 22 - 9 = 13$$
$$41.20 = \Sigma X^2 - 19.36 \times 5 \text{ or } \Sigma X^2 = 138$$
$$\Sigma X^2 = x_1^2 + x_2^2 + 1^2 + 2^2 + 6^2 = x_1^2 + x_2^2 + 41$$
$$x_1^2 + x_2^2 = 138 - 41 = 97$$
$$(x_1 + x_2)^2 = x_1^2 + x_2^2 + 2x_1 x_2$$
$$(13)^2 = 97 + 2x_1 x_2,$$
$$169 = 97 + 2x_1 x_2$$
$$x_1 x_2 = 36$$
$$(x_1 - x_2)^2 = 25$$
$$x_1 = 9, x_2 = 4$$

Example: Arithmetic mean and standard deviation of a series of 20 items in a ring frame store were calculated by a student as 20 cm and 5 cm, respectively. But while calculating an item 13 was misread as 30. Find the correct arithmetic mean and standard deviation.

Calculating correct mean

$$\overline{X} = \Sigma X / N, N \overline{X} = \Sigma X,$$
$$N = 20, \overline{X} = 20, \Sigma X = 400$$

Correct mean $= 400 - 30 + 13 = 383$
$$\overline{X} = 383/20 = 19.15$$
Calculation of correct standard deviation

$$\sigma^2 = \frac{\Sigma X^2}{N} - \left(\overline{X}\right)^2 = \frac{\Sigma X^2}{20} - (20)^2$$

implies $\Sigma X^2 = 8500$

Correct standard deviation
$\Sigma X^2 = 8500 - (30)^2 + (13)^2 = 7769$
Correct σ

$$\sqrt{\frac{\text{correct} \, \Sigma X^2}{N} - \left(\text{correct} \, \overline{X}\right)^2} = 4.55$$

Example: The mean and standard deviation of 200 items in a weaving store are found to be 60 and 20, respectively. If at the time of calculations two items were wrongly taken as 3 and 67 instead of 13 and 17. Find the correct mean and standard deviation. What is the correct coefficient of variation?

Solution: $\overline{X} = \Sigma X / N$, $\overline{X} = 60$, $N = 200$ $\Sigma X = 12000$
Correct $\Sigma X = 12000 - 3 - 13 + 17 = 11960$
∴ Correct mean $= 11960/200 = 59.8$

Correct deviation

$\Sigma X^2 = 400 \times 200 + 720000$
Correct $\Sigma X^2 = 800000 - 3^2 - (67)^2 + (13)^2 + (17)^2 = 795960$

Example: For two groups of observations the following results were available.

Group I	Group II
$\Sigma(X - 5) = 8$	$\Sigma(X - 8) = -10$
$N_1 = 20$	$N_2 = 21$

Find the $\overline{X}$ and SD of 45 observations obtained by combining the two groups.

Sol.

Group I	Group II
$\Sigma(X - 5) = 8$	$\Sigma(X - 8) = -10$
$\Sigma X = 108$	$\Sigma X = 190$
$\Sigma(X - 5)^2 = 40$	$\Sigma(X - 8)^2 = 70$
$\Sigma X^2 = 620$	$\Sigma X^2 = 1510$

For 45 combined observations are

$\Sigma X = 108+190 = 298$
$\Sigma X^2 = 620 + 1510 = 2130$

Combined mean $= 298/45 = 6.22$

$$\sigma = \sqrt{\frac{\Sigma X^2}{N} - \left(\overline{X}\right)^2} = 2.94$$

3.18   Problems on co-efficient of variation

Use of $\sigma = 1.25 \times$ Mean deviation   Mean deviation = 4/5 σ

Example: If the mean deviation and mean for a lea strength data for 2 set of yarns having normal distribution are 1.6 and 43, 2 and 45, respectively, which yarn is more uniform?

1st yarn σ $= 1.25 \times 1.6 = 2$
$\quad$ CV% $= 2/43 \times 100 = 4.65\%$
2nd yarn σ $= 1.25 \times 2 = 2.5$
$\quad$ CV% $= 2.5/45 \times 100 = 5.5\%$

First yarn is more uniform as compared to second yarn.

Example: A tensile test of certain yarns from two manufacturers is given below. Which is more uniform in its strength?

Manufacturer	First	Second					
1	2	X	$(X - \bar{X})$	$(X - \bar{X})^2$	Y	$(Y - \bar{Y})$	$(Y - \bar{Y})^2$
50	48	50	−2.16	4.66	48	−7.66	58.67
52	50	52	−0.16	0.02	50	−5.66	32.03
60	64	60	7.84	61.46	64	8.34	69.55
45	52	45	−7.16	51.26	52	−3.66	13.39
48	62	48	−4.16	17.30	62	6.34	40.19
58	58	58	5.84	34.10	58	−2.34	5.41
	313			168.8	334		219.3

First manufacturer

$$\sigma = \sqrt{\frac{\Sigma\left(X - \bar{X}\right)^2}{n - 1}} = \sqrt{168.8/5} = 5.81$$

$$CV\% = \frac{5.81}{52.16} \times 100 = 11.12\%$$

Second manufacturer

$$\sigma = \sqrt{\frac{219.3}{5}} = 6.62$$

$$CV\% = 11.89$$

Yarn supplied by first manufacturer is more uniform in its strength compared to yarn supplied by second manufacturer.

Example: The life test of certain component from two manufacturers is given below:

Length of life in hours	Manufacturers	
	A	B
700–900	10	3
900–1100	16	42
1100–1300	26	12
1300–1500	8	3

Which manufacturer's components are more uniform? Taking 100 hours = 1 hour

Manufacturer 1:

CI	Mid-point	F	d	fd	fd²
7–9	8	10	8 – 12 = –4	–40	160
9–11	10	16	10 – 12 = –2	–32	64
11–13	12	26	12 – 12 = 0	0	0
13–15	14	8	14 – 12 = 2	16	32
		60		–56	256

$A = 12$

$\bar{X} = A + (\Sigma fd/\Sigma f);\quad 12 + (-56/60) = 12.933$

$$\sigma = \sqrt{\frac{\Sigma d^2}{N} - \left(\frac{\Sigma fd}{N}\right)^2} = \sqrt{4.26 - 0.87} = 1.84$$

$CV\% = (1.84/12.93) \times 100 = 14.23\%$

Manufacturer 2:

CI	Mid-point	f	(X – A)	fd	fd²
7–9	8	3	–2	–6	12
9–11	10	42	0	0	0
11–13	12	12	2	24	48
13–15	14	3	4	12	48
		60		30	108

$A = 10$

$\bar{X} = A + (\Sigma fd/\Sigma f) = 10.5$

$$\sigma = \sqrt{\frac{108}{60} - (0.5)^2} = 1.24$$

$CV\% = (1.24/10.5) \times 100 = 11.85\%$

When compared, manufacturer 2 components are uniform.

3.18.1 Grouped data

Example: You are given below the daily wages paid to the workers in two factories X and Y

Daily wages	12–13	13–14	14–15	15–16	16–17	17–18	18–19
Factory X (no. of workers)	15	30	44	60	30	14	7
Factory Y (no. of workers)	25	40	60	35	12	15	5

Using appropriate measures explain:

i) Which factory pays higher average wage?
ii) Which factory has a consistent wage structure?

CI	X	f	d	fd	fd²	Y	f	fd'	fd'
12–13	12.5	15	–3	–45	135	–3	25	–75	225
13–14	13.5	30	–2	–60	120	–2	40	–80	160
14–15	14.5	44	–1	–44	44	–1	60	–60	60
15–16	15.5	60	0	0	0	0	35	0	000
16–17	15.5	30	1	30	30	1	12	12	12
17–18	17.5	14	2	28	56	2	15	30	60
18–19	18.5	7	3	21	63	3	5	15	45
		200		–70	448	15.5	192	–158	562

A = 15.5

$$\bar{X} = A + (\Sigma fd / N) = 15.15 \quad \bar{X} = A + (\Sigma fd/N) = 15.5 + 0.82 = 14.68$$

$$\sigma = \sqrt{\frac{448}{200} - (0.1225)} = 1.45 ... \sigma = \sqrt{\frac{562}{192} - (0.6724)} = 1.5$$

CV = 9.57%   CV = 10.22%

∴ Factory 'X' has consistent wage structure.

Example: From the data given below state, which series is most consistent?

Variable	10–20	20–30	30–40	40–50	50–60	60–70
Series A	20	18	32	40	22	18
Series B	13	22	40	32	18	10

Series A: A = 45; $\bar{X}$ = 42.14
              σ = 14.05
              CV = 33.34

Series B: A = 45; $\bar{X}$ = 37.86
              σ = 14.06
              CV = 37.14%

Example: Find the SD from the following data.

Age under	10	20	30	40	50	60	70	80
No. of persons dying	15	30	53	75	100	110	115	125

Age group	X	Cum f	Exact f	d	fd	fd²
1–10	5	15	15	–4	–60	240
10–20	15	30	15	–3	–45	135
20–30	25	53	23	–2	–46	92
30–40	35	75	22	–1	–22	22
40–50	45	100	25	0	0	0
50–60	55	110	10	1	10	10
60–70	65	115	5	2	10	20
70–80	75	125	10	3	30	90
			125		173	609

A = 45   A = 45 + (–123/125) × 10 = 35.16

$$\sigma = \sqrt{\frac{\Sigma fd^2}{N} - \left\{ \left(\frac{\Sigma fd}{N} \right)^2 \right\}} \times 10 = \sqrt{4.87 - 0.968} \times 10 = 19.75$$

When even number class intervals exist, to select A take the value n/2 class. Here it is 35.

Example: Find the standard deviation of the following distribution

Age	20–25	25–30	30–35	35–40	40–45	45–50
No. of persons	170	110	80	45	40	35

Age	Mid-point	f	d	fd	fd²
20–25	22.5	170	–2	-340	680
25–30	27.5	110	–1	–110	110
30–35	32.5	80	0	0	0
35–40	37.5	45	1	45	45
40–45	42.5	40	2	80	160
45–50	47.5	35	3	105	315
A = 32.5		489		220	1310

$$\sigma = \sqrt{\frac{1380}{480} - \left(\frac{-220}{480} \right)^2} \times 5 = 7.936$$

3.19   Calculation of standard deviation – discrete, individual

3.19.1 Individual scores

Following methods can be employed.

1. Deviations taken from actual mean

$$\sigma = \sqrt{\frac{\Sigma x^2}{N}} \text{where}(x) = (X - \overline{X})$$

2. Deviations taken from assumed mean

$$\sigma = \sqrt{\frac{\sum d^2}{N} - \left(\frac{\sum d}{N}\right)^2}$$

Example: Calculate SD from the following data: (actual mean)
240, 260, 290, 245, 255, 288, 272, 263, 277, 251

X	d	d²	
240	−24	576	
260	−4	16	
290	+26	676	
245	−19	361	
255	−9	81	
288	+24	576	
272	8	1	
263	1	1	
277	1	1	
251	−13	169	
2641	1	2689	A = 264

$$\sigma = \sqrt{\frac{\sum d^2}{N} - \left(\frac{\sum d}{N}\right)^2} = 16.369$$

3.19.2 Discrete series

(Actual mean or deviation (Assumed mean))

X	F	d	fd	fd²
3.5	3	−3	−9	27
4.5	7	−2	−14	28
5.5	22	−1	−22	22
6.5	60	0	0	0
7.5	85	1	85	85
8.5	32	2	64	128
9.5	8	3	24	72
	217		128	362

$45.5 = \sum X$

$$\sigma = \sqrt{\frac{362}{217} - \left(\frac{128}{217}\right)^2} = 1.149$$

A → here 'n' is odd therefore 6.5 is the middle term i.e., $\bar{X} = \sum X/N = 45.5/7 = 6.5$

3.19.2.1 *Discrete series – (step deviation method)*

Example: Find SD for the following distribution

X	4.5	14.5	24.5	34.5	44.5	54.5	64.5
f	1	5	12	22	17	9	4

x	F	d	fd	fd²
4.5	1	-3	-3	9
14.5	5	-2	-10	20
24.5	12	-1	-12	12
34.5	22	0	0	0
44.5	17	1	17	17
54.5	9	2	18	36
64.5	4	3	12	36
A = 34.5	70		22	130

Example: An analysis of the monthly wages paid to workers in two firms A and B belonging to the same industry, gives the following result.

	Firm A	Firm B
No. of employees	550	650
Average monthly wages	1450	1400
SD of wages	$\sqrt{10000}$	$\sqrt{19600}$

Answer the following questions with proper justifications.

a) Which firm A or B pays larger amount of weekly wages?
b) In which firm A or B is there greater variability in wages?
c) Calculate average weekly wages and SD of wages in two firms together.

a) Total wages of Firm A and Firm B.
   Firms A = 550 × 1450 = 797500
   Firms B = 650 × 1400 = 910000
   B pays larger amount as weekly wages.

b) $CV = \sigma / \bar{X} \times 100 = 6.89\%$
   $CV = 10\%$
   There is greater variation in wage distribution of wage.

c) Combined mean and standard deviation

$$\bar{X}_{1\&2} = \frac{N_1\bar{X}_1 + N_2\bar{X}_2}{N_1 + N_2} = \frac{(550\times1450)+(650\times1400)}{550+650} = 1422.9$$

$$\sigma_{12} = \sqrt{\frac{N_1\sigma^2_1 + N_2\sigma^2_2 + N_1d_1^2 + N_2d_2^2}{N_1 + N_2}}$$

$$d_1 = (\overline{X}_1 - \overline{X}_2) = (1450 - 1422.92) = 27.08$$
$$d_2 = (\overline{X}_2 - \overline{X}_{12}) = (1400 - 1422.92) = -22.92$$
$$\sigma_{12} = 39.78$$

Example: The first of the two sub-groups has 100 items with mean 15 and standard deviation 3. If the whole group has 250 items with mean 15.6 and SD $\sqrt{13.44}$. Find the SD of second group.

$$N_1 = 100, \ \overline{X} = 15, \ \sigma = 3, \ N_1 + N_2 = 250, \ \overline{X}_{12} = 15.6, \ \sigma_{12} = \sqrt{13.44}$$

$$\overline{X}_{12} = \frac{N_1\overline{X}_1 + N_2\overline{X}_2}{N_1 + N_2}; 15.6 = \frac{100 \times 15 + 150 \times \overline{X}_2}{250}; \text{implies} \overline{X}_2 = 16$$

$$\sigma_{12}^2 = \frac{N_1\sigma_1^2 + N_2\sigma_2^2 + N_1 d_1^2 + N_2 d_2^2}{N_1 + N_2}$$

$$d_1 = (\overline{X}_1 - \overline{X}_{12}) = (15 - 15.6) = -0.6$$
$$d_2 = (16 - 15.6) = 0.4$$

Therefore, $13.44 = \dfrac{100 \times 9 \times 150 \times \sigma_2^2 + 100 \times (0.36) + 150 \times 0.16}{250}$

$$\sigma_2^2 = 2400 \text{ or } \sigma_2 = 4$$

Example: The mean height of 150 students (boys and girls) is 60 kg. The mean weight of boys is 70 kg with a standard deviation of 10 kg. For the girls, the mean weight is 55 kg and the standard deviation is 15 kg. Find the number of boys and the combined standard deviation.

Solution: $N_1 + N_2 = 150, \ \sigma_{12} = ?$ $\overline{X}_{12} = 60$ $\overline{X}_1 = 70$ $\sigma_1 = 10$

$$N_2 = (150 - N_1) \qquad\qquad \overline{X}_2 = 55, \ \sigma_2 = 15.$$

$$60 = \frac{N_1 70 + (150 - N_1) 55}{150}$$

$$9000 = 70N_1 + 8250 - 55N_1, \ 15N_1 = 750, \ N_1 = 50, \ N_2 = 150 - 50 = 100$$

Number of boys = 50, number of girls = 100.

$$d_1 = (\overline{X}_1 - \overline{X}_{12}) = 70 - 60 = 10; \ d_2 = 55 - 60 = -5$$
$$\sigma_{12} = 15.28$$

3.20 Problems on "missing information" in properties of SD

Example: Find the missing information from the following data:

	Group I	Group II	Group III	Combined
Number	50	?	90	200
Standard Deviation	6	7	?	7.746
Mean	113	?	115	116

Solution: Let N_1, N_2, N_3 be the number of observations in the 1st, 2nd, 3rd group, respectively.

$N_1 + N_2 + N_3 = 200$, $N_1 = 50$, $N_2 = ?$ $N_3 = 90$, $N_2 = 200 - 90 - 50 = 60$

$\overline{X}_{12} = 116$, $\overline{X}_1 = 113$, $\overline{X}_{12} = ?$ $\overline{X}_3 = 115$

Implies $\overline{X}_2 = 120$

Finding SD of 3rd group

$$\sigma_{123} = \sqrt{\frac{N_1\sigma_1^2 + N_2\sigma_2^2 + N_3\sigma_3^2 + N_1 d_1^2 + N_2 d_2^2 + N_3 d_3^2}{N_1 + N_2 + N_3}}$$

Given $\sigma_{123} = 7.746$, $d_1 = 113 - 116 = -3$, $d_2 = 120 - 116 = 4$, $d_3 = 115 - 116 = -1$

This implies $\sigma_2 = 8$

Example: A collar manufacturer is considering the production of a new style of collar to attract young men. The following statistics of Neek circumferences are available based on the measurements of a typical group of college students.

Mid-value in inches	12	12.5	13	13.5	14	14.5	15	15.5	16
No. of students	2	16	36	60	76	37	18	3	2

Determine the largest and smallest size of the coller he should make in order to meet the needs of practically all the customers bearing in mind that collars are worn on an average 1 inch longer than need size.

Solution:

X	D	f	fd	fd²
12	-2	2	-4	8
12.5	-1.5	16	-24	36
13	-1	36	-36	36
13.5	-0.5	60	-30	15
14	0	76	0	0
14.5	0.5	37	17.5	8.75
15	1	18	18	18.00
15.5	1.5	3	4.5	6.75
16	2	2	4	8
250	-50	136.5		

$\bar{X} = 14 - 0.2 = 13.8$ $\sigma = 0.71$

Largest neek size = 13.8 + 3 × 0.71 = 15.93

Smallest neek size = 13.8 – 3 × 0.71 = 11.67

Since collars worn on an average are longer than neek size, we should add 0.5 to these limits.

(11.67 – 0.5) and (15.93+0.5)

3.21 "Inter-quartile range" problems, special problems on "SD", coefficient of SD

Inter quartile range $= Q_3 - Q_1$

Quartile deviation $= (Q_3 - Q_1)/2$

Coefficient of QD $= (Q_3 - Q_1)/(Q_3 + Q_1)$

3.21.1 "Individual" – Case (i)

Example: Find the quartile deviation and its coefficient from the following data:

Roll no.	1	2	3	4	5	6	7
Marks	20	28	40	12	30	15	50

Solution: First arrange the marks in ascending order:

12, 15, 20, 28, 30, 40, 50

Q_1 = Size of $(N+1)/4^{th}$ item = size of $(7+1)/4 = 2^{nd}$ item

Size of the 2nd item is 15, i.e. $Q_1 = 15$

Q_3 = Size of $3(N + 1)/4^{th}$ item = Size of $3(7 + 1)/4 = 6^{th}$ item

Size of the item is 40, i.e., $Q_3 = 40$.

Quartile Deviation $= (Q_3 - Q_1)/2 = (40 - 15)/2 = 12.5$

Co-efficient of Q.D. $= (Q_3 - Q_1)/(Q_3 + Q_1) = 25/55 = 0.455$

3.21.2 "Discrete" – Case (ii)

Example: Compute the co-efficient of quartile deviation from the following data:

Marks	10	20	30	40	50	60
No. of students	4	7	15	8	7	2

Solution:

Marks	f	c f	marks	f	cf
10	4	4	40	8	34
20	7	11	50	7	41
30	15	26	80	2	43

$Q_3 = 3(N + 1)/4^{th}$ item $= 3 \times 11 = 33^{rd}$ item, i.e. $Q_3 = 40$

Coefficient of QD $= 20/60 = 0.33$

$Q_1 = (N + 1)/4^{th}$ item, $= (43 + 1)/4 = 11^{th}$ item, i.e. $Q_1 = 20$, QD $= (Q_3 - Q_1)/2 = 20/2 = 10$

3.21.3 Continuous series – Case (iii)

Example: Compute quartile deviation and its coefficient from the following data.

X	: 10–20	20–30	30–40	40–60	60–70	70–80
f:	: 12	19	5	10	9	6

X	f	c. f		
10–20	12	12		QD $= (Q_3 - Q_1)/2$
20–30	19	31	Q_1 Class	$Q_1 =$ Size of N/4th item $= 61/4 = 15.25$
30–40	5	36		This value lies in 20–30 class
40–60	10	46	Q_3 class	
60–70	9	55		
70-80	6	61		

$$Q_1 = L + \frac{\dfrac{N}{4} - f_a}{f} \times i = 20 + \frac{15.25 - 12}{19} \times 10 = 21.71$$

$$QD = \frac{49.75 - 21.71}{2} = 14.02$$

Coefficient of QD $= (Q_3 - Q_1)/(Q_3 + Q_1) = 0.3$

$$Q_3 = L + \frac{\dfrac{3N}{4} - Cf_a}{f} \times i = 40 + \frac{45.75 - 36}{10} \times 10 = 49.75$$

Example: The mean and standard deviation of normal distribution are 60 and 5, respectively. Find the inter-quartile range and mean deviation of the distribution.

Solution: $\bar{X} = 60$, $\sigma = 5$, MD $= 4/5 \sigma = (4/5) \times 5 = 4$, QD $= 2/3 \sigma = (2/3) \times 5 = 10/3$

$(Q_3 - Q_1)/2 = 10/3$, $3(Q_3 - Q_1) = 20$; $Q_3 - Q_1 = 20/3 = 6.67$

3.21.4 Special cases

Example: Prepare a frequency table with each class intervals of 10 kg with first class interval as 40–50. Also find out the coefficient of variation thereon.

72	74	40	60	82	115	41	61	65	83
53	110	76	84	50	67	78	79	56	65
68	69	104	80	79	79	52	73	59	81
66	49	77	90	84	76	42	64	69	70
72	50	79	52	103	96	51	86	78	94

CI	Tally	f	Mid-point	d	fd	fd²
40–50	1111	4	45	−3	−12	36
50–60	1111111	8	55	−2	−16	32
60–70	11111111	9	65	−1	−9	09
70–80	1111111111111	16	75	0	0	00
80–90	11111	6	85	+1	6	06
90–100	111	3	95	+2	6	12
100–110	11	2	105	+3	6	18
110–120	11	2	115	+4	8	32
		50 = N			−11	145

$$\overline{X} = 75 - (110/50) = 72.8$$

$$\sigma = \sqrt{\frac{145}{50} - \left(\frac{-11}{50}\right)^2} \times 10 = 16.887$$

$$CV\% = (16.88/72.8) \times 100 = 23.2\%$$

*Example: A consignment of 180 articles is classified according to the size of the article as under. Find SD and its coefficient.

Measurement	No. of articles	Measurement	No. of articles
More than 80	5	more than 30	150
" 70	14	" 20	170
" 60	34	" 10	176
" 50	65	" 0	180
" 40	110	" 90	0

Solution: This is a cumulative distribution. First convert it into a simple distribution in an ascending order.

Measurement	f	Mid-point	D	fd	fd²
0–10	4	5	−4	−16	64
10–20	6	15	−3	−18	54
20–30	20	25	−2	−40	80
30–40	40	35	−1	−40	40

(Contd.)

Measurement	f	Mid-point	D	fd	fd^2
40–50	45	45	0	0	0
50–60	31	55	1	31	31
60–70	20	65	2	40	80
70–80	09	75	3	27	54
80–90	05	85	4	20	80
	180			4	510

$$\sigma = \sqrt{\frac{510}{180} - \left(\frac{4}{180}\right)^2} \times 10 = 16.83$$

Co-efficient of standard deviation

$\overline{X}$ = 44.78

Coefficient of SD = 16.83/44.78 = 0.376

3.22   Problems on "CI" determination from "SD", "mean", deviation and 'f'

Example: Mean and standard deviation of the following continuous series are 31 and 15.9, respectively. The distribution after taking step deviations is as follows:

d	−3	−2	−1	0	1	2	3
f	10	15	25	25	10	10	5

Determine the actual class intervals.

D	f	fd	fd^2
−3	10	−30	90
−2	15	−30	60
−1	25	−25	25
0	25	0	0
1	10	10	10
2	10	20	40
3	5	15	45
	100	−40	270

$$\sigma = \sqrt{\frac{270}{100} - \left(\frac{-40}{100}\right)^2} \times i;$$

This implies i =10.

$\overline{X}$ = A+ (−400/100) × 10
This implies A = 35

Hence, the assumed mean is 35 and the class interval is 10. The lower and upper limit of the class intervals is 30–40. The preceding CI is 20–30 and the succeeding CI is 40–50 and so on.

Solution:

CI	f
0–10	10
10–20	15
20–30	25
30–40	25
40–50	10
50–60	10
60–70	5

Example: If the values of the mean and SD of the following frequency distribution (obtained by step deviation method) are 135.3 and 9.6, respectively. Determine the actual CI.

d	–4	–3	–2	–1	0	1	2	3
f	2	5	8	18	22	13	8	4

Solution: A = 136.5   CI = 133.5 – 139.5

3.23   Harmonic Mean

Example: An automobile covers from plain to hill station 100 km distance at an average speed of 30 km/h. It then makes the return trip at average speed of 20 km/h. What is the average speed over the entire distance?

Example: It is not correct on our part to calculate AM because

$\bar{X}$ = (30 + 20)/2 = 25 km/h.

Harmonic mean would be the correct answer.

$$HM = \frac{2}{\dfrac{1}{20} + \dfrac{1}{30}} = \frac{2}{\dfrac{105}{60}} = \frac{120}{5} = 24 \text{ km/h.}$$

It can be proved that harmonic mean is the appropriate average in this case by tabulating the time and distance for each trip separately as follows:

	Distance (km)	Average speed (km/h)	Time taken
Going→	100	30	3 h 20 min
Returning ←	100	20	5 h

Total 200 km   Time taken = 8 h 20 min.

Thus the total time taken required for covering 200 km is 8 h 20 min which gives an average speed of 24 km/h and not 25 km/h.

Note: However if the above problem can be changed in such a manner that arithmetic mean is appropriate average. Suppose the driver makes the same trip but it is given that he travels at 30 km/h for half of the time and 20 km/h for other half of time. Now the correct answer about the average speed would be given by the arithmetic mean.

Average speed = (30 + 20)/2 = 25

To verify this result let us again prepare a table of time and distance at each speed.

Speed (km/h)	Distance	Time required
30	120 km	120/30 = 4 h
20	80 km	80/20 = 4 h

Thus, he has taken 8 h to travel 200 km, hence the average speed is 25 km/h.

The above example clearly shows that when distances are the same for the two speeds HM will give the correct answer and when times are same AM will give the correct answer.

Problem for practice

Problem 1: Given weight of yarn on full cones in grams. Compute measures of central tendency.

980   1005   1010   1012   995   990   1020   1016   1002   996
1000   984   994   999   1006   1000   1018   1011   1004   975

Measures of dispersion

4.1   Introduction

Measures of central tendency summarize only one special aspect of distribution. Any distribution has at least more than one more feature that must be summarized in some way. Distribution exhibit spread or dispersion, that tendency for observations to depart from central tendency. Variability or dispersion is thus an important concept in statistical enquiry. It reflects the poorness of central tendency as a description of a random-selected case, as it depicts the tendency of observations not to be like the average.

4.2   The measure of the variation of the items

The study of dispersion can be understood by citing the following example:
    Three sets of scores with equal means but different dispersions – an illustration.

Case (i)

S. no.	Set 1	Set 2	Set 3
1	10	13	19
2	10	12	16
3	10	11	13
4	10	10	10
5	10	9	7
6	10	8	4
7	10	7	1
Mean	10	10	10

All the 3 sets have mean equal to 10. The variability in case (i) is zero. As each score of the 7 scores is equal to the mean, the dispersion in set 3 is more than that in set 2. Therefore, the deviations of scores are more in set 3 than in set 2. But as far as set 1 is considered, we can say that the scores are free from dispersion.

    Similarly, we may have 2 groups of labourers with the same mean of salary and yet their distributions may differ widely.

4.3   Significance of measuring dispersion/variation

(a) To determine reliability of an average.

Measures of variation point out as to how far an average is representative of mass. When dispersion is less, the average is a typical value in the sense that it closely represents the individual value and is reliable. It is a good estimate of an average. On the other hand, if dispersion is more, then the average is not so typical and is unreliable.

(b) To serve as the basis for the control of variability.

Another important purpose of measuring the dispersion is to find out the nature and cause of variation in order to control it.

For example,

- In healthcare, variation in body temperature, pulse beat, are the basic guides for diagnosis.
- In engineering and industrial production, efficient operation requires control of quality variation; causes sought through inspection of SQL programs.
- In social sciences, measuring dispersion as the inequality of the distribution of income/health.

1) Measures of dispersion enable to compare two or more series with regard to their variability.

It helps in study of CV% of processing of two blends. High degree of variation would mean little uniformity or consistency and vice-versa.

2) To facilitate the use of other statistical measures.

Many powerful analytical tools in such as (i) correlation analysis, tests of significance, analysis of variance, SQL, etc.

Examples—

1. Mean count is 94.2^s, nominal count = 92^s
    S.D. = 2.2, n = 12; Is the spinning is too fire?
2. Lea strength values in lbs of 20^s hosiery spun on only ring from

Flexible	Metallic
$x_1 \, x_{12} \, x_{13} \cdots$	$y_1 \, y_{12} \, y_{13} \cdots$
$x_2 \, x_{21}, \, x_{23} \cdots$	$y_2 \, y_{21} \, y_{22} \cdots$

(Contd.)

Flexible	Metallic
$x_3, x_{31}, x_{32} \cdots$ .... $x_n, x_{n+1}, x_{n+2} \cdots$	$y_3, y_{31}, y_{32} \cdots$ $y_n, y_{n+1} \cdots$

Do you say that metallic card clothing is better?

1. Analysis of variance

20^s yarn was spun on 4-different OE spinners by feeding the same quality to all the frames. Strength index for each yarn is given below:

Tests	Frames			
	A	B	C	D
1	x_1	x_2	x_3	x_4
2	.	.	.	.
3	.	.	.	.
4	x_n	.	.	.

Is there any difference in quality of the yarn spun on different frames?

2. SQL

A large number of 80^s cons were produced in a textile mill. Some cones say 200 is selected at random and inspected for defective cones. Results of 15 trials are follows:

Trial	1	2	3	 15
Defective cone	8	11	12	....

Prepare suitable chart and comment.

Properties of a good average:

1. Should be simple to understand and compute.
2. Should be rigidly defined.
3. Should be based on every item in the population.
4. Should be subjectable to further algebraic treatment.

Methods of studying dispersion:

1. The range
2. The inter quartile range and quartile deviation
3. The average or mean deviation

4. Standard deviation
5. Lorenz curve

4.3.1   Absolute and relative measures of variation

Measures of dispersion may be absolute. Absolute measures of dispersion is expressed in the same statistical unit in which the original data are given such as rupees, kilograms, tones, etc. These values may be used to compare the variation in two distributions provided the variables are expressed in the same units and of the same average size.

The absolute measures of dispersion are not comparable. In such cases we go for relative dispersion measure.

A measure of relative dispersion is the ratio of a measure of absolute dispersion to an appropriate average. It is sometimes called as coefficient of dispersion.

4.4   Range and its importance

Range is the simplest method of studying dispersion. It is defined as the difference between the value of the smallest item and the value of the largest item included in the distribution. Symbolically, range $= L - S$, where L = largest item, S = smallest item.

Coefficient of range $= (L+S)/(L - S)$

4.4.1   Merits

Amongst all the methods of studying dispersion, range is the simplest to understand and the easiest to compute. It takes no time in calculation.

4.4.2   Limitations

1. Range is not based on each and every item of the distribution.
2. It is subject to fluctuations of considerable magnitude from sample to sample.
3. Range can't tell anything about the characteristics of distribution within the two extreme observations. For example, consider the following series:

Series	A	46	6	46	46	46	46	46	46
	B	6	10	6	6	46	46	46	46
	C	6	6	15	25	30	32	40	46

In all the 3 series range is same if $(46 - 6) = 40$. But it does not mean that series are alike range takes no account on the form of the distribution within the range. Range is therefore most unreliable as a guide to the dispersion of the values within a distribution.

4. Range can't be computed from opened distributions.

4.4.3   Applications of range

Despite serious limitations range is useful in the following cases:

i)   In quality control, range is given much importance. The range charts are constructed on the range basis only. The idea basically is that, if the range increases beyond a certain point, the production machinery should be examined to find out why the items produced have not followed their usual consistent pattern.

ii) Range will extremely be helpful for studying the fluctuations in the value of certain items like shares, stocks, etc.

iii) Most of the time we come across the usefulness of range in weather forecasts – indicating minimum and maximum temperature of the data.

iv) Range is most useful in our day-to-day life. For example, the expenditure of student refreshment is in the range of Rs. 200–300, etc.,

4.5   Quartile deviation

Range suffers from discrepancy. It is purely based on the two extreme items and fails to take account of the scatter within the range. Therefore, even after discarding the extreme items, range can be established in a more consistent way. For this purpose, there has been developed a measure called "Inter Quartile Range", which includes the middle of 50% of the distribution, i.e., one-quarter of observations at the lower end and another quarter of observations at the upper end of the distribution are excluded in computing inter quartile range. In other words, inter-quartile range represents the difference between the third quartile and the first quartile. Symbolically,

Inter Quartile Range = $Q_3 - Q_1$

Very often inter quartile range is reduced to form semi-quartile range or quartile deviation by dividing it by 2.

∴ Quartile Deviation = $(Q_3 - Q_1)/2$

This gives the average amount by which the two quartiles differ from the median. In a symmetrical distribution two quartiles Q_1 and Q_3 are equidistant from median.

Med – Q_1 = Q_3 – Med

Such difference can be taken as a measure of dispersion.

Median ± Qb covers exactly 50% observations. It is very difficult to get a symmetrical distribution. In a asymmetrical distribution Q_3 and Q_1 are not equidistant from median. As a result that type of distribution will have only 50% observations.

Coefficient of QD = $(Q_3 - Q_1)/(Q_3 + Q_1)$

Q_1 = size of (N/4)th term (in continuous series)

Q_3 = size of 3(N+1)/4 term (individual series)

Q_1 = size of (3N/4)th item (in continuous series)

Q_3 = size of (N+1)/4th item (individual observations and discrete series)

Theoretical distributions

5.1 Normal distribution

The normal curve is a bell-shaped symmetrical form of curve, also known as normal law or normal probability curve.

For example, reed space of looms, end breaks in weaving, dimensional variation produced in a component manufactured by an automatic machine.

5.1.1 Features of normal distribution

Following are the characteristics of normal distribution:

1. The curve is bell shaped and symmetrical about mean.
2. The mode, median and mean coincide.
3. The vertical height of the curve reduces in shape as the values move from mean faster at first and then less rapidly. In other words it can be said that the points of inflection occur at $\bar{x} \pm \sigma$.
4. Standard deviation = 1.25 × mean deviation (i.e., the mean deviation is 4/5 of the standard deviation).
5. Normal curve is unimodal (because of one maximum point or peak).
6. In normal distribution the variable is in "continuous" form.

The area under the curve can be considered as unity or 100%. In normal distribution the following points are found

- ±3 σ about   covers 99.7% at the area under the curve.
- ±2 σ about   covers 95.5% at the area under the curve.
- ±1 σ about $\bar{x}$ covers $\bar{x}$ 68% at the area under the curve.

7. The curve is covered by the mathematical law (where 'a' is standard deviation)

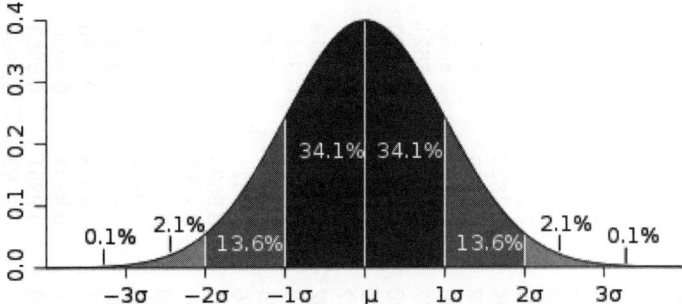

Dark grey is less than one standard deviation from the mean accounts for about 68% of area, while two standard deviations from the mean (medium and dark grey) account for about 95%, of area and three standard deviations (light, medium, and dark grey) account for about 99.7% area under the curve.

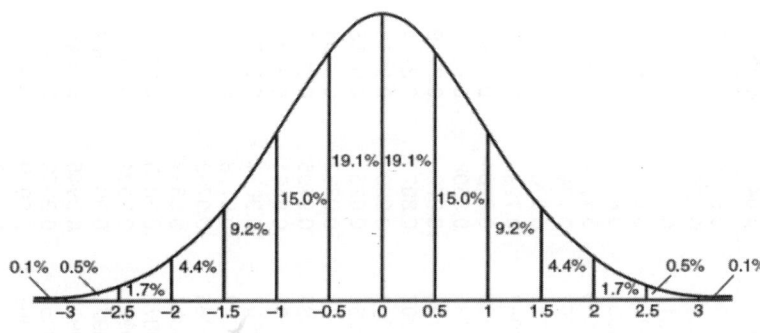

8. It is fully defined by mean and SD.

When the distribution is not known one way of dealing with large population (when there is insufficient data), following steps need to be taken:

(a) Consider a number of random observations from the distribution and find the AM with more number of replications.
(b) Means of these samples are plotted as a distribution to get a curve known as normal distribution curve.

Making predictions using normal curve:

To make predictions about a normally distributed population, the AM and SD of the population are used along with the table of areas under normal distribution curve.

Table 5.1 Normal distribution table

z	0	0.01	0.02	0.03	0.04	0.05	0.06	0.07	0.08	0.09
0.0	0.5000	0.5040	0.5080	0.5120	0.5160	0.5199	0.5239	0.5279	0.5319	0.5359
0.1	0.5398	0.5438	0.5478	0.5517	0.5557	0.5596	0.5636	0.5675	0.5714	0.5753
0.2	0.5793	0.5832	0.5871	0.5910	0.5948	0.5987	0.6026	0.6064	0.6103	0.6141
0.3	0.6179	0.6217	0.6255	0.6293	0.6331	0.6368	0.6406	0.6443	0.6480	0.6517
0.4	0.6554	0.6591	0.6628	0.6664	0.6700	0.6736	0.6772	0.6808	0.6844	0.6879
0.5	0.6915	0.6950	0.6985	0.7019	0.7054	0.7088	0.7123	0.7157	0.7190	0.7224
0.6	0.7257	0.7291	0.7324	0.7357	0.7389	0.7704	0.7454	0.7486	0.7517	0.7549
0.7	0.7580	0.7611	0.7642	0.7673	0.7704	0.7734	0.7764	0.7794	0.7823	0.7852
0.8	0.7881	0.7910	0.7939	0.7967	0.7995	0.8023	0.8051	0.8078	0.8106	0.8133
0.9	0.8159	0.8186	0.8212	0.8238	0.8264	0.8289	0.8315	0.8340	0.8365	0.8389
1.0	0.8413	0.8438	0.8461	0.8485	0.8508	0.8531	0.8554	0.8577	0.8599	0.8621
1.1	0.8643	0.8665	0.8686	0.8708	0.8729	0.8749	0.8770	0.8790	0.8810	0.8830
1.2	0.8849	0.8869	0.8888	0.8907	0.8925	0.8944	0.8962	0.8980	0.8997	0.9015
1.3	0.9032	0.9049	0.9066	0.9082	0.9099	0.9115	0.9131	0.9147	0.9162	0.9177
1.4	0.9192	0.9207	0.9222	0.9236	0.9251	0.9265	0.9279	0.9292	0.9306	0.9319
1.5	0.9332	0.9345	0.9357	0.9370	0.9382	0.9394	0.9406	0.9418	0.9429	0.9441
1.6	0.9452	0.9463	0.9474	0.9484	0.9495	0.9505	0.9515	0.9525	0.9535	0.9545
1.7	0.9554	0.9564	0.9573	0.9582	0.9591	0.9599	0.9608	0.9616	0.9625	0.9633
1.8	0.9641	0.9649	0.9656	0.9664	0.9671	0.9678	0.9686	0.9693	0.9699	0.9706
1.9	0.9713	0.9719	0.9726	0.9732	0.9738	0.9744	0.9750	0.9756	0.9761	0.9767
2.0	0.9772	0.9778	0.9783	0.9788	0.9793	0.9798	0.9803	0.9808	0.9812	0.9817
2.1	0.9821	0.9826	0.9830	0.9834	0.9838	0.9842	0.9846	0.9850	0.9854	0.9857
2.2	0.9861	0.9864	0.9868	0.9871	0.9875	0.9878	0.9881	0.9884	0.9887	0.9890
2.3	0.9893	0.9896	0.9898	0.9901	0.9904	0.9906	0.9909	0.9911	0.9913	0.9916
2.4	0.9918	0.9920	0.9922	0.9925	0.9927	0.9929	0.9931	0.9932	0.9934	0.9936
2.5	0.9938	0.9940	0.9941	0.9943	0.9945	0.9946	0.9948	0.9949	0.9951	0.9952
2.6	0.9953	0.9955	0.9956	0.9957	0.9959	0.9960	0.9961	0.9962	0.9963	0.9964
2.7	0.9965	0.9966	0.9967	0.9968	0.9969	0.9970	0.9971	0.9920	0.9973	0.9974
2.8	0.9974	0.9975	0.9976	0.9977	0.9977	0.9978	0.9979	0.9979	0.9980	0.9981
2.9	0.9981	0.9982	0.9982	0.9983	0.9984	0.9984	0.9985	0.9985	0.9986	0.9986

Table 5.1 (contd...) Normal distribution table

z	0	0.01	0.02	0.03	0.04	0.05	0.06	0.07	0.08	0.09
3.0	0.9987	0.9987	0.9987	0.9988	0.9988	0.9989	0.9989	0.9989	0.9990	0.9990
3.1	0.9990	0.9991	0.9991	0.9991	0.9992	0.9992	0.9992	0.9992	0.9993	0.9993
3.2	0.9993	0.9993	0.9994	0.9994	0.9994	0.9994	0.9994	0.9995	0.9995	0.9995
3.3	0.9995	0.9995	0.9995	0.9996	0.9996	0.9996	0.9996	0.9996	0.9996	0.9997
3.4	0.9997	0.9997	0.9997	0.9997	0.9997	0.9997	0.9997	0.9997	0.9997	0.9998
3.5	0.9998									
4.0	0.9997									
5.0	0.9999997									
6.0	0.999999999									

Example 1: From past experience an auto loom manufacturer concludes that the burnout time of a particular light bulb on the loom is normally distributed. A sample of 50 bulbs has been taken and tested. The average life found to be 60 days with a standard deviation of 20 days. How many bulbs in the entire population of light bulbs can be expected to require replacement after 100 days of life?

The middle point $\bar{x}$ = 60 days. The problem is to find the area under the curve beyond 100 days. The area beyond 100 days is the probability that a bulb will lost more than 100 days.

To find any area under a normal curve a fraction z is calculated by

$$Z = \frac{X - \bar{x}}{\sigma}$$ where Z is distance of x from $\bar{x}$ in unit of standard deviation.

Here, $Z = \dfrac{X - \bar{x}}{\sigma} + \dfrac{100 - 60}{20} = \dfrac{40}{20} = +2$

From tables of area under the normal curve, the area up to Z is 0.9773.

∴ Area beyond Z = 1 − 0.9773 = 0.0227

∴ % of bulbs that requires replacement after 100 days = 2.27%

Example 2: A normal curve has an average of 140.62 with standard deviation of 3.70. What percentage of the area under the curve will fall between the units of 135.5 and 142.5? What percentage of area falls beyond 145?

Given $\bar{x}$ = 140.62; SD = 3.70.

$$Z_1 = \frac{X_1 - \bar{x}}{\sigma} = \frac{135.5 - 140.62}{3.70} = -1.38$$

Area up to Z_1 from Table is 0.0838

$$Z_2 = \frac{X_2 - \bar{x}}{\sigma} = \frac{142.5 - 140.62}{3.7} = 0.5075$$

From Table area up to Z_2 is 0.6942

∴ Area between Z_2 and Z_1 is = 0.6942 − 0.0838 = 0.6104

∴ Percentage area between 135.5 and 142.5 = 61.04%

$$= \frac{X_3 - \bar{x}}{\sigma} = \frac{145 - 140.62}{3.7} = 1.183$$

Area up to Z_3 = 0.8816

∴ Area beyond 145 = 1 − 0.8816 = 0.1184 or 11.84%

Example 3: In a distribution exactly normal 7% of the items are under 35 and 89% are under 63, what are the mean and SD of the distribution?

$$Z_1 = \frac{X_1 - \bar{x}}{\sigma} = \frac{35 - \bar{x}}{\sigma}$$

From the table $Z_1 = -1.47$ for 0.07 area or 7%

$$\therefore \frac{35 - \bar{x}}{\sigma} = -1.47 \ ...(1)$$

$$Z_2 = \frac{X_2 - \bar{x}}{\sigma} = \frac{63 - \bar{x}}{\sigma}$$

Table time value of $Z_2 = +1.23$

$$\therefore \frac{63 - \bar{x}}{\sigma} = +1.23 \ ...(2)$$

$$(1) - (2) = \frac{35 - \bar{x} - 63 + \bar{x}}{\sigma} = -1.47 - 1.23$$

$$\therefore \sigma = \frac{28}{2.7} = 10.37$$

Substituting in (2) $\frac{63 - \bar{x}}{10.37} = 1.23$

$$-\bar{x} = 1.23 \times 10.37 - 63 = 12.75 - 63 = -50.25$$

$$\therefore \bar{x} = 50.25$$

Example 4: The time taken to complete a particular respective job is normally distributed with a mean of 40 minutes and SD of 8 minutes. Twenty five jobs are to be performed.

(1) How many jobs are expected to take more than 48 minutes?
(2) How many jobs are expected to be completed within 35 minutes?
(3) What is the expected total number of jobs that can be completed between 20 and 50 minutes?

Given $\bar{x} = 40$ $\sigma = 8$

(1) $Z_1 = \frac{X_1 - \bar{x}}{\sigma} = \frac{48 - 40}{8} = 1$

Area up to Z_1 from table = 0.8413

(2) $Z_2 = \frac{X_2 - \bar{x}}{\sigma} = \frac{35 - 40}{8} = -0.625$

Area up to Z_2 from table = 0.2659

(1) Area beyond 48 is $1 - 0.8413 = 0.1587$
(2) The number of jobs within 35 minutes
    $= 25 \times 0.2659 = 6.647 = 7$ jobs.

(3) $Z_3 = \dfrac{X_3 - \bar{x}}{\sigma} = \dfrac{20 - 40}{8} = \dfrac{-20}{8} = -2.5$

From table area up to $Z_3 = 0.0062$
From table area up to $Z_4 = 0.8944$.

$$Z_4 = \dfrac{X_4 - \bar{x}}{\sigma} = \dfrac{50 - 40}{8} = 1.25$$

$\therefore$ Area between 20 and 50 is $0.8944 - 0.0062 = 0.8882$
$\therefore$ Number of jobs $= 25 \times 0.8882 = 22$ jobs.

The following are some of the examples to illustrate how tables are to be consulted in order to obtain area under the normal curve.

Examples

a) Find the area under the normal curve for z = 1.54.

Solution: If we look to the table, the entry corresponding to z = 1.54, 0.4382 between z = 0 and . But since the curve is symmetrical, we can find the area between z = 0 and z = –1.54 by looking the area corresponding to z = 1.54.

If we wish to cut the area under normal curve to the right of a positive value of s, we should subtract the tabular value from 0.5000. The reason is that the normal curve is symmetrical, the area to the right of the mean is 0.5000 minus the tabular value given for z.

b)   Find the area to the right of z = 0.25.

Solution: Subtract 0.0987 (the entry, given in the table for z = 0.25) from 0.5000 getting (0.5000 – 0.0987).

If we wish to find out the area to the left of a positive value of z, we add 0.5 to the tabular value given for z.

Example 5: Find the area to the left of z = 1.96.

Solution: $(0.4750 + 0.5000) = 0.9750$

In some cases it may be of interest to determine area between two given lines of z. If both zs are on the same side of the mean, i.e., if they are both positive and both negative, the area between them is given by the difference of their tabular values. For example, the area between z = 0.60 and 1.80 is $(0.4641 - 0.2257) = 0.3811$.

If the two zs are on the opposite side of the mean, the area between them is given by the sum of their tabular values. For example, the area between $z = -0.4$ and $z = 0.6$ is $(0.1554 + 0.2257) = 0.3811$.

At times we may be given the area under the normal curve and asked to determine the corresponding value of z. For example, we may wish to find a z which is such that the area to its right is 0.2000 and the closest value in the table is $z = 0.84$.

Example 6: A normal curve has $\overline{x} = 20$ and $\sigma = 10$. Find the area between $X_1 = 15$ and $X_2 = 40$.

   Solution:

$$z_1 = \frac{X - \overline{X}}{\sigma} = \frac{15 - 20}{10} = -0.50$$

$$z_2 = \frac{40 - 20}{10} = 2.0$$

Consulting the table we find the areas corresponding to the z's are 0.1915 and 0.4772 and thus, the desired area between $x_1 = 15$ and $x_2 = 40$ is $(0.1915 + 0.4272) = 0.5687$.

5.1.2 Significance of the normal distribution

The normal distribution is mostly used for the following purposes:

1. To approximate or "fit" a distribution of measurement under certain conditions.
2. To approximate the binomial distribution and other discrete of continuous probability distributions under suitable conditions.
3. To approximate the distribution of means and certain other quantities calculated from samples, especially large samples.

The following examples shall illustrate the applications of normal distribution.

Example 7: Assume the mean height of Jacquard machine to be 68.22 inches with a variance of 10.8 inches. How many Jacquard in a group of 1,000 would you expect to be over six feet tall?

   Solution: Assume that the distribution of height is normal. Standard normal value or $z = \dfrac{X - \overline{x}}{\sigma}$

Area to the right of the ordinate at 1.15 from the normal table is $(0.5000 - 0.3749) = 0.1251$. Hence, the probability of getting Jacquards above six feet is 0.1251 and out of 1,000 Jacquards over six feet tall = 125.

Example 8: The diameter of crank shafts produced in a factory conforms to normal distribution. 31 percent of the shafts have a diameter less than 45 mm. and 8 percent have more than 64 mm. Find the mean and standard deviation of the diameter of shafts.

Solution:

$$\frac{\overline{X} - 45}{\sigma} = 0.5 \ or \ 0.5\sigma = \overline{X} - 45. \qquad \ldots \text{(i)}$$

8% of the items are above 64. Therefore, area to the right of the ordinate at 64 is 0.08. Area to the left of the ordinate at X = 64 up to mean ordinate is (0.5 − 0.08) = 0.42 and the value of z corresponding to this area is 1.4.

$$\frac{64 - \overline{X}}{\sigma} = 1.4 \ or \ 1.4\sigma = 64 - \overline{X} \qquad \ldots \text{(ii)}$$

Hence, From equation (i) and (ii)

$$1.4\sigma = 64 - \overline{X}$$
$$0.5\sigma = -45 + X$$
$$1.9\sigma = 19$$
$$\sigma = 10$$
$$\overline{X} - 0.5 \times 10 = 45$$
$$\overline{X} = 50$$

The mean of the distribution is 50 and standard deviation 10.

Example 9: The income of a group of 10,000 tenders was found to be normally distributed with mean = Rs.750 p.m. and standard deviation = Rs.50. Show that of this group about 95% had income exceeding Rs. 668 and only 5% had income exceeding Rs.832. what was the lowest income among the richest 100?

Solution: Standard normal variate or

$$Z = \frac{\left(X - \overline{X}\right)}{\sigma}$$

Hence, $X = 668$, $\overline{X} = 750$, $\sigma = 50$

$$Z = \frac{668 - 750}{50} = -\frac{82}{50} = -1.64$$

Area to the right of the ordinate at −1.64 is (0.4495 + 0.5000) = 0.9496

∴ The expected number of persons getting above Rs.668 = 10000 × 0.94950 = 9495

This is about 95% of the total i.e., 10,000

The standard normal variate corresponding to 832 is

$$Z = \frac{832 - 750}{50} = \frac{82}{50} = 1.64$$

Area to the right of ordinate at 1.64 is 0.5000 − 0.4495 = 0.0505

The number of persons getting above Rs. 832 is 10,000 × 0.0505 = 505

This is approximately 5%. Probability of getting richest 100 = 100 / 10000 = 0.01

Standard normal variate having 0.01 area to its right = 2.33

$$2.33 = \frac{X - 750}{50} \quad \text{implies } X = (2.33 \times 50)$$

$$X = (2.33 \times 50) + 750 = \text{Rs. } 866.5$$

Example 10: The mean weight of 500 fabrics is 151 lb, and the standard deviation is 15 lb. Assuming the weights are normally distributed find how many fabrics weigh (a) between 120 and 155 lb., and (b) more than 185 lb.

Solution: (a) Weights recorded as being between 120 and 155 lb. can actually have any value from 119.5 to 155.5 lb. Assuming they are recorded to the nearest pound.

Standard normal variate corresponding to 119.5 lb.

$$z = \frac{119.5 - 151}{15} = -2.1$$

Standard normal variate corresponding to 155.5 lb.

$$z = \frac{155.5 - 151}{15} = 0.3$$

Area between z = −2.10 and z = 0.30

$$= 0.4821 + 0.1179 = 0.6$$

∴ The number of fabrics weighing between 120 and 155 lb.

$$= 500 \times 0.6 = 300$$

(b) Fabrics weighing more than 185 lb, must weigh at least 185.5 lb

Standard normal variate corresponding to 185.5

$$z = \frac{185.5 - 151}{15} = 2.3$$

Area to the right of z = 2.3 is (0.5000 – 0.4893) = 0.0107
∴ Number of fabrics weighing more than 185 lb.

$$= 500 \times 0.0107 = 5.35 \text{ or } 5 \text{ approximately.}$$

Example 11: 1000 light bulbs with a mean life of 120 days are installed in a new textile factory; their length of life is normally distributed with standard deviation 20 days. (i) How many bulbs will expire in less than 90 days? (ii) If it is decided to replace all the bulbs together, what interval should be allowed between replacements if not more than 10 percent should expire before replacement?

Solution: (i) $\overline{X}$ = 120, σ = 20, X = 90
Standard normal variate or

$$z = \frac{90 - 100}{20} = -1.5$$

Area of the curve at (z = –1.5) up to the mean ordinate = 0.4332
Area of the left of –1.5 = 0.5 – 0.4332 = 0.0668.
Number of bulbs expected to expire in less than 90 days

$$= 0.0668 \times 1000 = 66.8 \text{ or } 67.$$

(ii) The value of standard normal variate corresponding to an area 0.4 (0.5 – 0.1) is 1.28

$$\frac{X - 120}{20} = -1.28$$

$$X = 120 - (1.28 \times 20) = 120 - 25.6 = 94.4 \text{ or } 94.$$

Hence, the bulbs will have to be replaced after 94 days.

Example 12: In an intelligence test administered to 1,000 students the average score was 42 and standard deviation 24. Find (a) the number of students exceeding a score 50. (b) the number of students lying between 30 and 54. (c) the value of score exceeded by the top 100 students.

Solution: (a) Given $\overline{X}$ = 42, X = 50, σ = 24

$$z = \frac{X - \overline{X}}{\sigma} = \frac{50 - 42}{24} = 0.333$$

Area to the right of ordinate at 0.333 is 0.5 − 0.1304 = 0.3696
∴ The expected number of children exceeding a score of 50

$$z = \frac{X - \overline{X}}{\sigma} = \frac{30 - 42}{24} = -0.5$$

$$= 0.3696 \times 1,000 = 369.6 \text{ or } 370$$

(b) Standard normal variate for score 30
standard normal variate for score 54

$$z = \frac{X - \overline{X}}{\sigma} = \frac{54 - 42}{24} = 0.5$$

Area to the right at 0.5 = 0.5 − 0.1915 = 0.3085
Area to the left at −0.5 = 0.3085
The probability of having children with score above 54 and below

$$= 0.3085 + 0.3085 = 0.6120$$

∴ the probability of having children between score 30 and 54

$$= 1 - 20.617 = 0.383$$

Thus, the number of children having score between 30 and 54.

$$= 0.383 \times 1000 = 383$$

(c) Probability of getting top 100 students = 100 / 1000 = 0.1
From table, for probability 0.1, Z = 1.231
Standard normal variate for score X

$$z = \frac{X - \overline{X}}{\sigma} \text{ implies } 1.281 = \frac{X - 42}{24} \text{ implies } 1.281 \times 24 = X - 42.$$

$$X = (1.281 \times 24) + 42 = 72.74 \text{ or } 73$$

Example 13: In a certain examination the percentage of passes and distinctions were 46 and 9 respectively. Estimate the average marks obtained by the candidates, the minimum pass and distinction marks being 40 and 75 respectively (assume the distribution of marks to be normal).

Also determine what would have been the minimum qualifying marks for admission to a re-examination of the failed candidates, had it been desired that the best 25% of them should be given another opportunity of being examined.

Solution: (a) Let X be the mean and σ be the standard deviation of the normal distribution. The area to the right of the ordinate at X = 40 is 0.46

and hence, the area between the men and the ordinate at X = 40 is 0.04. Now, from the table corresponding to 0.04, standard normal variate is 0.1

$$\frac{40 - \overline{X}}{\sigma} = 0.1$$

Similarly,

$$\frac{75 - \overline{X}}{\sigma} = 1.34$$

Or   40 – X = 0.1 σ   ... (i)
        75 – X = 1.34σ   ... (ii)

Subtracting (i) from (ii),

$$35 = 1.34\sigma$$

$$\sigma = 35 / 1.24 = 28.22$$

Putting the value of σ in the eq. (i)

$$\overline{X} = 37.18 \text{ or } 37.$$

Therefore, the average marks obtained by the candidates is 37.

(b) Let us assume that X_1 is the minimum qualifying marks for re-examination of the failed candidates.

The area to the right of X = 40 is 46%.

Percentage of students failing 54 and this is the area to the left of 40. We want that the best 25% of these failed candidates should be given a change to reappear. Suppose this area is 25% of 54 = 13.5

∴ Area between mean and ordinate at X_1 = – (0.135 – 0.04) = –0.095

(Negative sign is included because the area lies to the left of the mean ordinate).

Corresponding to this area, standard normal variate from the table is equal to –0.0378.

∴ $$\frac{X_1 - \overline{X}}{\sigma} = -0.0378$$

∴ $X_1 = \overline{X} - 0.0378\sigma = 37.2 - (0.0378 \times 28.2) = 37.2 - 1.066 = 36.134$ or 36 app.

Example 14: The results of a particular examination are given below in a summary form:

Result	% of candidates
(i) Passed with distinction	10
(ii) Passed	60
(iii) Failed	30

It is known that a candidate gets plucked if he obtains less than 40 marks (out of 100) while he must obtain at least 75 marks in order to pass with distinction. Determine the mean and standard deviation of the distribution of marks assuming this to be normal.

Solution: We have to calculate the mean and standard deviation from the given information.

We know that 30% students get less than 40 marks.

$\therefore$ From the table the z value corresponding to 0.2(20% area) = -0.524

$$\left(\begin{array}{l} z = 0.52 \text{ for } 0.1585 \\ z = 0.53 \text{ for } 0.2019 \\ z = 0.524 \text{ for } 0.2000 \end{array} \right)$$

Hence,

$$\frac{40 - \overline{X}}{\sigma} = -0524$$

10% students get distinction marks, i.e., 75 or more, from the table the z value corresponding to 0.4(40% area) = 1.28

Hence $\dfrac{75 - \overline{X}}{\sigma} = 1.28$

From equations (i) and (ii)

$$\overline{X} - 40 = 0.524\sigma$$
$$\underline{-\overline{X} + 75 = 1.280\sigma}$$
$$35 = 1.804\sigma$$

$\therefore$ $\sigma = \dfrac{35}{1.804} = 19.4$

$$40 - \overline{X} = -0.524 \times 19.4$$
$$-\overline{X} = -10.17 - 40 \text{ or } \overline{X} = 50.17$$

Hence the mean of the distribution is 50.17 and standard deviation

Example 15: The sample of 200 leas of yarn yielded a mean count of 37.22 and a standard deviation of 0.93. If the distribution of count of single leas is assumed to be normal with these values as the true mean and standard deviation, how many leas would be expected to have counts lower than 35.45 and 38.457. Consequently obtain the number of leas with counts between 35.45 and 38.45 and number finer than 38.45.

Solution: Given: n = 200 leas, $\bar{x}$ = 37.22, σ = 0.93, x = 35.45 and 38.45

$$z = \frac{x - \bar{x}}{\sigma} = \frac{35.45 - 37.22}{0.93} = -1.903$$

$$z = \frac{38.45 - 37.22}{0.93} = 1.323$$

The area corresponding to Z = 1.323 from the above problems is = 0.907.

The area corresponding to Z = –1.903 = 0.0268

(a) So the number of leas with count lower than 38.45 would be expected to equal 200 × 0.907 = 181 ½ .

(b) Number of leas with count lower than 35.45 would be 200 × 0.0268 = 5.36 leas = 5 leas approximately.

(c) Number of leas with counts between 35.45 and 38.45 will be (0.5 – 0.0268) + (0.907 – 0.5) = 0.4732 + 0.407 = 0.8802
0.8802 × 200 = 176.04 = 176 leas approximately.

(d) Number of leas with counts finer than 38.45 will be 1 – 0.907 = 0.093
Therefore 0.093 × 200 = 18.6 = 19 leas.
Fractional frequency less than (–Z) = 1 – fractional frequency less than Z.

Example 16: From a large number of weighting reprocessed the standard deviation of 45 lb finisher laps produced on a certain scutcher is 0.2 lb. If the rule is adopted that all laps deviating from 45 lb by 0.5 lb or more are reprocessed, what is the minimum number of laps per hundred reprocessed, assuming the frequency distribution of lap weight to be normal.

Solution: Mean = 45 lb., x = 44.5 and 45.5 lb. and SD = 0.2 lb.

$$Z = \frac{X - \bar{x}}{\sigma} = \frac{445 - 45}{0.2} = \frac{-0.5}{0.2} = -2.5z$$

$$Z = \frac{45.5 - 45}{0.2} = \frac{0.5}{0.2} = 2.5$$

$$= 1 - 0.9938 = 0.0062$$

$$0.0062 \times 2 = 0.0124$$

0.0124 × 300 = 3.72 laps in 300 will be reprocessed.

b) Suppose that the overlooker of question (a) wishes to narrow the tolerance limits of lap weight and, in order to do this, is willing to reprocess upto 2% of the laps, where should be set the limits?

2% laps includes 1% on either side i.e., 2% / 2 = 1%

$$Z = \frac{X - \bar{x}}{\sigma}$$

$\bar{x} = 45\ lb.$

$\sigma = 0.47\ lb.$

$Z = ?$

The area beyond the ordinates is 0.01.

In the table we can get area to left of ordinate at Z. hence we should know area to the left the ordinate Z i.e., 1 − 0.01 = 0.99.

Area of left of ordinate at Z	Z^1
0.9901	2.33
0.9925	2.43
For a change of area = 0.24	change in Z = 0.1

Therefore, (0.9901 − 0.99)

$$= \frac{0.0001}{0.24} \times 0.1 = 0.00004$$

$Z = 2.33$

$$Z = \frac{X - \bar{x}}{\sigma} = 2.33 = \frac{X - \bar{x}}{0.2} \quad \text{implies} \quad X - \bar{x} = 2.33 \times 0.2 = 0.466\ \text{lbs.}$$

Therefore, x = $\bar{x}$ + 0.466 lb or x − 0.466 lb.

Or approximately 7 ozs above and below the required lap weight.

Example 17: When a large number of single threads of sized yarn are extended by 2% of their length, 1.43% of them break, and when they are extended by 5% further 77.08% of them break. Assuming the distribution of single thread extensibility to be normal, what are the mean and standard deviation?

Solution: 5% extension also includes 2% extension. Hence, the area under the normal curve to the left of the ordinate at 5% extensibility is = 0.7708 − 0.0143 = 0.7851

Similarly the area to left of ordinate at 2% extensibility is = 0.0143.

The standardised ordinates for area = 0.7851 is + 0.79

The standardised ordinates for area = 0.0143 is − 2.19

$$Z = \frac{X - \bar{x}}{\sigma} = 0.79 = \frac{5 - \bar{x}}{\sigma}$$

Similarly $-2.19 = \dfrac{2 - \bar{x}}{\sigma}$

$$5\ \bar{x} = 0.79\sigma \qquad \qquad \dots (1)$$
$$2 - \bar{x} = 2.19\sigma \qquad \qquad \dots (2)$$
$$0.79\sigma + \bar{x} = 5 \qquad \qquad \dots (3)$$
$$-2.19\sigma + \bar{x} = 2 \qquad \qquad \dots (4)$$
$$(-) \qquad (-)$$
$$2.98\sigma = 3$$
$$\sigma = 3\ /\ 2.98 = 1.01\% \text{ extension.}$$

Substitute 1.01% in equation 3 or 4.
$$0.79\ (1.01) + \bar{x} = 5$$
$$\bar{x} = 5 - 0.7979 = 4.20\% \text{ extension.}$$

Example 18: The mean and standard deviation of yarn count are 44.1 and 1.8 respectively. Assuming the distribution of count to be normal, calculate how many leas in two hundred would be expected to yield a count lower than 40.95 and lower than 45.45. Consequently obtain the number of leas with counts between 40.95 and 45.45 and the number finer than 45.45.

Solution: $\bar{x} = 44.1 \quad n = 200\ \sigma = 1.8$

(a) Less than 40.95
(b) lower Jho 45.45
(c) between 40.95 and 45.45
(d) finer than 45.45

a) $Z = \dfrac{40.95 - 44.1}{1.8} = -1.75$

When $Z = 1.75$ area to the left of the ordinate is 0.0401.
Therefore $0.0401 \times 200 = 8$ leas would be expected to yield a count lower than 40.95.

b) $Z = \dfrac{45.45 - 44.1}{1.8} = 0.75$

Area to the left to Z, i.e., 0.75 is 0.7734.
Therefore, $0.7734 \times 200 = 154.68 = 155$ approximately.
Leas would be expected to yield a counter lower than 45.45.

c) $1 - 0.7734 = 0.2266 = (0.5 - 0.2266 + 0.5 - 0.0401) = 0.7333$

Therefore $0.7333 \times 200 = 146.66 = 147$ leas approximately would be expected to lie between 40.95 and 45.45.

d) The number finer than 45.45 i.e., $= 0.2266 \times 200 = 45.32 = 45$ leas.

Example 19: a) The coefficient of variation of lea CSP of a certain yarn is 8.4%. How many leas in 500 have strength less than 90% of the mean?

b) The mean count strength product of the above yarn is 2000 what is the % of leas have less than 1700.

Solution: Given CV = 8.4%, n = 500, M = 100% less than 90% of mean

a) $Z = \dfrac{90-100}{8.4} = -1.19 = 0.1170$

Therefore, $500 \times 0.1170 = 58.5 = 59$ leas have strength less than 90% of the mean.

Area to the left of $-1.78 = 0.0375$

Therefore, $500 \times 0.0375 = 18.75$ leas = 19 leas have C.S.P. less than 1700 or 3.7%.

Problem 1: A bore in picking element of a projectile loom part produced is found to have a mean diameter of 2.498 cm. With a SD of 0.012 cm. Determine the percentage of pieces produced you would except to lie outside of the drawing limits of 2.5 ± 0.02 cm.

Given $\overline{X} = 2.498$ cm

S. D. = 0.012 cm

Upper drawing limit = 2.52

Lower limit = 2.48

$$Z_1 = \frac{x_1 - \overline{x}}{\sigma} = \frac{2.48 - 2.498}{0.012} = -1.5$$

Area upto $Z_1 = 0.0668$

% Area upto $Z_1 = 6.68\%$

$$Z_2 = \frac{x_2 - \overline{x}}{\sigma} = \frac{2.52 - 2.498}{0.012} = 1.83$$

Area upto $Z_2 = 0.9664$

Area beyond $Z_2 = 1 - 0.9664 = 0.0336 = 3.36\%$

$\therefore$ % of units falling outside the drawing limits = 6.68% + 3.36% = 10.04%

Example 20: Plastic strips that are used in uster evenness tester (a sensitive electronic device are manufactured to a maximum specification of 305.7 mm and a minimum specification of 304.55 mm. If the strips are less than minimum specification they are scrapped. If they are greater than maximum specification, they are reworked. The part dimensions are normally distributed with a mean of 305.20 mm and SD of 0.25 mm. What % of product is scrapped and what % is reworked. How can the process be centered to eliminate all but 0.1% of the scrap? What is the rework % now?

$\bar{x}$ = 305.20 mm, σ = 0.25 mm

$$Z_1 = \frac{X_1 - \bar{x}}{\sigma} = \frac{304.55 - 305.20}{0.25} = -2.6$$

$\therefore$ Area upto Z_1 we will get from the table = 0.0047
$\therefore$ The % of product scrapped = 0.47%

$$Z_2 = \frac{x_2 - \bar{x}}{\sigma} = \frac{305.7 - 305.20}{0.25} = 2$$

Area upto Z_2

The % of product reworked

$\therefore$ = 1 – 0.9773 = 0.0227 = 2.27%
If % of the product scrapped is 0.1%
Then area upto Z_1 = 0.001
We know

$$Z_1 = \frac{x_1 - \bar{x}}{\sigma}$$

$$-3.09 = \frac{304.55 - \bar{x}}{0.25}$$

$$-3.09 \times 0.25 + 304.55 = +\bar{x}$$

$$\therefore \bar{x} = 305.32$$

$\therefore$ Z_1 = –3.09 from the tables

To find rework when $\bar{x}$ = 305.32

$$Z_2 = \frac{x_2 - \bar{x}}{\sigma} = \frac{305.7 - 305.32}{0.25} = 1.52$$

Area upto Z_2 from the table is = 0.9357

∴ % of rework is equal to $1 - 0.9357 = 0.0643$

∴ % of rework = 6.43%

Example 21: 2000 electronic relays used in textile machines were tested and it was observed that the life time of relay was normally distributed with an average of 2040 hours SD of 60 hours. Compute the number of bulbs that are expected to burn for

(i)   More than 2150 hours

(ii) Less than 1960 hours

$$Z_1 = \frac{x_1 - \bar{x}}{\sigma} = \frac{1960 - 2040}{60} = -1.33$$

Given $\bar{x} = 2040$ hours $\sigma = 60$ hours

Area upto Z_1 from table = 0.0918 or 9.18%.

The number of bulbs that are expected to burn less than 1960 hours = $0.0918 \times 2000 = 183.6 = 184$ bulbs.

$$Z_2 = \frac{x_2 - \bar{x}}{\sigma} = \frac{2150 - 2040}{60} = 1.833$$

From table area upto $Z_2 = 0.9664$

∴ Area beyond $Z_2 = 1 - 0.9664 = 0.0336$

The number of bulbs that burn beyond 2150 hours = $0.0336 \times 2000 = 67.2$ or 67 bulbs.

5.2   Patterns of variation

Variables of statistics are sometimes distributed according to some definite probability and which can be expressed mathematically. Some of them are the following:

a) Binomial distribution

b) Poisson's distribution

c) Exponential distribution

d) Hypergeometric distribution

5.2.1   Binomial distribution

When a random experiment is performed repeatedly and if the occurrence of an event in any trial is called a success and its non-occurrence as a failure, then, for 'n' (n being finite) trials, the probability 'p' of success in any trial is constant for each trial. Then $q = 1 - p$ is the probability of failure in any trial.

The probability of 'x' successes and (n – x) failures 'n' independent trials, in a specified order is given by the compound probability theorem.

For example: Say the order of successes and failures are

S, S, F, F, F, S, F, S, F, F, S, S, F,...F, S, F

$$= P(S, S, F \ldots F, SF /$$
$$= P(S) \times P(S) \times P(F) \times P(F)\ldots\times P(F) \times P(S) \times P(F)$$

$$= P.P.P \quad \ldots\ldots\ldots \quad q, q, q$$

(x factors)   (n × x) factors

$$= p^x \times q^{n-x}$$

But 'x' successes in 'n' trials can occur in nC_x ways and the probability for each of these ways is $p^x \times q^{n-x}$

Hence, the probability of 'x' successes in any order whatsoever is given by the addition theorem of probability by the explanation.

$$P(x) = nC_x \, p^x \, q^{n-x}$$

Where x = 0, 1, 2,................n

The probability distribution of the number of successes so obtained is called "Binomial distribution" for the above reason that the probability of 1, 2,......n successes q^n, $nC_1 \, q^{n-1} \, P$,

$nC_2 \, q^{n-2} \, p^2 \ldots\ldots\ldots p^n$ are the successive terms of the Binomial expansion, $(q + P)^n$

The two independent constants 'n' and 'p' in the distribution are known as the parameters of the distribution.

It is a descrete distribution as 'x' can take only values like 0, 1, 2,........n. Any variable which follows a binomial distribution is known as a binomial variate.

Let us suppose that 'n' trials constitute an experiment. Then if this experiment is repeated 'N' times, the frequency function of binomial distribution is given by

$$f(x) = N \, P(x) = N. \, nC_x \, p^x \, q^{n-x}$$

$$x = 0, 1, 2\ldots\ldots..n$$

Characteristics

1. The binomial distribution is a distribution of discrete variable.
2. The formula for a distribution is $P(x) = nC_x \, p^x \, q^{n-x}$
   Or

$$P(x) = \frac{\angle n_1}{x1(n-x)1} p^x (1-p)^{n-x}$$

3. An example of binomial distribution may be P(x) is the probability of x defective items in a sample size of 'n' when sampling from on infinite universe which is fraction 'p' defective.
4. Mean of binomial distribution is given by mean $\bar{x}$ = np
5. Standard deviation is given by $\sigma x = \sqrt{nP(1 - P)}$ or $\sigma x = \sqrt{npq}$
    These are the formulas used in "acceptance sampling" and in control charts.
6. When P = 0.5, the binomial distribution is symmetrical around its mean.
    When P > 0.5, the right hand tail of distribution is longer.
    When P < 0.5, the left hand tail of distribution is longer.
7. The standard deviation of the binomial distribution has its maximum value where P = 0.5.

Example 22: 10 coins are thrown simultaneously. Find the probability of getting atleast seven heads.

Solution: P = Probability of getting a head = ½; q = Probability of not getting a head = ½.

Probability of getting x heads in a thrown of 'n' coins is $P(x) = nC_x \, p^x \, q^{n-x}$

$$P(7) = 10 \ C_7 \ P^7 \ q^{10-7} = 10C_7 \ (1/2)^{10}$$
$$P(8) = 10 \ C_8 \ (1/2)^{10}$$
$$P(9) = 10 \ C_9 \ (1/2)^{10}$$
$$P(10) = 10C_{10} \ (1/2)^{10}$$

Or probability of getting at least 7 heads

$$P(x = 7) = P(7) + P(8) + P(9) + P(10)$$
$$= (1/2)^{10} \ [C_7 + 10C_8 + 10C_9 + 10C_{10}]$$
$$= (1/2)^{10}[120+45+10+1]$$
$$= 176 / 1024 = 0.1718$$

5.2.2   The Poisson distribution

Poisson distribution is a limiting case of the binomial distribution, under the following conditions:

(i)   n, the number of trials is indefinitely large i.e., n $\rightarrow \infty$
(ii) p, the constant probability of success for each trial is indefinitely small. Is P$\rightarrow$0?
(iii) N p = m (say) is finite.
      i.e., P = m/n, q = 1 – (m/n)
      The probability of x success in a series of independent trials
      $P(x) = nC_x \, p^x \, q^{n-x}$

x = 0, 1, 2,...n

$$\lim_{n\to\infty} P(x) = \lim_{n\to\infty} \frac{n!}{x!(n-x)!}\left(\frac{m}{n}\right)^x\left(1-\frac{m}{n}\right)^{n-x}$$

$$P(x) = \frac{e^{-m}m^x}{x!} \quad for \quad x = 0,1,2,3,...n$$

Here 'm' is known as parameter of the Poisson distribution.

The Poisson process may also be obtained independently. i.e., (without considering it as a limiting form of the binomial distribution) as follows:

Let x_i be the number of telephone calls received in time interval 't' on a telephone switch board.

If λ is the mean arrival time, then it can be shown that the probability of getting x calls in time 't' is given by

$$P_x(t) = \frac{e^{-\lambda t}(\lambda t)^x}{x1} \quad x = 0,1,2,...$$

which is a Poisson distribution with parameter λt.

Application of Poisson distribution

1. To find no. of suicides reported in a particular city.
2. To find no. of defective material in a packing manufactured by a company
3. To find no of air accidents in some limit of time
4. To find no. of faulty blades in a packet of 1000
5. To find no. of patients arriving in a hospital
6. To find no. of cars passing across a busy street point/min
7. To find the emission of radioactive particles
8. To find no. of break downs of machinery/day

Poisson distribution is used in the sampling inspection.

1. Mean of poison distribution $\bar{x} = \lambda t = n.p.$
2. Standard deviation $= \sqrt{\lambda t} = \sqrt{n.p.}$

Example 23: A manufacture of cotter pins knows that 5% of his product is defective. If he sells cotter pins in boxes of 100 and guarantees that not more than 10 pins will be defective, then what is the approximate probability that a box will meet the guaranteed quality?

Here, n = 100

P = probability of defective pin = 5% = 0.05

m = mean number of defective pins in a box of 100 = np = 100 × 0.05 = 5

Since 'p' is small, poison distribution is used. Probability of 'x' defective pins in a box of 100.

$$P(x) = \frac{e^{-m} m^x}{x1} = \frac{e^{-5} 5^x}{x1}$$

Probability that a box fails to meet the guaranteed quality, P(x >10) = 1 – P(x ≤ 10)

$$= 1 - \sum_{x=0}^{10} \frac{e^{-5} 5^x}{x1} = 1 - e^{-5} \sum_{x=0}^{10} \frac{5^x}{x1}$$

$$= 1 - e^{-5} \left[\frac{5^0}{01} + \frac{5^1}{11} + \frac{5^2}{21} + \frac{5^3}{31} + \frac{5^4}{41} + \frac{5^5}{51} + \frac{5^6}{61} + \frac{5^7}{71} + \frac{5^8}{81} + \frac{5^9}{91} + \frac{5^{10}}{101} \right]$$

5.2.3   Exponential distribution

1. The exponential probability function follows the law, $y = 1 / \mu \; e^{-x/M}$ where μ = mean of distribution

2. In case of exponential distribution, the variable 'x' takes continuous values, i.e., it is a continuous function.

3. *Applications*
   a)   The exponential distribution can be used to predict the probability of failure of a particular equipment during a specified period.
   b)   It can also be used to determine the probability of a m/c repair completed in a specific period.
   c)   Mean of distribution = $\Sigma x / n = \mu$
        Standard deviation = Mean = μ

5.2.4 Hyper geometric distribution

The hyper geometric distribution occurs when the universe is finite and the random sample is taken without replacement.

Let there be 'a' defectives and 'b' good units in a box.

Suppose we draw 'n' units at random (without replacement) from the box, then the probability of getting 'x' defectives out of 'n' (x < n) is given by

$$P(x) = \frac{aC_x \; bC_{n-x}}{(a+b)C_n} \qquad \text{where } x = 0, 1, 2, \ldots \ldots n$$

or

$$P(x) = \frac{\dfrac{a\mathrm{l}}{x\mathrm{l}(a-x)\mathrm{l}} \dfrac{b\mathrm{l}}{(n-x)\mathrm{l}\,(b-n+x)\mathrm{l}}}{\dfrac{a+b}{(a+b-n)\mathrm{l}}}$$

This probability function gives a distribution known as hyper geometric distribution.

1. It is also a descrete function.
2. Mean of the distribution = n (a / a + b) = n. p.
3. *Applications*

$$\text{Standard deviation} = \sqrt{npq\,\frac{(a+b-n)}{(a+b-1)}}$$

The hyper geometric distribution looks very much like a binomial distribution and used in "Acceptance sampling." P(x) is the probability of getting 'x' defectives in a random sample of 'n' taken without replacement from a lot of N items of which 'a' are defective.

5.3   Tchebycheff's inequality

When we do not have a formula for a distribution and know nothing about the pattern of variation, then Tchebycheff's inequality is of some use.

This mathematical theorem states that "More than 1½ of any set of finite members must fall within closed range $\bar{x} \pm 3\sigma$, $\bar{x}$ and $\bar{\sigma}$ are computed from the numbers.

In other words less than 1/9 of the numbers can fall outside these limits. The actual fraction falling outside $\bar{x} \pm 3\,\sigma$ may be much less than 1/9. The Tchebycheff's inequality simply states that it cannot be as much as 1/9.

An extension of the above inequality by Camp and Meidell states that under certain circumstances (where mode and $\bar{x}$ are same) that more than $1 - (1/2.25t^2)$ of any distribution will fall within the closed range $\bar{x} \pm t\,\sigma$.

Problem 2: A lot of 10 articles contain 3 defectives. A random sample of 2 articles is selected from this lot. What are the respective probability that this random samples will contain

1) No defectives
2) One defectives
3) Two defectives
4) At least one defectives

Using hyper geometric distribution

$$P(x) = \frac{aC_x \times C_{n-x}}{(a+b)C_n}$$

Here, a = 3 defectives; b = 7 good ones; n = sample size = 2

∴ (1) Probability that the sample containing number defectives

$$= P(O) = \frac{3C_o \times 7C_{2-0}}{10C_2} = \frac{1 \times \dfrac{7 \times 6}{1 \times 2}}{\dfrac{10 \times 9}{1 \times 2}} = \frac{42}{90} = 0.467 = 46.7\%$$

(2) Probability that the sample contain one defective

$$P(1) = \frac{3C_1 \times 7C_{2-1}}{10C_2} = \frac{3 \times 7}{\dfrac{10 \times 9}{1 \times 2}} = \frac{42}{90} = 0.467$$

(3) Probability that the sample contain two defectives

$$P(2) = \frac{3C_2 \times 7C_{2-2}}{10C_2} = \frac{\dfrac{3 \times 2}{1 \times 2} \times 1}{\dfrac{10 \times 9}{1 \times 2}} = \frac{6}{90} = 0.067$$

(4) Probability that the sample contain atleast one defective

$$= P(1) + P(2) = 0.467 + 0.067 = 0.534.$$

Example 24: From a box containing 150 picking bolts of which 8 are defective a sample of 10 picking bolts is taken randomly.

1. What is the probability that the sample will have exactly three defectives.

2. Less than three defectives using hyper geometric distribution,

$$P(x) = \frac{aC_x \times bC_{n-x}}{(a+b)C_n}$$

1. Probability that the sample contain exactly three defectives.

$$= P(3) = \frac{8C_3 . 142C_{10-3}}{150C_{10}} =$$

$$= \frac{\dfrac{8 \times 7 \times 6}{1 \times 2 \times 3} \times \dfrac{142 \times 141 \times 140 \times 139 \times 138 \times 137 \times 136}{1 \times 2 \times 3 \times 4 \times 5 \times 6 \times 7}}{150 \times 149 \times 148 \times 147 \times 146 \times 145 \times 144 \times 143 \times 142 \times 141} =$$

$$= 0.00951$$

2. Probability that the sample contain less than three defectives.

$$P(O) = \frac{8C_o.142C_{10-0}}{150C_{10}} =$$

$$= 1 \times \frac{142 \times 141 \times 140 \times 139 \times 138 \times 137 \times 136 \times 135 \times 134 \times 133}{\dfrac{1 \times 2 \times 3 \times 4 \times 5 \times 6 \times 7 \times 8 \times 9 \times 10}{1.16955 \times 10^{15}}} =$$

$$= 0.507$$

$$P(1) = \frac{8C_1.142C_{10-1}}{150C_{10}} = 0.030$$

$$P(2) = \frac{8C_2.142C_{10-2}}{150C_{10}} = 0.08$$

$\therefore$ The probability that the sample contains less than the defectives.
$= P(0) + P(1) + P(2) = 0.567 + 0.034 + 0.08 = 0.681$

Example 25: A factory finds that an average of 20% picking cams produced by a given machine will be defective. If 10 picking cams are selected at random from a day's production of this machine, find the probability that:
a) Exactly two will be defective.
b) Two or more will be defective.
c) More than 5 will be defective.

If 1000 samples of 10 bolts each taken in the above problem, then how many of the samples you expect to find exactly two defective bolts, or two or more defective bolts.

Using binomial distribution

$$P(x) = nC_x \, p^x \, q^{n-x}$$

a) $P(2)$ = Probability that exactly two will be defective = $10C_2$ $(0.2)^2.(0.8)^8 = 0.301$. Using Poisson distribution.

$$P(x) = \frac{e^{-m} \, m^x}{x1}$$

$$P(2) = \frac{e^{-2} (2)^2}{21} = 0.271$$

Here m = n.p. = 10 × 0.2 = 2

b) Probability that the sample containing two or more defectives

$$P(\geq 2) = 1 - P(<2)$$

P $(<2) = P(0) + P(1)$

P $(0) = n C_x p^x q^{n-x} = 10C_0 (0.2)^0 . (0.8)^{10} = 1 \times 1 \times 0.1073 = 0.1073$

P $(1) = 10C_1 (0.2)^1 (0.8)^9 = 10 \times 0.2 \times 0.1342 = 0.2684$

∴ Probability $= 1- P(0) + P(1) = 1 - 0.1073 + 0.2684 = 0.6242$

c) Probability that the sample contain more than 5 defectives,

P $(>5) = 1 - P(\leq5)$

$= 1 - [P(0) + P(1) + P(2) + P(3) + P(4) + P(5)]$

d) Probability that each sample contain exactly 2 defectives = 0.301
∴ Out of 1000 samples no. of samples having 2 defectives = 0.301 × 1000 = 301 samples.
Probability that each sample contain 2 or more defectives = 0.6242
∴ Out of 1000 samples no. of samples having 2 or more defectives = 0.6242 × 1000 = 624 samples.

Example 26: Use hyper geometric distribution to find the probability that a batch of 140 pieces containing 5 defectives will give a sample of 10 pieces of which 2 are exactly defective.

$$P(x) = \frac{aC_x bC_{n-x}}{(a+b)C_n} = \frac{5C_2 135C_{10-2}}{140C_{10}} = 0.0386$$

Here, a = 5, b = 135, n = 10 and x = 2.

5.4   Normal approximation to binomial distribution

Under certain conditions the normal probability distribution will approximate the binomial probability distribution. The method is explained by means of the following example.

Example 27: It is required to find the probability of getting 2, 3, or 4 tails in 12 tosses of a coin by normal approximation to the binomial.

Answer: The two parameters for the normal curve are average and standard deviation. For binomial distribution

Average $= \bar{x} = np = 12 \times ½ = 6$
And standard deviation $= \sigma = \sqrt{npq} = \sqrt{12 \times ½ \times ½} = 1.73$

Since the data must be continuous for the normal curve, the probability of obtaining 2 to 4 tails is considered to be from 1.5 (lower boundary of cell whose mid point is 2) to 4.5 (upper boundary of the all whose mid is at 4).

Then $Z_1 = \dfrac{x_1 - \bar{x}}{\sigma} = \dfrac{1.5 - 6}{1.73} = -2.6$

and $Z_2 = \dfrac{x_2 - \bar{x}}{\sigma} = \dfrac{4.5 - 6}{1.73} = -0.87$

From table of area under normal curve, for Z_2 of -0.87 i.e., area $A_3 = 0.1922$.

And area of upto Z_1 of -2.6 (area of A_2) $= 0.0047$
Area A_1 enclosed between these limits $= 0.1922 - 0.0047 = 0.1875$
Thus the probability is $P(2,3,4$ or 4 tails$) = 0.1875$

Let us compare this with binomial distribution,

P_2 $= n\, C_x\, p^x\, q^{n-x} = 12\, C_{2(1/2)}\, 2\, _{(1/2)}10$
    $= (12 \times 11) / (1 \times 2) \times (1 / 2)^2 \times (1 / 2)^{10} = 66(1 / 2)^{12}$
$P(3) = 220(1 / 2)^{12}$ and $P(4) = 495(1 / 2)^{12}$

Hence $P(2$ to 4 tails$) = 66(1 / 2)^{12} + 220(1 / 2)^{12} + 495(1 / 2)^{12} = 0.1906$
From the above, it is seen that the normal distribution will give almost the same value of the probability (little less than actual).

Example 28: Random samples of 80 items are taken from a continuous process which is known to produce 30% defectives. Determine the probability of finding more than 15 defectives in the sample.

a)   Using normal approximation to binomial
b)   Using Poison approximation

Which do you think is better to present the true value of the binomial?

Solution: (a) *Normal approximation to binomial*

Average $= n\, \bar{p} = 80 \times (30 / 100) = 24$ defectives
Standard deviation $= \sqrt{npq} = 80 \times 0.3 \times 0.7 = 4.1$

Probability of more than 15 defectives, means that the probability of 15.5 or more because normal distribution is a continuous curve.

∴ $Z = \dfrac{15.5 - 24}{4.41} = -2.07$

From table of area under normal curve, for value of $Z = -2.07$ the area up to Z is equal to 0.0191.

∴ $P\,(>15.5) = 1 - 0.0191 = 0.9809$

b) *Using Poisson approximation*

From Poisson table, for a value of np = 24 and c = 15,

The probability upto 15 = 0.034
∴ Probability (> 15) = 1 - 0.034 = 0.966

  The normal distribution will give better approximation to binomial when $\overline{p}$ is in the vicinity of 0.5. But in this case, $\overline{p}$ = 0.3 which is nearer to zero, and when $\overline{p}$ is small Poisson gives a better approximation of the true probability, than the normal distribution.

Example 29: If the probability of defective bolts is 0.1, find (a) the mean and standard deviation for the distribution of defective bolts in a total of 500; and (b) the moment coefficients of skewness and kurtosis of the distribution.

Solution: (a) p = 0.1, n = 500
Mean = np = 500 × 0.1 = 50
Thus we can expect 50 bolts to be defective, $\sigma = \sqrt{npq}, n = 500, p = 0.1$ and q = 0.9.

$$\sigma = \sqrt{500 \times 0.1 \times 0.9} = 6.91$$

b) Moment coefficient of skewness, i.e., γ_1

$$\gamma_1 = \sqrt{p_1} = \sqrt{\frac{(q-p)^2}{npq}}$$

$$= \frac{q-p}{\sqrt{npq}} = \frac{(0.9-0.1)}{0.71} = \frac{0.8}{0.71} = 0.119$$

Since γ_1 is more than zero the distribution is positively skewed. However, the skewness is very moderate.
Moment coefficient of Kurtosis $\gamma_2 = \beta_2 - 3$
Since γ_2 is positive the distribution is platykurtic

$$\beta_2 = 3 + \frac{1 - 6pq}{npq} = 3 + \frac{1 - 6(0.1)(0.9)}{44.9}$$

$$= 3 + \frac{0.46}{44.9} = 3.01$$

$$\gamma_2 = 3.01 - 3 = +0.01$$

$(q + p)^2 = q^4 + 6q^6 p + 6q^3 p^2 + 20q^3 p^5 + 15q^2 p^4 + 6q\, p^5 + p^4$

Example 30: The coincidence of occupational disease in a glass fibre industry is such that the workmen have a 25% chance of suffering from it. What is the probability that out of 6 workmen 4 or more will contact the disease?

Solution: Let q denote chance of suffering and p chance of not suffering.

$\therefore$ q = 25% = ¼ and p = 3

The binomial expression is

$$(q + p)^n = (1 / 4 + ¾)^4$$

Or $q^3 + 6q^4 p + 15q^4 p^2 + 15q^2 p + 6q\ p^5$

The probability of 4 or more (that is, 4, 5 and 6 successes is)

$$= 15q^4 p^2 + 6q^2 + q^4$$

Substituting the values, we get

$$= 15\left(\frac{1}{4}\right)^4 \left(\frac{3}{4}\right)^2 + 6\left(\frac{1}{4}\right)^5 \left(\frac{3}{4}\right) + \left(\frac{1}{4}\right)^6$$

$$= \frac{15 \times 9}{4096} + \frac{6 \times 3}{4096} + \frac{1}{4096} = \frac{135 + 18 + 1}{4096} = \frac{154}{4096} = 0.0376$$

5.5   The binomial distribution

If n events are taken, the number of sets having n successes, (n – 1) successes, n (–2) successes, etc., will be given by the terms of the binomial distribution.

$$(p + q)^n$$

The probability of getting r successes, in n independent trials is given by

$$f(r) = n\ C_r\ p^r\ q^{n-r}$$

Or $f(r) = n\ C_r\ p^r\ (1-p)^{n-r}$ for r = 0, 1, 2,................., or n

5.5.1   Assumptions made in binomial distribution

1. The number of trials (attempts, or repetitions) is fixed.
2. The probability of a success is the same for each trial.
3. The trials all independent, that is, what happens in any one trial does not affect the probability of a success in any other trial.

Mean of probability distribution μ = Er f (r)

Mean of binomial distribution μ $= nP$
Variance of probability distribution $\sigma^2 = E (r - \mu)^2, f(r)$

Example 31: During an efficiency survey of a weaving shed, 64 observations of the six looms of one weaver were made, i.e., sixty four 'map-readings' in which the number of stopped looms is recorded in the brief instant of observation. It was found that distribution of the number of stopped looms was as follows:

Number of stopped looms	0	1	2	3	4	5	6
Frequency		30	22	8	2	2	0	0

Can this distribution be represented by the binomial distribution?

The number of 'sets of events' in this case is 64, i.e., N – 64. The 'n' events are the stoppages of the looms, i.e., n = 6. Hence, the binomial expansion in this example may be written.

$$(p + q)^n$$

For a binomial distribution arithmetic mean = nP
Arithmetic mean = $\Sigma fx / \Sigma f$

$$= \frac{(30\times0)+(22\times1)+(8\times2)+(2\times3)+(2\times4)+(0\times5)+(0\times6)}{64} = \frac{52}{64}$$

Since, n = 6, arithmetic mean = nP

$$p = 52/64 \times 1/6 = 0.135$$

Since, p + q =1, q = 0.865, expansion becomes $(0.135 + 0.865)^6$
Success in this case is stopped loom.
The probability that none of the loom were stopped is (r) = $nC_r\, p^r\, q^{n-r}$

$$P (0) = 6C_0 (0.135)^0 (0.865)^{6-0} = 0.865^6 = 0.4218$$

The number of times that there were no stopped looms is given by the last term, i.e.,

$$64 \times 0.865^6 = 27 \text{ approximately.}$$

The probability that 1 out of 6 looms was stopped is given

$$p(1) = 6C_1(0.135)^1 (0.865)^5 = 0.3906$$

The number of times that 1 out of 6 looms was stopped is = 64×0.865^6 = 0.3906 × 64 = 25.
Similarly, the number of times looms were stopped at p(2), p(4), p(3), p(5), p(6), are 10, 2, 0.23, 0, 0 respectively.

Hence, the distribution is as follows:

Number of looms stopped   0, 1, 2, 3, 4, 5, 6
Frequency   27, 25, 10, 2, 0.23, 0, 0.

Comparing the calculated and the actual distributions, we observe that there is a reasonable agreement between them. We therefore, conclude that the actual distribution follows the binomial distribution.

Example 32: In the above problem find the probability that

(1)   Exactly 3 looms were stopped at a given time.
(2)   Less than 3 looms were stopped at a given time.
(3)   More than 2 looms were stopped at a given time.

Answer: p (2) 0.1562, p(3) p.08125, p(4) 0.0036, p(5) 0.00, p(6) 0.

1) p(3) = $6C_3$ $(0.135)^3$ $(0.865)^3$ = 0.03125
2) Probability that less than 3 looms were stopped at a given time is
        = 1 – p(3) + p(4) + p(5) – p(6)
        = 1 – (0.03125 + 0.0036 + 0 + 0) = 0.96515
3) Probability that more than 2 looms were stopped at a given time is
        = 1 – p(0) + p(1) + p(2) = 1 – (0.4218 + 0.03906 + 0.1512)
        = 0.364

Example 33: In a binomial distribution, the mean np = 6 and the variance npq = 2. Determine the distribution.

$$np = 6 \qquad \qquad \ldots \text{(i)}$$
$$npq = 2 \qquad \qquad \ldots \text{(ii)}$$

Substituting p = 6/n in Equation (ii), we get

$$n\frac{6}{n}\left(1-\frac{6}{n}\right) = 2.$$

$$6 n - 36 = 2n$$
$$4n = 36$$
$$n = 9$$

Substitution in Equation (i) np = 6

$$p = 6 / 9 = 0.66$$

∴   q = 1 – 066 = 0.33.

The binomial expansion may be written as $(0.66 + 0.33)^6$

Distribution

$$P(0) = 6C_0 (0.66)^0 (0.33)^6$$

$$P(1) = 6C_1 (0.66)^1 (0.33)^5$$

$$P(2) = 6C_2 (0.66)^2 (0.33)^4$$

$$P(3) = 6C_3 (0.66)^3 (0.33)^3$$

$$P(4) = 6C_4 (0.66)^4 (0.33)^2$$

$$P(5) = 6C_5 (0.66)^5 (0.33)^1$$

$$P(6) = 6C_6 (0.66)^6 (0.33)^0$$

Example 34: A sample of 86 cotton fibres has been examined for maturity, and 55% of them are found to be 'normal' (in the sense used in the maturity test). Within what limits would the true percentage of 'normal' fibres be expected to lie?

Answer: P = 0.55 SE of proportion

$$\sqrt{\frac{0.55(1-0.55)}{86}} = 0.054 \ or \ 5.4\%$$

Maximum error E = 1.96 × 0.054 = 0.1058 or 10.58%

Confidence interval

True percentage of normal fibres is likely to be 55 ± 10.58 i.e., between 44.22 and 65.58.

Confidence interval for proportion

$$np = Z\frac{\alpha}{2}\sqrt{np(1-p)} < x < np + Z\frac{\alpha}{2}\sqrt{np(1-p)}$$

$$or \ as \ \frac{\overline{x}}{n} - Z\frac{\alpha}{2}\sqrt{\frac{p(1-p)}{n}} < p < \frac{x}{n} + Z\frac{\alpha}{2}\sqrt{\frac{p(1-p)}{n}}$$

$$\sqrt{\frac{p(1-p)}{n}}$$

is called the SE of a proportion.

$$\frac{x}{n} - Z\frac{\alpha}{2}\sqrt{\frac{\frac{x}{n}\left(1-\frac{x}{n}\right)}{n}} < p < x/n + Z\frac{\alpha}{2}\sqrt{\frac{\frac{x}{n}\left(1-\frac{x}{n}\right)}{n}}$$

Sample size

$$n = p(1-p)\frac{Z\frac{\alpha}{2}}{E}$$

Since the unknown population proportion p appears in this formula, it cannot be used unless we have some information about the possible values p might assume. If we have no such information, we make use of the fact that p(1 − p) is ¼ when p = ½, and less than ¼ for all other values of p. Hence, if we use the formula

$$\text{Sample size } n = \frac{1}{4}\left(\frac{Z\frac{\alpha}{2}}{E}\right)^2$$

Test whether the Poisson distribution is applicable to the snap study readings given below. The number of end breakages in 12 periods of 1 hour's spinning with 160 spindles.

Answer:

6   4   8   10   7   4   8   9   9   5   8   6
Mean number = 7.00, variance = 4.00, F = variance/mean = 0.57

With V_1 = 11, V_2 = ∞, F tab. For 5% level of significance, 0.57 < 1.8. Hence, the value 0.57 is not significant and we conclude that there is no evidence to suggest that the variation in number of end breakage is not random. Hence, Poisson distribution is applicable.

Test whether the Poisson distribution is applicable to the snap study readings given below.

Number of end breakages in eight periods of 1 hour's spinning with 400 spindles 15, 10, 20, 25, 18, 10, 20, 23.

Σx = (141, Σx^2 = 2703, σ = 55)
σ^2 31.12 = variance $\bar{x}$ = 17.62
F = variance / mean = 31.12 / 17.62 = 1.76
With V_1 = 8 − 1 = 7 and V_2 = ∞
F tab. Value at 5% level of significance is 2.00

F calculated value 1.76 is less than F tab value of 2.0. Hence, the variation in number of end breakages is not significant. Hence, Poisson distribution is applicable.

Suppose the number of warp breakages per unit length of 5 yd. is studied and the results are as follows:

Breaks per length	Frequency	Breaks × frequency
0	15	0
1	26	26
2	21	42
3	19	57
4	8	32
5	3	15
6	0	0
7	0	0
8	0	0
Total	92	172

Test whether the Poisson distribution is applicable.

The mean   = 172 / 92 = 1.87

The variance = 1.78

Assuming for the moment that the distribution nearly follows the Poisson distribution, let $\mu = 1.87$.

The calculated frequency of

$$f(0)\text{Breaks '}92\left(\frac{e^{-1.87}1.87^0}{01}\right) = 92 \times 0.154\ldots14.2$$

$$f(1)\text{Breaks '}92\left(\frac{e^{-1.87}1.87^1}{11}\right) = 92 \times 0.154 \times 1.87\ldots26.6$$

$$f(2)\text{Breaks '}92\left(\frac{e^{-1.87}1.87^2}{21}\right) = \ldots24.8$$

$f(3)$ Breaks 15.4

$f(4)$ Breaks 7.2

$f(5)$ Breaks 2.7

$f(6)$ Breaks 0.8

$f(7)$ Breaks 0.2

$f(8)$ Breaks 0.1

The calculated frequency distribution of the breaks to be expected is in reasonable agreement with the actual distribution. Hence, it follows Poisson distribution.

Neps in a card web are estimated by placing over the web templates with many circular holes, each one square inch in area, and counting the proportion of holes that are free from neps and the number that contain one nep or more. If 72 holes are examined and 60 are free from neps, what is the estimate of the mean number of neps per 100 square inches? (It may be assumed that the frequency distribution of holes with 0, 1, 2, etc., neps is a Poisson distribution).

Answer:

$$p(0) = \frac{e^{-\mu}\mu^0}{x!} = e^{-\mu} = \frac{60}{72} = 5/6$$

= probability of holes with zero neps.

Taking log on both sides

$$-\mu \log e = \log 5 - \log 6.$$
$$\mu \log e = \log 5 + \log 6$$
$$\mu \log e = \log (6/5)$$
$$= 0.079 / 0.434 = 0.18$$

$$\mu = \frac{\log\left(\frac{6}{5}\right)}{\log e}$$

The neps per 100 square inches are thus estimated to be 18.

5.6   The central limit theorem

The central limit theorem defines the limit to which the distribution of sums of independent random variables converge. If x_1, x_2, ...x_k are k independent random variables, then any linear function of the variables say,

$$y = \sum_1^k a_i x_i$$

will tend to be normally distributed, irrespective of the distributions of the individual variables entering into the expression, provided that none of the individual variances S_i^2 (i = 1,2,.....k) is large compared to the sum of the other variances, i.e., provided S_i^2 is not large compared to $S_1^2 + S_2^2 + S_{i-1}^2 + S_{i+1}^2 +..........+S_k^2$ for all values of i (i = 1,2,.....k).

The larger the value of k, the nearer will be the distribution of y to the normal. Consider an example, x_1 is a random variable which can take values 1, 2, 3, 4 with equal probabilities, while x_2, is another variable which can take values 1, 2, 3, 4, 5, 6 with equal probabilities. Distribution of x_1:

Variate value	1	2	3	4
Probability	¼	¼	¼	¼

Distribution of X2

Variate value	1	2	3	4	5	6
Probability	1 / 6	1 / 6	1 / 6	1 / 6	1 / 6	1 / 6

The distribution of the sum (X1 + X2) will be

Variate value	2	3	4	5	6	7	8	9	10
Probability	1 / 24	1 / 12	1 / 8	1 / 6	1 / 6	1 / 6	1 / 8	1 / 12	1 / 24

The distributions are plotted in Fig. 4.2.

It is seen that even where only two variables are summed, the resulting distributions has become symmetrical. The central limit theorem explains why many of the distributions converge to the normal for large populations sizes.

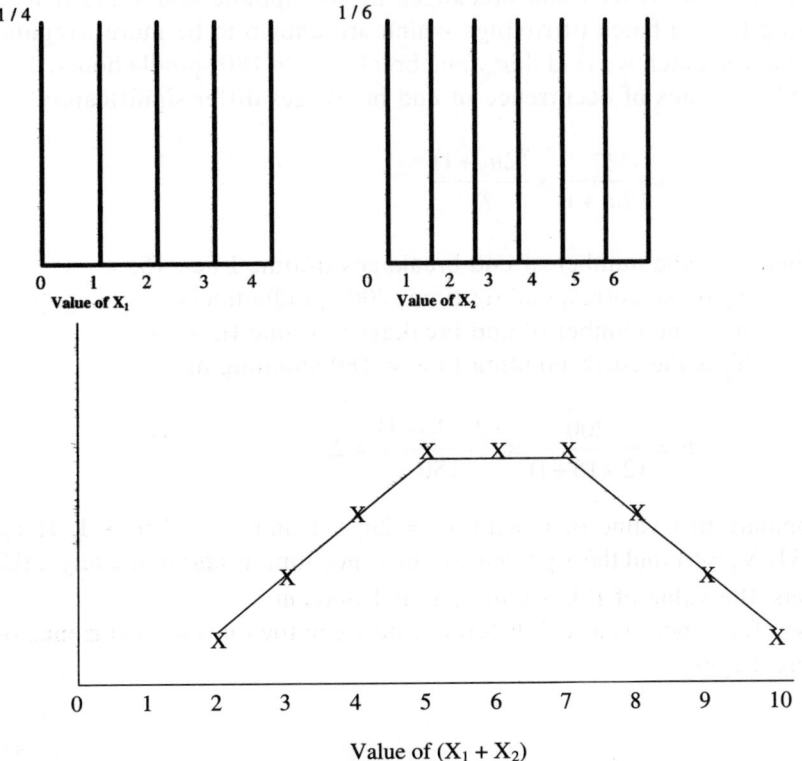

4.2 Distributions of X_1, X_2 and (X_1+X_2).

Example 35: A manufacturer has based the work-load of weavers and the assumption of 1.0 warp breaks per loom per hour, and has agreed to take action if, for any set of warps, the observed breakage rate raises above 1.25 per loom per hour. For how many hours must observations be taken in order to give the manufacturer reasonable confidence that he does not take action when the true breakage ratio is 1.0 (assume that warp breaks are distributed randomly in time).

Maximum error E = 1.25 − 1 = 0.25 E = 1
S.E. of single estimate of E = $\sqrt{E}$ / $\sqrt{T}$ 1.96
$\sqrt{T}$ = (1 / 0.25) × 1.96
T = 61.46 h.

5.7   Significance test for the difference between two rates of occurrence

Example 36: Suppose that we know from past experience that the Poisson distribution can be used to describe the distribution of end breakage in spinning on a certain frame. Suppose that in spinning from one batch of rovings we find fifteen end breakages in 200 spindle hours and that in spinning from a batch of rovings which are known to be more irregular than the first batch we find thirty end breakages in 180 spindle hours. Test whether the rates of occurrence of end breakages differ significantly?

$$F = \frac{T_1}{(2n_1 + 1)} \times \frac{(2n_2 + 1)}{T_2}$$

When n_1 is the number of end breakages in time I i.e., 15.
     T_1 is the corresponding time: 200 spindle hours.
     n_2 is the number of end breakages in time II, ≈ 30.
     T_2 is the corresponding time = 180 spinning hrs.

$$F = \frac{200}{(2 \times 15 + 1)} \times \frac{(2 \times 30 + 1)}{180} = 2.1$$

Compare this value of F with $V_1 = 2n_1 + 1$ and $V_2 = 2n_2 + 1$. Here, $V_1 = 31$, $V_2 = 61$ and the 1 percent significance limit is approximately 2.03.

Thus, the value of F is significant at 1 percent.

Therefore, there is a real difference between the rates of occurrence of end breakages.

5.8   Confidence interval for mean rate of occurrence

Example 37: Suppose that we count 64 warp breakages in 500 hours on a certain loom. We may wish to give a confidence interval for the population breakage rate (i.e., the average rate at which breakages would occur in a very long time).

The general formula is that if n events occur in time T, the 95% confidence interval for the mean rate of occurrence is

$$n\sqrt{T} \pm 1.96\frac{\sqrt{n}}{T}$$

$$\frac{64}{500} + 1.96\frac{\sqrt{64}}{500} \quad or \quad 0.128 \pm 0.031$$

In our particular example, the 95 percent is the confidence interval.

This result enables us to decide what sample size is necessary to attain an assigned accuracy. If we want to know the rate of occurrence of end breakages to an accuracy of 20%, we must observe end breakages until about 100 have occurred.

$$\frac{\dfrac{1.96\sqrt{n}}{T}}{n\sqrt{T}} = 0.20$$

$$Hence \quad n = \left(\frac{1.96}{0.20}\right) = 96$$

Example 38: The average end-breakage rates observed with two different types of top roller covering A and B were 10 and 12 per 100 spindle hours respectively. Each of this average is based on 2000 spindle hours test whether the difference is significant.

Answer:

$$F = \left(\frac{100}{(2\times10)+1}\right) \times \left(\frac{(2\times12)+1}{100}\right) = \frac{25}{21} = 1.19$$

Compare this value of F with $V_1 = (2n_1+1)$ and $V_2 = 2n_2+1$. Here $V_1 = 19$, $V_2 = 23$. Thus the value of F tab for 5% level of significance is 2.15 approximately. Hence, the difference in breakage rate is insignificant.

Alternative method

For comparing breakage rates for two different conditions, the observed difference in end breaks is real only if

$$\frac{(A-B)^2}{A+B} > 4$$

Where A = Total number of end breaks counted for one condition.
B = Total number of end breaks counted for the other condition for the same number of spindle hours.

$$= \frac{(12-10)^2}{12+10} = \frac{4}{22} = 0.18 < 4.$$

Hence, the difference is insignificant.

Example 39: During the spinning of a certain yarn, 112 breaks were observed and of these 24 were due to waste and fly on the yarn. For another yarn, 83 out of 218 breaks were due to waste and fly. Is the difference in proportions a change effect?

It is assumed that the bulk of fibres has been so well mixed, or the sampling technique has been so arranged, that the probability of each fibre being 'normal' is constant.

Answer: SE_1 of proportion

$$\sqrt{\frac{p(1-p)}{n}} = \sqrt{\frac{\frac{24}{112}\left(1-\frac{24}{112}\right)}{112}} = 0.03877$$

$$SE_2 \text{ of proportion} = \sqrt{\frac{p(1-p)}{n}} = \sqrt{\frac{\frac{83}{218}\left(1-\frac{83}{218}\right)}{218}} = 0.032288$$

SE_{1-2} (Standard error of difference in proportion) =

$$= \sqrt{SE_1^2 + SE_2^2} = \sqrt{0.0015 + 0.00108} = 0.05079$$

Maximum error E

Maximum difference in sample proportion

$$(83 / 218) - (24 / 112) = 0.1664$$

Since, the actual error is greater than the maximum error, difference very unlikely to have been a change effect (i.e., it is not due to the change effect).

Example 40: In a snap-reading survey of weavers it is required to estimate the percentage of time spent in mending warp-breaks so that the error is unlikely to exceed ± 1% of the 'weavers' time. Usually, these weavers spend about 10% of their time in mending warp-breaks. If there are 16 weavers, how many snap observations must be made of each?

Answer: E = ± 1%

$$\text{Maximum error} = Z\alpha\frac{1}{2}\sqrt{\frac{p(1-p)}{n}} => 0.01 = 1.96\sqrt{\frac{0.1(0.9)}{n}}$$

$$n = \frac{0.1 \times 0.9}{(0.01)^2} \times (1.96)^2 =$$

$$= 3457.44 \text{ observations of 16weavers}$$

∴ For 1 weaver it is = 216 observation.

It is assumed that the operatives spend a constant proportion of their time in general supervision and relaxation or that, if this is not so, the observations are substantially distributed at random over the time. That is of interest.

Example 41: If the weight of laps coming from the scoutcher is correctly controlled one half will be heavier than the specified weight and one half lighter. A manager makes a spot check and finds that 46 out of 64 laps are 'heavy' is this evidence that the average lap weight is away from the specified value.

Answer: SE of proportion

$$\sqrt{\frac{p(1-p)}{n}} = \sqrt{\frac{\frac{46}{64}\left(1-\frac{46}{64}\right)}{64}} = 0.056$$

Maximum error = 0.056 × 1.96 = 0.1097
  Actual error = 0.5.

Example 42: Spinning breaks have been counted on the frames of one tenter for 27 hours (i) before and (ii) after changing to rovings from a new mixing of cotton, and the separate hourly observations were as follows:

(i) Before	24	18	27	15	17	17	18	17	25
	22	28	17	15	21	16	20	20	15
	17	25	18	18	22	14	22	28	21
(ii) Before	29	30	30	27	36	30	33	34	23
	22	24	21	26	17	22	30	21	21
	34	22	21	19	21	33	17	17	28

a) Estimate directly the standard deviation of a single hourly observation for each series and compare the result given by equation standard deviation of single estimate of $\mu = \sqrt{\mu}$. Do the Poisson formula apply?

b) Is there any evidence of a real change in breakage rate? (Answer this question in two ways.)

(a) (i) *Direct method*

$$n = 27 \quad \Sigma x = 540$$

$$SD = \sqrt{\frac{n \in x^2 - (\in x)^2}{n(n-1)}} = \sqrt{\frac{27(11266) - (540)^2}{27(27-1)}} = 4.23$$

By using the formula i.e., Standard deviation of single estimate of $\mu = \sqrt{\mu}$

Here μ is nothing but mean $= \overline{x} = 540 / 27 = 20$

$$= \sqrt{20} = 4.47$$

ii) *Direct method*

$$n = 27, \quad \in x = 688 \quad \in x^2 = 18406$$

$$SD = \sqrt{\frac{27(18406) - (688)^2}{27(26)}} = 5.80$$

Standard deviation of single estimate of $\mu = 25.48$ and $688/27 = 25.48$

5.8.1   To test whether Poisson distribution is applicable or not

$$F = variance/mean$$

i) Direct method: Variance $= \sigma^2 = 4.23^2 = 17.89$

Mean $= \overline{x} = 20 \quad F = (17.89) / 20 = 0.89$

The value of F tab for $V_1 = 27 - 1 = 26$ and $V_2 =$ at 5% level of significance is 1.50 approximately. 0.89 is less than 1.5. Hence, the Poisson formulae give a reasonably close approximation to the directly estimated standard deviation.

ii) Assuming Poisson formula

$$Variance = 5.8^2$$
$$\overline{x} = 25.48$$
$$F = 33.64 / 25.48 = 1.32$$

Again 1.32 is less than 1.5 (i.e., 5% table value for 26 and degrees of freedom). Hence, the Poisson formula can be applicable to the directly estimated standard deviation.

b) Direct estimate of SD

SE$_1$ (i.e., SE of standard deviation)

$$\frac{S.D}{\sqrt{2n}} = \frac{4.23}{\sqrt{2 \times 27}} = 0.57$$

Since actual error is less than the maximum error, the difference in end breakage rate is not significant. Hence, the difference is due to change effect.
Using Poisson formulae:
SE of mean of n estimates of $\mu = \mu / \sqrt{n}$

$$SE_{(ii)} = \frac{\sqrt{25.48}}{\sqrt{27}}$$

$$SE_{(i)-(ii)} = \sqrt{(SE_i)^2 + (SE_{ii})^2} = \sqrt{\frac{20}{27} + \frac{25.48}{27}} = 1.29$$

Maximum error = 1.29 × 1.96 = 2.5284
Actual error = $\mu_i - \mu_{ii}$ = 25.48 – 20 = 5.48

Since the actual error is greater than maximum error the actual difference in end breakage rate is significant (when Poisson formula is made use of). Hence, the difference is due to the assignable causes.

Example 1: Find the coefficient of correlation between the ends/inch (X) and picks per inch (Y).

x	23	27	28	28	29	30	31	33	35	36
y	18	20	22	27	21	29	27	29	28	29

Solution:

X-series			Y-series			
x	d_x	d^2_x	y	d_y	d^2_y	$d_x \times d_y$
23	−7	49	18	−7	49	49
27	−3	9	20	−5	25	15
28	−2	4	22	−3	9	6
28	−2	4	27	2	4	−4
29	−1	1	21	−4	16	4
30	0	0	29	4	16	0
31	1	1	27	2	4	2
33	3	9	29	4	16	12
35	5	25	28	3	9	15
36	6	36	29	4	16	24
$\Sigma x = 300$	$\Sigma d^2_x = 138$		$\Sigma y = 250$	$\Sigma d^2_y = 164$	$\Sigma d_x d_y = 123$	

Mean of X-series = $\Sigma x/n = 300/10 = 30$
Mean of Y-series = $\Sigma y/n = 250/10 = 25$

$$\sigma_x = \sqrt{\frac{\Sigma d^2_x}{n}} = \sqrt{\frac{138}{10}} = 3.7 \,(App.)$$

$$\sigma_y = \sqrt{\frac{\Sigma d^2_y}{n}} = \sqrt{\frac{164}{10}} = 4 \,(App.)$$

$$r = \frac{\Sigma d_x d_y}{n\sigma_x\sigma_y} = \frac{123}{10\times3.7\times4} = +0.831$$

Thus, it is a case of +ve correlation.

Example 2: A basic scutcher has a piano feed regulating motion with cone drums. Find the coefficient of correlation between them.

Top cone   89 86   74 65 65   63 66   67 72   79
(Drum diameter in mm)

Bottom cone   82 91.5 84 75 73.5 72 70.5 75 77.5 84
(Drum diameter in mm)

Let provisional mean in X-series = 76 and in Y-series = 81

X-series	D_x	D^2_x	Y-series	D_y	D^2_y	$D_x \times D_y$
89	13	169	82	1	1	13
86	10	100	91.5	10.5	110.25	105
74	-2	4	84	3	9	-6
65	-11	121	75	-6	36	66
65	-11	121	73.5	-7.5	56.25	82.5
63	13	169	72	-9	81	117
66	-10	100	70.5	-10.5	110.25	105
67	-9	81	75	-6	36	54
72	-4	16	77.5	-3.5	12.25	14
79	3	9	84	3	9	9
Total 726	-34	890	785	-25	461	559.5

$$\sigma x = \sqrt{\frac{\sum D_x^2}{n} - \left(\frac{\sum D_x}{n}\right)^2} = \sqrt{\frac{890}{10} - \left(-\frac{34}{10}\right)^2} = \sqrt{77.4} = 8.8$$

$$\sigma y = \sqrt{\frac{\sum D_y^2}{n} - \left(\frac{\sum D_y}{n}\right)^2} = \sqrt{\frac{461}{10} - \left(-\frac{25}{10}\right)^2} = \sqrt{39.85} = 6.3$$

$$r = \frac{\frac{\sum D_x D_y}{n} - \frac{\sum D_x}{n} \times \frac{\sum D_y}{n}}{\sigma_x \sigma_y} = \frac{\frac{559.5}{10} - \left(-\frac{34}{10}\right)\left(\frac{-25}{10}\right)}{8.8 \times 6.3}$$

$$= \frac{55.95 - 8.5}{55.44} = \frac{47.45}{55.44} = +0.856$$

Hence, the diameters are positioning correlated.

Grouped data

If correlation table is given, the following formulae are used.

$$(1) \quad r = \frac{\sum fd_x d_y}{n\sigma_x \sigma_y}$$

$$(2) \quad r - \dfrac{\dfrac{\sum fD_x D_y}{n} - \dfrac{\sum fD_y}{n} \times \dfrac{\sum dD_y}{n}}{\sigma_x \sigma_y} \text{(short-cut method)}$$

The method is the same as illustrated in the previous example.

Example 3: Calculate 'r' between percentage of photocell surviving and mortality rate of feelers.

Mortality rate of feeler	Percentage of photocell surviving more than two weeks					
	1.5–4.5	4.5–7.5	7.5–10.5	10.5–13.5	13.5–16.5	16.5–19.5
36–46	5	–	–	–	–	–
46–56	9	1	–	–	–	–
56–66	10	4	1	–	–	1
66–76	4	7	5	2	–	–
76–86	2	5	4	1	1	–
86–96	–	2	2	2	–	1
96–106	–	1	2	2	1 1	
106–116	–	1	–	1	–	–

$\sum fD_x D_y = 5 \times (-6) \times (-30) + 9 \times (-6) \times (-20) + 10 \times (-6) \times (-10) + 4 \times (-6) \times 0 + 2 \times (-6) \times 10 + 1 \times (-3) \times (-20) + 4 \times (-3) \times (-10) + 7 \times (-3) \times 0 + 5 \times (-3) \times 10 + 2 \times (-3) \times 20 + 1 \times (-3) \times 30 + 1 \times (-3) \times (40) + 1 \times 0 \times 10 + 5 \times 0 \times 0 + 4 \times 0 \times 10 + 2 \times 0 \times 20 + 2 \times 0 \times 30 + 2 \times 3 \times 0 + 1 \times 3 \times 10 + 2 \times 3 \times 20 + 2 \times 3 \times 30 + 1 \times 3 \times 40 + 1 \times 6 \times 10 + 1 \times 6 \times 30 + 1 \times 9 \times (-10) + 1 \times 9 \times 20 + 1 \times 9 \times 30$

$= 900 + 1080 + 600 + 0 - 120 + 60 + 120 + 0 - 150 - 120 - 90 - 120 + 0 + 0 + 0 + 0 + 0 + 0 + 30 + 120 + 180 + 120 + 60 + 180 - 90 + 180 + 270 = 3210$

$$\sigma_x = \sqrt{\dfrac{\sum fD_x^2}{n} - \left(\dfrac{\sum fD_x}{n}\right)^2} = \sqrt{\dfrac{1656}{78} - \left(\dfrac{-180}{78}\right)^2} = \sqrt{16.07} = 4$$

$$\sigma_y = \sqrt{\dfrac{\sum fD_y^2}{n} - \left(\dfrac{\sum fD_y}{n}\right)^2} = \sqrt{\dfrac{23700}{78} - \left(\dfrac{50}{78}\right)^2} = \sqrt{303.59} = 17.42$$

$$r = \dfrac{\dfrac{\sum fD_x D_y}{n} - \dfrac{\sum fD_x}{n} \times \dfrac{\sum fD_y}{n}}{\sigma_x \sigma_y} = \dfrac{\dfrac{3210}{78} - \dfrac{-180}{78} \times \dfrac{50}{78}}{4 \times 17.42}$$

$$= \dfrac{41.15 + 1.48}{69.68} = \dfrac{42.63}{69.68} = 0.61$$

In the previous paragraphs

Hint: (1) For finding σ_x and σ_y, separate tables for X-series and Y-series should be framed ignoring Y-series in former case and X-series in the later case. The total number of frequencies in each row and column will be the frequencies of the corresponding central value of X-series and Y-series, respectively.

(2) In correlation table use short-cut method.

σ_x can be found by making a separate table in the following way:

Central value	f	D_x	D_x^2	fD_x	fD_x^2
3	30	−6	36	−180	1080
6	21	−3	9	−63	189
9	14	0	0	0	0
12	8	3	9	24	72
15	2	6	36	12	72
18	3	9	81	27	243
Totals	**78**			**180**	**1656**

$$\sigma_x = \sqrt{\frac{\sum fD_x^2}{n} - \left(\frac{\sum fD_x}{n}\right)^2}$$

$$= \sqrt{\frac{1656}{78} - \left(\frac{-180}{78}\right)^2} = \sqrt{16.07} = 4(\text{App.})$$

Similarly, σ_y can be calculated.

Table for calculating the values of $\sum fD_x D_y$ can be done in the following way:

Table for calculating the value of $\sum fD_x D_y$

$D_x \rightarrow$ $D_y \downarrow$	−6	−3	0	3	6	9	Total $fD_x D_y$
−30	+180 5 900						900
−20	+120 9 1080	+60 1 60					1440
−10	+60 10 600	+30 4 120	0 1 0			−90 1 −90	630

(Contd.)

$D_x \rightarrow$ $D_y \downarrow$	−6	−3	0	3	6	9	Total fD_xD_y
0	0 4 0	0 7 0	0 5 0	0 2 0			0
10	−60 2 −120	−30 5 −150	0 4 0	30 1 30	60 1 60		−180
10		−80 3 −240	−40 2 −80	0 1 0	40 1 40	80 5 400	120

Method:

1) In each cell the number in the left hand upper corner is the product of D_x and D_y (e.g. in cell 1, the number in the left hand upper corner is −6 × −30 = +180.
2) In the middle is the frequency (f).
3) In each cell, the right hand lower corner gives the product of fD_xD_y (In cell 1 product is 180 × 5 = 900).

Important note:

In the above table, D_x = −6, −3, 0, 3, 6, 9
(for simplifying the procedure)
→ We can also take D_x = −2, −1, 0, 1, 2, 3
  Similarly, D_y = −30, −20, −10, 0, 10, 20, 30, 40
→ We can also take D_y = −3, −2, −1, 0, 1, 2, 3, 4

Example 4: Find the coefficient of correlation between yarn linear density and threads/set in fabrics.

	4–8	8–12	12–16	16–20	20–24	24–28	Total
5–10	2	–	1	3	–	–	6
10–15	–	5	4	11	3	–	23
15–20	–	–	7	9	16	1	33
20–25	–	–	12	15	5	3	35
25–30	–	–	–	1	22	7	30
30–35	–	3	2	1	1	5	12
35–40	1	4	9	–	–	–	14
Total	**3**	**12**	**35**	**40**	**47**	**16**	**153**

$$\sigma_x = \sqrt{\frac{\sum fD_x^2}{n} - \left(\frac{\sum fD_x}{n}\right)^2} = \sqrt{\frac{3536}{153} - \left(\frac{44}{153}\right)^2} =$$

$$= \sqrt{23.1 - 0.0841} = \sqrt{23.0159} = 4.8$$

$$\sigma_y = \sqrt{\frac{\sum fD_y^2}{n} - \left(\frac{\sum fD_y}{n}\right)^2} = \sqrt{\frac{9575}{153} - \left(\frac{-5}{153}\right)^2} =$$

$$= \sqrt{62.6 - 0.0009} = \sqrt{62.5991} = 7.9$$

$$r = \frac{\dfrac{\sum fD_xD_y}{n} - \dfrac{\sum fD_x}{n} \times \dfrac{\sum fD_y}{n}}{\sigma_x \times \sigma_y} = \frac{\dfrac{280}{153} - \dfrac{44}{153} \times \dfrac{-5}{153}}{4.8 \times 7.9} =$$

$$= \frac{1.83 + 0.0087}{37.92} = 0.048$$

Note: We can also take $D_x = -3, -2, -1, 0, 1, 2.$
$D_y = -3, -2, -1, 0, 1, 2, 3.$

Table for calculating $\sum f D_x D_y$

$D_x \rightarrow$ $D_y \downarrow$	−12	−8	−4	0	4	8	Total fD_xD_y
−15	+180 2 360		+60 1 60	0 3 0			420
−10		+80 5 400	+40 4 160	0 11 0	−40 3 −120		440
−5			+20 7 140	0 9 0	−20 16 −320	−40 1 −40	−220
0			0 12 0	0 15 0	0 5 0	0 3 0	0
5				0 1 0	20 22 440	40 7 280	720
10		−80 3 −240	−40 2 −80	0 1 0	40 1 40	80 5 400	120
15	−180 1 −180	−120 4 −480	−60 9 −540				−1200
Total fD$_x$D$_y$	**180**	**−320**	**−260**	**0**	**40**	**640**	**280**

Example 5: Calculate the coefficient of concurrent deviation.

Mean breakages per 100 spindle hours	Deviation with direction	Piecing rate	Deviation with direction	Concurrent deviations
35.3	–	20.8	–	CD
33.5	Less 1.8 (-ive)	19.4	Less 1.4 (-ive)	CD
31.4	Less 2.1 (-ive)	18.9	Less 0.5 (-ive)	CD
30.5	Less 0.9 (-ive)	18.7	Less 0.2 (-ive)	CD
29.3	Less 1.2 (-ive)	17.7	Less 1.0 (-ive)	CD
28.2	Less 1.1 (-ive)	16.0	Less 1.7 (-ive)	CD
26.3	Less 1.9 (-ive)	14.7	Less 1.3 (-ive)	CD
23.6	Less 2.7 (-ive)	14.3	Less 0.4 (-ive)	CD
20.1	Less 3.5 (-ive)	14.4	More 0.1 (+ive)	X
19.9	Less 0.2 (-ive)	12.2	Less 2.2 (-ive)	CD
16.7	Less 3.2 (-ive)	12.1	Less 0.1 (-ive)	CD

Concurrent deviations (CD) are those deviations which have the same sign in both sides.

Number of concurrent deviations, i.e., C = 9

Number of total deviations, i.e., N = 10

Now $\dfrac{2C-N}{N} = \dfrac{2\times 9-10}{10} = \dfrac{8}{10}(+\text{ive})$

i.e. + sign should be taken at both places.

$\therefore$ Coefficient of CD $= +\sqrt{+\dfrac{2C-N}{N}} = +\sqrt{+\dfrac{2\times 9-10}{10}} = +\sqrt{0.8} = 0.89.$

Example 6: Calculate 'r' for short-term oscillations of an Uster stapler for the following indices while testing Jayadhar cotton.

X	116	114	111	91	98	95	92	93	96	104
Y	78	84	93	117	97	102	108	105	96	77
X	107	104	98	100	108					
Y	68	77	93	89	83					

X	5 years total	Average (App.)	d_{ix}	d^2_{ix}	Y	5 years totals	Average	d_{iy}	d^2_{iy}	$d_{ix} \times d_{iy}$
116					78					
114					84					
111	530	105	5	25	93	469	94	−1	1	−5
91	509	102	−11	121	117	493	99	18	324	−198
98	487	97	1	1	97	517	103	−6	36	−6
95	469	94	1	1	102	529	106	−4	16	−4
92	474	95	−3	9	108	508	102	6	36	−18
93	480	96	−3	9	105	488	98	7	49	−21

(Contd.)

X	5 years total	Average (App.)	d_{ix}	d^2_{ix}	Y	5 years totals	Average	d_{iy}	d^2_{iy}	$d_{ix} \times d_{iy}$
96	492	98	-2	4	96	454	91	5	25	-10
104	504	101	3	9	77	423	85	-8	64	-24
107	509	102	5	25	68	411	85	-14	196	-70
104	513	103	1	1	77	404	81	-4	16	-4
98	517	103	-5	25	93	410	82	11	121	-55
100	–	–	–	–	89	–	–	–	–	–
108	–	–	–	–	83	–	–	–	–	–
Total				230					884	-415

n = number of moving averages = 11

$$\sigma_X = \sqrt{\frac{\sum d_{ix}^2}{n}} = \sqrt{\frac{230}{11}} = \sqrt{20.9} = 4.57$$

$$\sigma_y = \sqrt{\frac{\sum d_{iy}^2}{n}} = \sqrt{\frac{884}{11}} = \sqrt{80.36} = 8.96$$

$$r = \frac{\sum \left(d_{ix} x d_{iy} \right)}{n\sigma_x \sigma_y}$$

$$= \frac{-415}{11 \times 4.57 \times 8.96} = \frac{-415}{450.42} = -0.92$$

Example 7: Find the coefficient of rank correlation.

Marks

FSD –I	29	32	53	47	45	32	70	45	70	53
FSD –II	56	60	72	48	72	35	67	67	75	31

Paper – I		Paper – II			
Marks	Rank	Marks	Rank	d_r	d^2_r
29	10	56	7	+3	9
32	$\frac{8+9}{2} = 8.5$	60	6	2.5	6.25
53	$\frac{3+4}{2} = 3.5$	72	$\frac{2+3}{2} = 2.5$	1	1
47	5	48	8	-3	9

(Contd.)

Paper – I		Paper – II			
Marks	Rank	Marks	Rank	d_r	d^2_r
32	$\dfrac{8+9}{2} = 8.5$	35	9	−0.5	0.25
*70	$\dfrac{1+2}{2} = 1.5$	67	$\dfrac{4+5}{2} = 4.5$	−3	9
45	$\dfrac{6+7}{2} = 6.5$	67	$\dfrac{4+5}{2} = 4.5$	2	4
*70	$\dfrac{1+2}{2} = 1.5$	75	1	0.5	0.25
53	$\dfrac{3+4}{2} = 3.5$	31	10	?6.5	42.25

Hence, n = 10 $\Sigma d^2_r = 97.00$

Coefficient of rank correlation $r_r = 1 - \dfrac{6\Sigma d^2_r}{n(n-1)} = 1 - \dfrac{6 \times 97}{10(100-1)}$

$$= 1 - 0.588 = 0.412$$

*70 is the highest value. There are two 70s.

Therefore, each rank = $\dfrac{1+2}{2} = 1.5$

Example 8: Calculate the correlation coefficient between x and y for the following data collected from 160 cards.

Sum of x-values = 548   Sum of y-values = 156
Sum of squares of x = 21522   Sum of squares of y = 1675
Sum of products of x and y = 4883

Solution:

Given n = 160, $\Sigma x = 548$, y = 156, $\Sigma x^2 = 21522$, $\Sigma y^2 = 1675$, $\Sigma xy = 4883$

If 0 (zero) is the provisional mean (PM), then

$D_x = x - PM = x - 0 = x$ and $D_y = y - 0 = y$
$\Sigma D_x = \Sigma x = 548$; $\Sigma D_y = \Sigma y = 156$; $\Sigma D_x D_y = \Sigma xy = 4883$
$\Sigma D^2_x = \Sigma x^2 = 21522$; $\Sigma D_y^2 = \Sigma y^2 = 1675$

$$\sigma_x = \sqrt{\dfrac{\Sigma D_x^2}{n} - \left(\dfrac{\Sigma D_x}{n}\right)^2} = \sqrt{\dfrac{\Sigma x^2}{n} - \left(\dfrac{\Sigma x}{n}\right)}$$

$$= \sqrt{\frac{21522}{160} - \left(\frac{548}{160}\right)^2} = \sqrt{134.51 - 11.73} = \sqrt{122.78} = 11.08$$

$$\sigma_y = \sqrt{\frac{\sum y^2}{n} - \left(\frac{\sum y}{n}\right)^2} = \sqrt{\frac{1675}{160} - \left(\frac{156}{160}\right)^2} = \sqrt{10.47 - 0.95} = \sqrt{9.52} = 3.08$$

$$r = \frac{\dfrac{\sum D_x D_y}{n} - \dfrac{\sum D_x}{n} \times \dfrac{\sum D_y}{n}}{\sigma_x \times \sigma_y}$$

$$= \frac{\dfrac{\sum xy}{n} - \dfrac{\sum x}{n} \times \dfrac{\sum y}{n}}{\sigma_x \times \sigma_y}$$

$$= \frac{\dfrac{4883}{160} - \dfrac{548}{160} \times \dfrac{156}{160}}{11.08 \times 3.08} = \frac{30.52 - 3.34}{34.13} = \frac{27.18}{34.13} = 0.79$$

6.1   Partial and multiple correlations

6.1.1   Introduction

Simple correlation, which is also called 'bivariate correlation', gives us an idea of connection or relationship between two variates.

But sometimes there are three or more variates and a dependent variable may be influenced by more than one independent variable. For example, yield of crop depends not only on rainfall but on other factors also such as fertility of the soil, sunshine, number of plough units, etc.; in other words, yield may partly be influenced by rainfall. It may depend partly on the amount of fertilizers used and partly on plough units. All these factors influence the yield. Similarly, weight depends not only upon height but also on age. In other words, weight depends partly on height and partly it is influenced by age. It may be further pointed that height and age are also mutually correlated.

In the above examples, two or more variates influence a variate. This partial influence of each of the factors is also evident from the fact that the coefficient of correlation between two variates is generally less than 1. Therefore, there must be other factors influencing the dependent variable.

When there are three or more mutually correlated variates and we are required to measure the separate effect of each of the variates on the dependent variate, then we have to use partial correlation. Thus, in partial correlation, we are required to separate out these effects. This can be done, if the effect of all other factors is eliminated. This can also be done if the effect of other variates remains unchanged or constant.

6.2   Partial correlation

Partial correlation is the correlation between two variables when the effect of the other variates has been eliminated. It is relationship between independent and dependent variable when the effect of other independent variable remains unchanged (i.e., constant).

If x, y, z are three mutually correlated variates, we may be required to measure the relationship between x and y when the influence of z is eliminated. This is given by the coefficient of partial correlation.

6.2.1   Coefficient of partial correlation

First order: When x, y, z are three variates, then the coefficient of correlation between x and y with the effect of z eliminated is called coefficient of partial correlation of first order and is denoted by r_{xyz}. This is also termed as partial correlation coefficient.

Note: r_{xy} is correlation of zero order.

Second order: When there are four variates, viz., x, y, z, u then the coefficient of correlation between x and y with the effect of z, u eliminated (or keeping z and u constant) is called partial correlation coefficient of second order and is denoted by $r_{xy.zu}$.

Similarly, $r_{xy.suv}$ is partial correlation coefficient or third order and is coefficient of correlation between x and y keeping z, u, y constant).

Note: The order of a partial r is determined by the number of secondary subscripts. In $r_{xy.zuv}$, x and y are primary subscripts and z, u, v are secondary subscripts.

$r_{12.3}$ means r between (1) and (2) with effect of (3) eliminated.

$r_{13.2}$ means r between (1) and (3) with effect of (2) eliminated.

$r_{12.34}$ means r between (1) and (2) with effect of (3) and (4) eliminated.

6.3   How to find partial correlation coefficients?

The following formulae are used

1) $$r_{x.yz} = \frac{r_{xy} - r_{xz}.r_{yz}}{\sqrt{1-r_x^2}.\sqrt{1-r_{yz}^2}}$$

Where, r_{xy} means coefficient of correlation between x and y.

r_{xz} means coefficient of correlation between x and z.

r_{yz} means coefficient of correlation between y and z.

$$r_{12.3} = \frac{r_{12} - r_{13}.r_{23}}{\sqrt{1 - r_{13}^2}\sqrt{1 - r_{23}^2}}$$

2) $$r_{xy.zu} = \frac{r_{xy.z} - r_{xu.z}.r_{yu.x}}{\sqrt{1 - r_{xu.z}^2}\sqrt{1 - r_{yu.x}^2}}$$

$$r_{12.34} = \frac{r_{12.3} - r_{14.3}.r_{24.3}}{\sqrt{1 - r_{14.3}^2},\sqrt{1 - r_{24.3}^2}}$$

3) $$r_{xy.xuv} = \frac{r_{xy.zu} - r_{xv.zu}.r_{yv.zu}}{\sqrt{1 - r_{xy.zu}^2},\sqrt{1 - r_{yv.zu}^2}}$$

$$r_{12.345} = \frac{r_{12.34} - r_{15.34}.r_{25.34}}{\sqrt{1 - r_{15.34}^2},\sqrt{1 - r_{25.34}^2}}$$

Example 1: Given the following correlations for KESF tests of 200 fabrics:

$r_{ia} = 0.41$; $r_{is} = 0.71$; $r_{as} = 0.5$ where i denotes parameter; a, GSM, and s, constant.

Find $r_{is.a}$, $r_{ia.s}$, $r_{as.i}$

Solution:

$$r_{is.a} = \frac{r_{is} - r_{ia}.r_{sa}}{\sqrt{1 - r_{ia}^2}\sqrt{1 - r_{sa}^2}} = \frac{0.71 - 0.41 \times 0.5}{\sqrt{1 - (0.41)^2}\sqrt{1 - (0.5)^2}}$$

$$= \frac{0.71 - 0.205}{0.91 \times 0.87} = \frac{0.505}{0.79} = 0.63$$

$$r_{ia.s} = \frac{r_{ia} - r_{is}.r_{as}}{\sqrt{1 - r_{is}^2}\sqrt{1 - r_{as}^2}} = \frac{0.41 - 0.71 \times 0.5}{\sqrt{1 - (0.71)^2}\sqrt{1 - (0.5)^2}}$$

$$= \frac{0.41 - 0.355}{0.7 \times 0.87} = \frac{0.055}{0.609} = 0.09$$

$$r_{as.i} = \frac{r_{as} - r_{ai}.r_{si}}{\sqrt{1-r_{ai}^2}\sqrt{1-r_{si}^2}} = \frac{0.5 - 0.41 \times 0.71}{\sqrt{1-(0.41)^2}\sqrt{1-(0.71)^2}}$$

$$= \frac{0.5 - 0.29}{0.91 \times 0.7} = \frac{0.21}{0.637} = 0.33$$

Example 2: Given $r_{12.3} = -3.4$, $r_{14.3} = -0.43$, $r_{24.3} = 0.187$, $r_{14.2} = -0.43$, $r_{13.2} = -0.62$, $r_{34.2} = 0.2$.

Find the values of $r_{12.34}$ and $r_{14.23}$

Solution: The following formulae shall be used:

1) $r_{12.34} = \dfrac{r_{12.3} - r_{14.3}.r_{24.3}}{\sqrt{1-r_{14.3}^2}\sqrt{1-r_{24.3}^2}} = \dfrac{0.34 - (-0.43) \times 0.187}{\sqrt{1-(0.43)^2}\sqrt{1-(0.187)^2}}$

$$= \frac{0.34 + 0.08}{0.9 \times 0.982} = \frac{-0.26}{0.883} = -0.3(App.)$$

2) $r_{14.23} = \dfrac{r_{14.2} - r_{13.2}.r_{43.2}}{\sqrt{1-r_{13.2}^2}\sqrt{1-r_{43.2}^2}} = \dfrac{0.43 - (-0.62) \times 0.2}{\sqrt{1-(0.62)^2}\sqrt{1-(0.2)^2}}$

$$*[r_{43.2} = r_{34.2}]$$

$$= \frac{0.43 + 0.124}{0.78 \times 0.98} = \frac{-0.306}{0.76} = 0.4$$

$*r_{34.2}$ means r between (3) and (4) keeping (2) as constant.
$r_{43.2}$ means r between (4) and (3) keeping (2) as constant.

Reverse case: Suppose there are three variates x, y, z and three partial correlation coefficients $r_{xy.z}$, $r_{xz.y}$, $r_{yz.x}$ are given, then we can find r_{xy}, r_{yz}, r_{zx} by using the following formula.

$$r_{xy} = \frac{r_{xy.z} + r_{xz.y}.r_{yz.x}}{\sqrt{1-r_{xz.y}^2}, \sqrt{1-r_{yz.x}^2}}$$

Or if (1), (2) and (3) are three variates

Then $r_{12} = \dfrac{r_{12.3} + r_{13.2}.r_{23.1}}{\sqrt{1-r_{13.2}^2}, \sqrt{1-r_{23.1}^2}}$

Similarly, $r_{yz} = \dfrac{r_{yz.x} + r_{xy.z}.r_{zx.y}}{\sqrt{1 - r_{xy.z}^2}, \sqrt{1 - r_{zx.y}^2}}$

$$r_{23} = \dfrac{r_{23.1} + r_{12.3}.r_{13.2}}{\sqrt{1 - r_{12.3}^2}\sqrt{1 - r_{13.2}^2}}$$

Example 3: Given $r_{is.a} = 0.63$, $r_{ia.s} = 0.09$, $r_{as.i} = 0.33$. Find $r_{ia,}$ $r_{is,}$ $r_{as.}$.

Solution: By formula:

1) $r_{ia} = \dfrac{r_{ia.s} + r_{is.a}.r_{as.i}}{\sqrt{1 - r_{is.a}^2}\sqrt{1 - r_{as.i}^2}} = \dfrac{0.09 + 0.63 \times 0.33}{\sqrt{1 - (0.63)^2}\sqrt{1 - (0.33)^2}}$

$= \dfrac{0.09 + 0.2}{0.78 \times 0.94} = \dfrac{0.29}{0.7} = 0.41$

2) $r_{is} = \dfrac{r_{is.a} + r_{ia.s}.r_{as.i}}{\sqrt{1 - r_{ia.s}^2}\sqrt{1 - r_{as.i}^2}} = \dfrac{0.63 + 0.09 \times 0.33}{\sqrt{1 - (0.9)^2}\sqrt{1 - (0.33)^2}}$

$= \dfrac{0.63 + 0.3}{0.99 \times 0.94} = \dfrac{0.66}{0.93} = 0.71$

3) $r_{as} = \dfrac{r_{as.s} + r_{ia.s}.r_{is.a}}{\sqrt{1 - r_{ia.s}^2}\sqrt{1 - r_{is.a}^2}} = \dfrac{0.33 + 0.09 \times 0.63}{\sqrt{1 - (0.9)^2}\sqrt{1 - (0.63)^2}}$

$= \dfrac{0.33 + 0.06}{0.99 \times 0.78} = \dfrac{0.39}{0.77} = 0.5$

Example 4: If $r_{12} = k$, $r_{23} = -k$; show that r_{13} will lie between -1 and $1 - 2k^2$

Solution: We know a partial correlation coefficient is ≤ 1

$$| \, r_{12.3} \, | \le 1 \text{ or } r^2_{12.3} \le 1$$

Now $\quad r_{12.3} = \dfrac{r_{12} - r_{13}r_{23}}{\sqrt{1 - r_{13}^2}\sqrt{1 - r_{23}^2}}$

$\therefore \quad r^2_{12.3} = \left[\dfrac{r_{12} - r_{13}r_{23}}{\sqrt{1 - r_{13}^2}\sqrt{1 - r_{23}^2}} \right]^2$

$$= \frac{k - r_{13}(-k)}{\sqrt{1 - r_{13}^2}\sqrt{1 - (-k)^2}}$$

$$= \frac{[k + r_{13}k]^2}{(1 - r_{13}^2)(1 - k^2)}$$

As $r^2{}_{12.3} \leq 1$

$\therefore$
$$\frac{k^2 + k^2 r^2{}_{13} + 2k^2 r_{13}}{(1 - r_{13}^2)(1 - k^2)} \leq 1$$

Or $k^2 + k^2 r^2{}_{13} + 2k^2 r_{13} \leq (1 - r^2{}_{13})(1 - k^2)$

Or $k^2 + k^2 r^2{}_{13} + 2k^2 r_{13} \leq 1 - k^2 - r^2{}_{13} + k^2 r^2{}_{13}$

Or $r^2{}_{13} + 2k^2 r_{13} + (2k^2 - 1) \leq 0$

Or $(r_{13} + 1)(r_{13} + 2k^2 - 1) \leq 0$

$\therefore r_{13}$ lies between -1 and $-2k^2 + 1$

i.e., r_{13} lies between -1 and $1 - 2k^2$

6.4   Method to calculate multiple correlation coefficients

Multiple correlation coefficient is found with the help of partial standard deviation. Just as we have partial correlation coefficients, similarly we can have partial standard deviations. If x, y, z, u are variates, then $\sigma_{x.yz}$ is the partial standard deviation of x, free of influence of y and z.

$\sigma_{x.yzuv}$ is the standard deviation of x, which has been freed of the influence exerted upon its variability by variables y, z, u and v.

Formulae to find partial standard deviations

1) $\sigma_{x.y} = \sigma_x \cdot \sqrt{1 - r_{xy}^2}$

Or

$\sigma_{1.2} = \sigma_1 \sqrt{1 - r_{12}^2}$

2) $\sigma_{x.yz} = \sigma_x \sqrt{1 - r_{xy}^2} \cdot \sqrt{1 - r_{xz.y}^2}$

Or

$\sigma_{1.23} = \sigma_1 \cdot \sqrt{1 - r_{12}^2} \cdot \sqrt{1 - r_{13.2}^2}$

3) $\sigma_{x.yzu} = \sigma_x \cdot \sqrt{1 - r_{xy}^2} \cdot \sqrt{1 - r_{xz.y}^2} \cdot \sqrt{1 - r_{xu.yz}^2}$

Or

$\sigma_{1.234} = \sigma_1 \sqrt{1 - r_{12}^2} \cdot \sqrt{1 - r_{13.2}^2} \cdot \sqrt{1 - r_{14.23}^2}$

4) $\sigma_{x.yzuv} = \sigma_x \cdot \sqrt{1 - r_{xy}^2} \cdot \sqrt{1 - r_{xz.y}^2} \cdot \sqrt{1 - r_{xu.yz}^2} \cdot \sqrt{1 - r_{xy.yzu}^2}$

Or

$\sigma_{1.2345} = \sigma_1 \sqrt{1 - r_{12}^2} \cdot \sqrt{1 - r_{13.2}^2} \cdot \sqrt{1 - r_{14.23}^2} \cdot \sqrt{1 - r_{15.234}^2}$

General formula:

$$\sigma_{1.234....n} = \sigma_1 \sqrt{1 - r_{12}^2} \cdot \sqrt{1 - r_{13.2}^2} \cdot \sqrt{1 - r_{14.23}^2} \cdot \sqrt{1 - r_{15.234}^2} \cdots \sqrt{1 - r_{1n.234......n-1}^2}$$

6.4.1   Multiple correlation coefficient

If multiple correlation coefficient is denoted by $R_{1.234....n}$ then

$$R_{1.23.....n} = \sqrt{1 - \frac{\sigma^2_{1.23........n}}{\sigma_1^2}}$$

Where $\sigma_{1.23...n} = \sigma_1 \sqrt{1 - r_{12}^2} \cdot \sqrt{1 - r_{13.2}^2} \cdot \sqrt{1 - r_{14.23}^2} \cdot \sqrt{1 - r_{15.234}^2} \cdots \sqrt{1 - r_{1n.234......n-1}^2}$

The formula is

$$R^2_{1.23.......n} = \sqrt{1 - \frac{\sigma^2_{1.23........n}}{\sigma_1^2}}$$

If there are three variates, then

$$R^2_{12.3} = \sqrt{1 - \frac{\sigma^2_{1.23}}{\sigma_1^2}}$$

Another formula for finding the multiple correlation coefficient when there are only three variates is

$$R^2_{12.3} = \frac{r_{12}^2 + r_{13}^2 - 2r_{12}r_{13}r_{23}}{1 - r_{23}^2}$$

Example 5:

Given $r_{13} = 0.583$, $r_{14} = 0.546$, $r_{34} = 0.396$, $\sigma_1 = 9.1$. Find $R_{1.34}$

Solution:

First method

$$\sigma_{1.34} = \sigma_1 \sqrt{1 - r_{13}^2} \sqrt{1 - r_{14.3}^2} \qquad \qquad \dots (1)$$

$$r_{14.3} = \frac{r_{14} - r_{13}.r_{34}}{\sqrt{1-r_{13}^2}\sqrt{1-r_{34}^2}} = \frac{0.546 - 0.583 \times 0.396}{\sqrt{1-(.583)^2}\sqrt{1-(0.396)^2}}$$

$$= \frac{0.546 - 0.231}{\sqrt{1-0.3398}\sqrt{1-0.1568}} = \frac{0.315}{0.81 \times 0.91} = \frac{0.315}{0.737} = 0.428$$

From (1) $\sigma_{1.34} = 9.1\sqrt{1-(0.583)^2}\sqrt{1-(0.428)^2}$

$$= 9.1 \times 0.81 \times 0.903 = 6.656$$

$$R_{1.34} = \sqrt{1 - \frac{\sigma_{1.34}^2}{\sigma_1^2}} = \sqrt{1 - \frac{6.656^2}{9.1^2}} = \sqrt{1 - \frac{44.3}{82.8}} = \sqrt{0.465} = 0.678$$

Second method: As there are three variates (1), (3) and (4)

$$\therefore \qquad R_{1.34}^2 = \frac{r_{13}^2 + r_{14}^2 - 2r_{13}r_{14}r_{34}}{1 - r_{34}^2}$$

$$= \frac{(0.583)^2 + (0.546)^2 - 2(0.583)(0.546)(0.396)}{1 - (0.396)^2}$$

$$= \frac{0.340 + 0.298 - 0.252}{1 - 0.1568} = \frac{0.386}{0.8432} = 0.46$$

$$R_{1.34} = \sqrt{0.46} = 0.677$$

Another method of writing the general formula,

$$R_{1.234....n} = \sqrt{1 - \frac{\sigma_{1.234...n}^2}{\sigma_1^2}}$$

$$= \sqrt{1 - \frac{\left(\sigma_1\sqrt{1-r_{12}^2}\sqrt{1-r_{13.2}^2}........\sqrt{1-r_{1n.234,,,,,,,n-1}^2}\right)^2}{\sigma_1^2}}$$

$$\therefore \qquad R_{1.234..n} = \sqrt{1 - \left[\left(1-r_{12}^2\right)\left(1-r_{13.2}^2\right).........\left(1-r_{1n.234......n-1}^2\right)\right]}$$

Example 6: If $r_{23}=0$ prove that $R^2_{1(23)} = r^2_{12} + r^2_{13}$

Note: $R_{1.23}$ is also expressed as $R_{1(23)}$

We know $R^2_{1(23)} = \dfrac{r_{12}^2 + r_{13}^2 - 2r_{12}r_{13}r_{23}}{1 - r_{23}^2}$ ... (1)

Put $r_{23} = 0$ in (1)

$\therefore \qquad R^2_{1(23)} = \dfrac{r_{12}^2 + r_{13}^2 - 2r_{12}r_{13}x0}{1 - 0} = r_{12}^2 + r_{13}^2$

*$\sigma_{1.23}$ is also known as standard error of estimate.

Example 7: The correlation between intelligence ratio and height of 406 students was 0.24, that between their age and height was 0.85 and the correlation between the age and intelligence ratio was 0.007. Taking heights as character 1, age 3 and intelligence ratio 2, $\sigma_1 = 15.22$. Find the standard error of estimate and coefficient of multiple correlation.

First method:

Solution:

Given, $r_{12} = 0.24$, $r_{13} = 0.85$, $r_{23} = 0.007$, $\sigma_1 = 15.22$

$$\sigma_{1.23} = \sigma_1 \sqrt{1 - r_{12}^2} \sqrt{1 - r_{13.2}^2}$$

We are required to find the value of $r_{13.2}$

$$r_{13.2} = \frac{r_{13} - r_{12}.r_{23}}{\sqrt{1 - r_{12}^2}\sqrt{1 - r_{23}^2}} = \frac{0.85 - 0.24 \times 0.007}{\sqrt{1 - (0.24)^2}\sqrt{1 - (0.007)^2}}$$

$$= \frac{0.85 - 0.00168}{\sqrt{0.9424}\sqrt{0.999951}} = \frac{0.84832}{0.97 \times 0.99} = \frac{0.8483}{0.9608} = 0.88$$

$$\sigma_{1.23} = \sigma_1 \sqrt{1 - r_{12}^2}\sqrt{1 - r_{13.2}^2} = 15.22 \times \sqrt{1 - (0.24)^2}\sqrt{1 - (0.88)^2}$$

$$= 15.22 \times 0.97 \times 0.475 = 7.014$$

$$R_{1.23} = \sqrt{1 - \frac{\sigma_{1.23}^2}{\sigma_1^2}} = 1 - \frac{7.014^2}{(15.22)^2} = 1 - \frac{49.14}{231.65} = 1 - 0.2121$$

$$R^2_{1(23)} = 0.7879$$

$$R_{1(23)} \sqrt{0.7879} = 0.88$$

Second method:

$$\therefore \quad R_{1.23}^2 = \frac{r_{12}^2 + r_{13}^2 - 2r_{12}r_{13}r_{23}}{1 - r_{23}^2}$$

$$= \frac{0.24^2 + 0.85^2 - 2(0.24)(0.85)(0.007)}{1 - (0.007)^2}$$

$$= \frac{0.0576 + 0.7225 - 0.0029}{1 - 0.000049} = \frac{0.7772}{0.9999} = 0.77$$

$$R_{1(23)} = 0.88$$

Example 8: Given $\sigma_1 = 44.7$, $r_{12} = -0.5$, $r_{13.2} = -0.62$, $r_{14.23} = -0.405$. Find $\sigma_{1.234}$ and $R_{1.234}$.

Solution:

$$\sigma_{1.234} = \sigma_1 \sqrt{1 - r_{12}^2}\sqrt{1 - r_{13.2}^2}\sqrt{1 - r_{14.23}^2}$$

$$= 44.7\sqrt{1 - (-5)^2}\sqrt{1 - (-0.62)^2}\sqrt{1 - (-0.405)^2}$$

$$= 44.7\sqrt{1 - 0.25}\sqrt{1 - 0.3844}\sqrt{1 - 0.164025}$$

$$= 44.7\sqrt{0.75}\sqrt{0.6156}\sqrt{0.835975}$$

$$= 44.7 \times 0.87 \times 0.78 \times 0.914 = 27.72$$

$$R_{1.234}^2 = 1 - [(1 - r_{12}^2)(1 - r_{13.2}^2)(1 - r_{14.23}^2)]$$

$$= 1 - [0.75 \times 0.6156 \times 0.835975] = 1 - 0.3845 = 0.6156$$

$$R_{1.234} = \sqrt{0.6155} = 0.78$$

Example 9: Given $R_{1.234} = 0.78$, $R_{1.23} = 0.74$, $r_{12} = -0.5$. Find $r_{13.2}$ and $r_{14.23}$ taking negative signs.

Solution:

(i) $\quad r_{13.2}^2 = \dfrac{R_{1.23}^2 - r_{12}^2}{1 - r_{12}^2}$

$$= \frac{(0.74)^2 - (-0.5)^2}{1 - (-0.5)^2} = \frac{0.55 - 0.25}{1 - 0.25} = \frac{0.30}{75} = 0.40$$

$$r_{13.2} = \pm\sqrt{0.40} = -0.63 \text{ (Taking negative sign)}$$

(ii) $r_{14.2}^2 = \dfrac{R_{1.234}^2 - r_{12.3}^2}{1 - R_{12}^2}$

$$= \frac{(0.78)^2 - (0.74)^2}{1 - (0.74)^2} = \frac{0.6194 - 0.5476}{1 - 0.5476}$$

$$= \frac{0.0718}{0.4524} = 0.16 \,(\text{App.})$$

$$r_{14.23} = \pm\sqrt{0.16} = -0.4 \,(\text{Taking negative sign})$$

6.5   Regression equations and regression coefficients

If there are three variables x_1, x_2, and x_3 then the regression equations for three variables are

1) $x_1 = b_{12.3}\, x_2 + b_{13.2}x_3$
2) $x_2 = b_{23.1}x_3 + b_{21.3}\, x_1$
3) $x_3 = b_{31.2}\, x_1 + b_{32.1}\, x_2$

$b_{12.3}$, $b_{23.1}$, $b_{23.1}$, $b_{31.2}$, $b_{32.1}$ are called regression coefficients.

6.5.1 Regression coefficients

The following formula is used to find the regression coefficients.

$$b_{12.3} = r_{12.3} \times \frac{\sigma_{1.23}}{\sigma_{2.12}}$$

Similarly $b_{13.2} = r_{13.2} \times \dfrac{\sigma_{13.2}}{\sigma_{3.12}}$

Example 10: Given $r_{12} = 0.28$, $r_{23} = 0.49$, $r_{31} = 0.51$
$\sigma_1 = 2.7$, $\sigma_2 = 2.4$; $\sigma_3 = 2.7$
Find the regression equation of x_3 and x_1 and x_2.

Solution:

The regression equation of x_3 on x_1 and x_2 is

$$x_3 = b_{31.2}\, x_1 + b_{32.1} \cdot x_2$$

Where $b_{31.2} = r_{31.2} \times \dfrac{\sigma_{3.12}}{\sigma_{1.23}}$ and $b_{32.1} = r_{32.1} \times \dfrac{\sigma_{3.12}}{\sigma_{23.1}}$. Find $r_{31.2}$, $r_{32.1}$, $\sigma_{3.12}$, $\sigma_{2.31}$.

$$r_{31.2} = \frac{r_{31} - r_{23}r_{12}}{\sqrt{1-r_{23}^2}\sqrt{1-r_{12}^2}} = \frac{0.51 - 0.49 \times 0.28}{\sqrt{1-(0.49)^2}\sqrt{1-(0.28)^2}}$$

$$= \frac{0.51 - 0.14}{0.87 \times 0.96} = \frac{0.37}{0.84} = 0.44$$

$$r_{32.1} = \frac{r_{32} - r_{31}r_{12}}{\sqrt{1-r_{31}^2}\sqrt{1-r_{12}^2}} = \frac{0.49 - 0.51 \times 0.28}{\sqrt{1-(0.51)^2}\sqrt{1-(0.28)^2}}$$

$$= \frac{0.49 - 0.14}{0.86 \times 0.96} = \frac{0.35}{0.83} = 0.42$$

$$\sigma_{3.12} = \sigma_3 \sqrt{1-r_{31}^2}\sqrt{1-r_{32.1}^2}$$

$$= 2.7\sqrt{1-(0.51)^2}\sqrt{1-(0.42)^2}$$

$$= 2.7 \times 0.86 \times 0.91 = 2.1$$

$$\sigma_{1.23} = \sigma_1 \sqrt{1-r_{12}^2}\sqrt{1-r_{13.2}^2}$$

$$= 2.7\sqrt{1-(0.28)^2}\sqrt{1-(0.44)^2}$$

$$= 2.7 \times 0.96 \times 0.9 = 2.3$$

$$\sigma_{2.31} = \sigma_2 \sqrt{1-r_{23}^2}\sqrt{1-r_{12.3}^2}$$

$$= 2.4\sqrt{1-(0.49)^2}\sqrt{1-(0.04)^2}$$

$$= 2.4 \times 0.86 \times 0.99 = 2.04$$

$$r_{12.3} = \frac{r_{12} - r_{13}r_{23}}{\sqrt{1-r_{13}^2}\sqrt{1-r_{23}^2}} = \frac{0.28 - 0.51 \times 0.49}{\sqrt{1-(0.51)^2}\sqrt{1-(0.49)^2}}$$

$$= \frac{0.28 - 0.25}{0.86 \times 0.87} = \frac{0.03}{0.75} = 0.4$$

$$b_{31.2} = r_{31.2} \times \frac{\sigma_{3.12}}{\sigma_{1.23}}$$

$$= 0.44 \times \frac{2.1}{2.3} = 0.40$$

$$b_{32.1} = r_{32.1} \times \frac{\sigma_{3.21}}{\sigma_{2.31}} = 0.42 \times \frac{2.1}{2.04} = 0.43$$

Substituting the values of $b_{31.2}$ and $b_{32.1}$ in (1) the regression equation is

$$x_3 = 0.40 \; x_1 + 0.43 \; x_2$$

Similarly $b_{12.3} = r_{12.3} \times \dfrac{\sigma_{1.23}}{\sigma_{2.13}}$

$$= 0.04 \times (2.3 \,/\, 2.04) = 0.045$$

And $\quad b_{13.2} = r_{13.2} \times \dfrac{\sigma_{1.32}}{\sigma_{3.12}}$

$$= 0.44 \times (2.3 \,/\, 2.1) = 0.48$$

Regression equation of x_1 on x_2 and x_3 is

$$x_1 = b_{12.3} \; x_2 + b_{13.2} \; x_3$$

Or $\qquad x_1 = 0.045 \; x_2 + 0.48 \; x_3$

Linear regression

7.1   Introduction

Regression analysis is a technique of estimating the unknown values of one variable from the known values of another variable. In other words, if an independent variable is X used to predict the value of required variable or dependent variable is Y. The technique is known as simple (as there is one independent variable) linear regression analysis. The relation between X and Y is defined by

$$Y = a + bx \text{ (Equation of straight line)}$$

It is known as regression line. Regression analysis is also used to obtain the measure of error involved in the estimation using regression lines as basis. Correlation coefficient is also calculated with the help of Regression coefficients. The degree of association of correlation between two variables is described by "Co-efficient of determination" and is given by r2.

7.2   Regression equations and coefficients

Regression equations are algebraic expressions of the regression lines. If X and Y are two variables, two regression lines are described as regression of X on Y and regression of Y on X. Former gives probable values of X for different values of Y and the later gives probable values of Y for given values of X. Hence, two regression equations are described.

7.2.1   Regression equation of Y on X:

It is represented by

$$Y = a + bX$$

Values 'a' and 'b' are given by solving the normal equations.

$$\Sigma Y = Na + b\Sigma x,$$

$$\Sigma XY = a\Sigma X + b\Sigma X2$$

7.2.2   Regression equation of X on Y

It is given by

$$X = a + bY$$

The following normal equations give the values of a and b.

$$\Sigma X = Na + b\Sigma Y$$
$$\Sigma XY = a\Sigma Y + b\Sigma Y^2$$

Example 1: In the manufacture of tyre the effect of processing tension on modulus of elasticity was noted. Give the regression equations.

Processing (X) tension	5	7	9	10	11	12	13
Modulus (Y)	30.1	32.1	32.2	32.9	34.9	34.7	35.5

X	Y	X^2	XY	Y^2
5	301	25	150.5	906.00
7	32.1	49	224.7	1030.42
9	32.2	81	289.8	1036.80
10	32.9	100	329.0	1082.41
11	32.9	121	361.9	1082.41
12	34.7	144	416.4	1204.09
13	35.5	169	461.5	1260.25
$\Sigma X = 67$	$\Sigma Y = 230.4$	$\Sigma X^2 = 689$	$\Sigma XY = 2233.8$	$\Sigma Y^2 = 7602.42$

Regression equation of Y on X

$$Y = a + b\Sigma X$$

$$\Sigma Y = Na + b\Sigma X, \quad \Sigma XY = a \Sigma X = a\Sigma X + b\Sigma X^2$$

$$230.4 = 7a + 67b, \quad 2233.8 = 67a + 689b$$

$$7a + 67b = 230.4 \qquad\qquad \dots (1) \times 67$$

$$67a + 689b = 2233.8 \qquad\qquad \dots (2) \times 7$$

$$469a + 4489b = 15436.8$$
$$469a + 4823b = 15636.6$$
$$\underline{(-) \quad (-)}$$
$$-334b = -199.8$$
$$b = 0.6$$
$$a = 27.18$$
$$Y = 27.2 + 0.6 \ X$$

Regression equation of X on Y:

$$67 = 7a + 230.4b \times 230.4$$
$$2233.8 = 230.4a + 7602.42b \times 7$$

$$1612.8a + 53084.16b = 15436.8$$
$$1612.8a + 53216.94b = 15636.6$$
$$(-) \quad (-) \qquad\qquad (-)$$

$$\overline{\qquad -132.78b \quad = -199.8 \qquad}$$

b = 1.504
a = 0.02
X = 0.02 + 1.5 Y

Example 2: You are given the results of area-shrinkage tests on a fabric treated with shrink resist finish. Workout the regression equations.

Strength of (X)   0   0.3   0.6   0.9   1.2   1.5   1.8   2.1
S-R Finish

X	Y	X2	XY	Y2
0	36	0	0	1296
0.3	21	0.9	6.3	441
0.6	12	0.36	7.2	144
0.9	9.8	0.81	8.82	96.04
1.2	8.8	1.44	10.56	77.44
1.5	4.0	2.25	6.00	16
1.8	2.5	3.24	4.5	6.25
2.1	2.1	4.41	4.41	4.41
ΣX = 8.4,	ΣY = 96.2	ΣX2 = 13.41	ΣXY = 47.79	ΣY2 = 2081.14

Regression equation of Y on X

$$Y = a + bX \quad 96.2 = 8a + 8.4b, \quad \times 8.4$$

$$47.79 = 8.4a + 13.41b \quad \times 8$$

$$808.08 = 67.2a + 70.56b$$

$$382.32 = 67.2a + 107.28b$$
$$(-) \qquad\qquad (-)$$

$$\overline{\qquad\qquad\qquad\qquad\qquad\qquad\qquad -}$$

$$425.76 = -36.72b$$
$$b = -11.59$$
$$a = 24.19$$
$$Y = 24.19 - 11.59 X$$

The reader is instructed to workout regression equatio n of X on Y.

Example 3: Following table gives the result of an experiment to investigate the relationship between loop length and the courses per unit length is as follows:

X	1.7	1.5	1.3	1.2	1.1	1.0
Y	8.6	7.3	7.0	6.9	6.7	5.8

Solution: Problem is solved by deviations taken from arithmetic mean

X	(X – ΣX)		Y	(Y – ΣY)		
	x	x²		y	y²	xy
1.7	0.4	0.16	8.6	1.55	2.40	0.62
1.5	0.2	0.04	7.3	0.25	0.62	0.05
1.3	0	0	7.0	–0.05	0.0025	0
1.2	–0.1	0.01	6.9	–0.15	0.0225	0.015
1.1	–0.2	0.04	6.7	–0.35	0.1225	0.07
1.0	–0.3	0.09	5.8	–1.25	1.5625	0.375
ΣX = –7.8	Σx = 0	Σx2 = 0.34	ΣY = 42.3	Σy = 0	Σy2 = 4.73	Σxy = 1.13

$$\overline{X} = 1.3 \quad \overline{Y} = 7.05$$

Regression equation of X on Y:

$$X - \overline{X} = r \frac{\sigma x}{\sigma y}(Y - \overline{Y})$$

$$r \frac{\sigma x}{\sigma y} = \frac{\Sigma xy}{\Sigma y^2} = \frac{1.13}{4.73} = 0.238$$

$$X - 1.3 = 0.238 \,(Y - 7.05)$$
$$X - 1.3 = 0.238 \,Y - 1.68$$
$$X = 0.238 \,Y - 0.38$$

Regression equation of Y on X:

$$Y - \overline{Y} = r \frac{\sigma y}{\sigma x}(X - \overline{X})$$

$$r \frac{\sigma y}{\sigma x} = \frac{\Sigma xy}{\Sigma x^2} = \frac{1.13}{0.34} = 3.32$$

$$Y - 7.05 = 3.32 \,(X - 1.3)$$
$$Y = 3.32 \,X - 4.316 + 7.05$$
$$Y = 3.32 \,X + 2.734$$

Example 4: The following data show the relation between relative viscosity of a dye liquor and dye uptake on certain fabric.

X	0	3	5	6	8	11
Y	1	2	6	7	8	12

Give the regression equations

Solution: Problem is solved by taking deviations from assumed mean.

X	(X – 5) = dx	dx²	Y	(Y – 6) = dy	dy²	dx dy
0	–5	5	1	–5	25	25
3	–2	4	2	–4	16	8
5	0	0	6	0	0	0
6	1	1	7	1	1	1
8	3	9	8	2	4	6
11	6	36	12	6	16	36
ΣX = 33	Σdx = 3	Σdx2 = 75	ΣY = 36	Σdy = 0	Σdy2 = 62	Σdx dy = 76

$$\overline{X} = 33 / 6 = 5.5 \qquad \overline{Y} = 36 / 6 = 6$$

Regression equation of X on Y:

$$X - \overline{X} = b_{xy} = (Y - \overline{Y})$$

$$b_{xy} = \frac{\sum dxdy - \dfrac{\sum dx \times \sum dy}{N}}{\sum dy^2 - \dfrac{(\sum dy)^2}{N}}$$

$$= \frac{76 - \dfrac{3 \times 36}{6}}{62 - 0} = \frac{58}{62} = 0.935$$

$$X - 5.5 = 0.935 \ (Y - 6)$$
$$X - 5.5 = 0.935Y - 5.61$$
$$\mathbf{X = 0.935Y - 0.11}$$

Regression equation of Y on X:

$$Y - \overline{Y} = b_{yx} = (X - \overline{X})$$

$$b_{xy} = \frac{\sum dxdy - \dfrac{\sum dx \times \sum dy}{N}}{\sum dx^2 - \dfrac{(\sum dx)^2}{N}}$$

$$= \frac{76 - 18}{75 - (9/6)} = \frac{58}{73.5} = 0.79$$

$$Y - 6 = 0.79 \ (X - 5.5)$$
$$Y = 0.79X - 4.345 + 6$$
$$\mathbf{Y = 0.79X + 1.66}$$

Example 5: The data given below relate the thickness loss during calendering of a viscose needle punched fabric and the load on the calender bowl.

Load X (tons)	0.5	1.0	1.5	2.0	2.5	3.0
Thickness less (%) Y	4	13	14	20	24	33

Fit the regression equations.

Solution:

X	$(X - \Sigma X) = x$	x^2	Y	$(Y - \Sigma Y) = y$	y^2	xy
0.5	−1.25	1.562	4	−14	196	15.25
1.0	−0.75	0.5625	13	−5	25	3.75
1.5	−0.25	0.625	14	−4	16	1.00
2.0	0.25	0.625	20	2	4	0.50
2.5	0.75	0.5625	24	6	36	4.50
3.0	1.25	1.562	33	15	225	18.75
$\Sigma X = 10.5$	$\Sigma x = 0$	$\Sigma x^2 = 5.5$	$\Sigma Y = 108$	$\Sigma y = 502$		$\Sigma xy = 43.75$

$$\overline{X} = 1.75 \qquad \overline{Y} = 108 / 6 = 18$$

Regression equation of X on Y:

$$X - \overline{X} = r\frac{\sigma x}{\sigma y}\left(Y - \overline{Y}\right)$$

$$X - 1.75 = \frac{\Sigma xy}{\Sigma y^2}(Y - 18)$$

$$X - 1.75 = \frac{43.75}{502}(Y - 18)$$

$$X - 1.75 = 0.077(Y - 18)$$

$$X = 0.087Y - 1.568 + 1.75$$

$$X = 0.087\ Y + 3.318$$

Regression equation of Y on X:

$$Y - \overline{Y} = r\frac{\sigma y}{\sigma x}\left(X - \overline{X}\right)$$

$$Y - 18 = \frac{\sum xy}{\sum x^2}(X - \overline{X})$$

$$Y - 18 = \frac{43.75}{5.5}(X - \overline{X})$$

$$Y - 18 = 7.95X - 13.92$$

$$Y = 7.95X + 4.07$$

Example 6: The analysis of two groups of plain fabrics revealed the following data:

	Long cloth – A	Long cloth – B
Mean	65	67
S.D.	2.5	3.5
r	0.8	

Find the regression equations of A on B.

Regression equation of A on B

$$X - \overline{X} = r\frac{\sigma x}{\sigma y}\left(Y - \overline{Y}\right)$$

$$X - 65 = 0.8\frac{2.5}{3.5}(Y - 67)$$

$$X = 0.5714Y + 26.72$$

Example 7: Two fabric primary handle values like koshi and numeri are described by two regression equations.

$$5X - 6Y = -90$$
$$15X - 8Y = 130$$

What is the mean and 'r'.

Solution: By solving the above equations we get X = 30 ($\overline{X}$ = 30) and Y = 40 ($\overline{Y}$ = 40)

'r' can be found out by considering any one of the equation

$$5X = 6Y - 90 \qquad \qquad \qquad ... (1)$$
$$X = 6/5Y - 18 \text{ or } b_{xy} \ 6/5$$
$$-8Y = -15X + 130$$
$$Y = (15/8)X - 130/8 \text{ or } b_{yx} = 15/8$$

As it can be noted b_{xy} and b_{yx} values are more than one, hence, the equation are reconsidered as follows:

$-6Y = -5X - 90$, $6Y = 5X + 90$, $b_{yx} = 5 / 6$
$15\ X = 130 + 8Y$, $b_{xy} = 8 / 15$

$$r = \sqrt{b_{xy} \times b_{yx}} = 0.66$$

Example 8: M/s. Universal textiles has given the details about advertisement for new dress material as following:

	Advertisement expenses (Lakhs)	Sales (Lakhs)
X	20	120
S.D.	5	25
r = 0.8		

Find the likely sales when advertisement expenditure is Rs.25 lakhs. What is the advertisement expense for sales of Rs.150 lakhs.

Solution: Regression equation of advertisement on sales

$$X - \overline{X} = r\frac{\sigma x}{\sigma y}\left(Y - \overline{Y}\right)$$

$$X = 0.16Y + 0.8 \qquad\qquad \dots (1)$$

Regression equation of sales on advertisement

$$Y - \overline{Y} = r\frac{\sigma y}{\sigma x}\left(X - \overline{X}\right)$$

$$Y = 4X + 40 \qquad\qquad \dots (2)$$

Substituting Y = 150 in (1) we get,

$$X_{150} = 0.16\ (150) + 0.8 = 24.8 \text{ lakhs}$$

Similarly substituting X = 25 in (2)

$$Y_{25} = 4(25) + 40 = 140 \text{ lakhs.}$$

Example 9: From the following details on linear density in tex of two filaments workout regression equations and find the value of correlation coefficient.

X	6	2	10	4	8
Y	9	11	5	8	7

Solution: On computation we get

$\Sigma X = 30$ $\Sigma x = 0$ $\Sigma x^2 = 40$ $\Sigma Y = 40$
$\Sigma y = 0$
    $\Sigma y^2 = 20$ $\Sigma xy = -26$

Regression equation of X on Y

$$X - \overline{X} = b_{xy} (Y - \overline{Y})$$
$$X = -1.3Y + 16.4$$
$$Y - \overline{Y} = b_{yx} (X - \overline{X})$$
$$Y = -0.65 X + 11.9$$

$$r = \sqrt{b_{xy} \times b_{yx}} = -\sqrt{1.3 \times 6.5} = -0.919$$

7.3   Standard error of estimate

Regression equations perfect prediction is impractical in some situations. Hence, a measure is required to indicate the precise prediction of Y based on X and the measure is standard error of estimate (S_{yx}). In other words, standard error estimate measures the dispersion about an average line, called the regression line.

S_{yx} = the standard error of regression of X values from X_c

Also $S_{yx} = \sigma y \sqrt{1 - r^2}$

$$S_{xy} = \sqrt{\frac{\Sigma (X - X_c)^2}{N}}$$

Also $S_{xy} = \sigma y \sqrt{1 - r^2}$

Example 10: Given regression equations of fibre length and fibre fineness calculate the standard error of the estimate.

$Y = 11.9 - 0.65X$, $X = 16.4 - 1.3Y$

X	Y	Yc	Xc	$(Y - Yc)^2$	$(X - Xc)^2$
6	9	8	4.7	1.00	1.69
2	11	10.6	2.1	0.16	0.01
10	5	5.4	9.9	1.16	0.01
4	8	9.3	6.0	1.69	4.00
8	7	6.7	7.3	0.09	0.49
$\Sigma X = 30$	$\Sigma Y = 40$	$\Sigma Yc = 40$	$\Sigma Xc = 30$	$\Sigma (y - yc)^2 = 3.1$	$\Sigma (X - Xc)^2 = 6.2$

In the above table values of X and Y are assumed and the values of Y_c and X_c are obtained by substituting the values of X and Y in respective regression equations.

$$S_{yx} = \sqrt{\frac{3.1}{5}} = 0.787$$

$$S_{xy} = \sqrt{\frac{6.2}{5}} = 1.114$$

7.4   Ratio of variation

We know that the value of 'r' lies between +1 and –1. The correlation is positive if increase (or decrease) in one series is associated with the increase (or decrease) of the other. The correlation between the two series may be perfect but the proportional movements in the two series may be very different.

Supposing we have to find the variation in one series corresponding to a given variation in other series, i.e. if we are interested in knowing the relative variations of the two series, then we will have to find the ratio of variation.

The ratio of variation is useful for finding the extent or proportion to which a variable varies corresponding to a given variation in the other variable. For example, price and demand of a commodity may have a high degree of correlation (negative), yet the movements in price may not be proportionally the same as the movements in the demand. In case we want to measure the proportionate contraction of demand in response to a given rise in price, then we are required to calculate the ratio of variation.

There are two methods for finding ratio of variation.

Method 1

When the series are regular, ratio of variation is calculated as follows:
    Let there are two series: Y-series (relative) and X-series (subject).

(1)   Find the mean of Y-series.
(2)   Convert the values in Y-series into percentages of the mean. (In other words, find index numbers with mean as base).

Formula: Percentage = value / mean × 100

(3)   Find deviations of the percentages from average (i.e. 100)
(4)   Repeat the same process in case of X- series.

(5) Find the ratios between the corresponding percentage deviations from Y and X-series.
(6) Add the ratios and find the average.

This average is the required ratio of variation.

Example 1: Compute the ratio of variation mathematically.

Subject (X):	18	20	22	27	21	29	27	29	28	29
Relative (Y):	24	27	27	27	30	30	30	33	36	36

Y	Percentage of mean	Percentage deviations Dy	X	Percentage of mean	Percentage deviations Dx	DxDy
24	80	−20	18	72	−28	+0.71
27	90	−10	20	80	−20	+0.50
27	90	−10	22	88	−12	+0.83
27	90	−10	27	108	+8	−1.25
30	100	0	21	84	−16	0
30	100	0	29	116	+16	0
30	100	0	27	108	+8	0
33	110	+10	29	116	+16	+0.63
36	120	+20	28	112	+12	+1.67
36	120	+20	29	116	+16	+1.25
300		250				4.34

Mean = 300 / 10 = 30   Mean = 250 / 10 = 25

$$\text{Ratio of variation} = \frac{\Sigma \dfrac{D_y}{D_x}}{n} = \frac{4.34}{10} = 0.43$$

Method 2:

The above method is suitable only when the series are regular. For irregular series, ratio of variation is obtained graphically. The graph which is used for calculating ratio of variation is known as "Galton graph".

7.5   Galton graph and regression line

If subjects and relatives are given, then we have to follow the following steps to draw the "Galton graph":

1) Convert the values of both the series into index numbers with respective averages of the series as the base.
2) Index numbers of the subject are to be taken along the vertical scale.
3) Index numbers of the relative are to be taken along a horizontal scale.
4) The corresponding index numbers of the subject and relatives are the points which are to be plotted on the graph.

5) These points will be scattered and form a scattered diagram.
6) Draw a line showing a general trend through these points.

The following precautions are to be observed:

i) The line may be drawn in such a way that approximately an equal number of points lie on each side of the line.
ii) The points on either side may be equidistant from the line.
iii) The line should pass through the averages of the series, i.e., through the point (100, 100).

This general trend line is called the line of regression and the graph is called the "Galton graph".

7.5.1 Interpretation

a) If the angle between the line of regression and the vertical is < 45° (or > 45° with the horizontal), then the changes in the relative are less in proportion to those in the subject.
b) If the angle between the line of regression and the vertical is >45° (or < 45° with the horizontal), then the changes in the relative are greater in proportion to those in the subject.
c) If the angle between the line of regression and the vertical (or horizontal) is equal to 45°, then both the series change in the same proportion and the ratio of variation is unity. Such a line is called as line of equal variation.

Thus, the smaller is this angle, the slighter is the degree of correlation.

Ratio of variation is the tangent of the angle which a regression line makes with the vertical. If θ be the angle between the line of regression and the vertical, then

Ratio of variation = tan θ = perpendicular / base = AB / BC (in the figure).

Other inferences:
d) All the points lying in a straight line, the correlation is perfect.
e) If the line rises from left to right, the correlation is direct.
f) When the line slopes to the right, the correlation is inverse.

7.5.2   Uses of Galton graph

From the above study, we are in a position to enumerate the advantages of the Galton graph which helps us to find out:

1) Whether or not there is any correlation between two series
2) If the correlation exists, whether it is positive or negative
3) Whether the correlation is perfect or not
4) The ratio of variation
5) That the line of regression is the line of the best fit and we can find the best expected value of the relative for a given value of the subject in the graph and
6) The ratio of regression.

Ratio of regression = 1 – ratio of variation.

Example 2: Draw a Galton graph and show the ratio of variation between the following eight years.

Subject: (X)	79	52	33	55	46	62	31	34
Relative (Y):	49	40	25	35	35	34	34	28

Solution: Average of X = 392 / 8 = 49
Average of Y = 280 / 8 = 35

X	Index numbers (49 as base)	Y	Index numbers (35 as base)
79	79/49 × 100 = 161	49	49 / 35 × 100 = 140
52	52/49 × 100 = 106	40	40 / 35 × 100 =114
33	67	25	71
55	112	35	100
46	94	35	100
62	127	34	97
31	63	34	97
34	69	28	80

1) Plot index numbers of X along the vertical scale
2) Plot index number of Y along the horizontal scale
3) Plot the following points.
   Along horizontal axis: Y=140, 114, 71, 100, 100, 97, 97, 80
   Along vertical scale: X =161, 106, 67, 112, 94, 127, 63, 69.
4) Thus, draw the scattered diagram and draw a straight line showing the general trend. Draw the line through (100, 100).
5) Find the tangent of the angle which this line makes with the vertical.

Note: The series with larger average percentage deviation are generally taken as subject

Ratio of variation = tan θ = AB / BC = 20 / 31 = 0.6452

If we measure θ with the help of a protractor, then

θ = 32.8° (app.); tan 32.8° = 0.65 (app.)

It is < 45°, therefore, the changes in the relative are less in proportion to those in the subject.

7.6   How to find the ratio of regression?

Ratio of regression = 1 − ratio of variation

$$1 - 0.6452 = 0.3548$$

Ratio of variation thus, tells us the variation in one series corresponding to a given variation in the other series. In Galton graph, the line of regression helps us to find whether the changes in the relative are proportionally less, greater or equal corresponding to those in the subject.

Example: In a partially destroyed laboratory record of an analysis of correlation data, the following results are legible.

Variance of X = 9

Regression equations: (1) Regression equation of Y on X

8X − 10Y + 66 = 0.

(2) Regression equation of X on Y, 40X − 18Y = 214

What were: (a) The mean values of X and Y,
           (b) Standard deviation of Y,
           (c) Coefficient of correlation between X and Y.

Solution: As the regression lines pass through the means, therefore, their point of intersection gives the mean values.
Equations are:

$$8X - 10Y + 66 = 0 \text{ or, } 8X - 10Y = -66 \qquad ... (1)$$

$$40X - 18Y = 214 \qquad ... (2)$$

Multiple (1) by 5

∴ $40X - 50Y = -330 \qquad ... (3)$

Subtract (3) from (2), then 32Y = 544

Y = 17

Put Y = 17 in (2)
        40 X − 18 X 17 = 214
             40 X = 214 + 306 = 520
               X = 13

∴ $\overline{X} = 13, Y = 17$

Now $\sigma x = \sqrt{\text{variance}} = \sqrt{9} = 3$

Equations of regression lines are

$$X-\overline{X}=r\frac{\sigma x}{\sigma y}(Y-\overline{Y}) \quad \text{or} \quad X=r\frac{\sigma x}{\sigma y}(Y-\overline{Y})+\overline{X} \qquad \ldots (1)$$

$$Y-\overline{Y}=r\frac{\sigma y}{\sigma x}(X-\overline{X}) \quad \text{or} \quad Y=r\frac{\sigma y}{\sigma x}(X-\overline{X})+\overline{Y} \qquad \ldots (2)$$

Now equations are as follows:

$$8X - 10Y + 66 = 0 \qquad \ldots (1)$$

Or
$$10Y = 8X + 66$$
$$Y = (8/10)X + (66/10)$$

$$40X - 18Y = 214 \qquad \ldots (2)$$

$$40X = 18Y + 214$$
$$X = (18/40)Y + (214/40)$$

Regression coefficient in (1) = $r\dfrac{\sigma y}{\sigma x} = 8/10$

Coefficient of regression in (2) = $r\dfrac{\sigma x}{\sigma y} = 18/40$

Now coefficient of correlation

$$r = \sqrt{\text{Product of regression coefficients}}$$

$$\left[\because r\frac{\sigma y}{\sigma x} \times r\frac{\sigma x}{\sigma y} = r^2 \right]$$

$$\therefore r = \sqrt{\frac{8}{10} \times \frac{18}{40}} = \sqrt{\frac{144}{400}} = 12/20 = 0.6$$

$$Now \quad r\frac{\sigma y}{\sigma x} = \frac{8}{10}; \quad \sigma x = 3; \quad r = 12/20$$

$$\therefore \frac{12}{20} \times \frac{\sigma y}{3} = \frac{8}{10} \qquad \therefore \sigma y = \frac{8}{10} \times \frac{20 \times 3}{12} = 4$$

$$\therefore \ \overline{X} = 13, \ Y = 17, \ \sigma_y = 4, \ r = 0.6$$

Example : Given $\bar{X} = 726 / 10 = 72.6$, $\bar{Y} = 785 / 10 = 78.5$, r = 0.856, $\sigma_x = 8.8$, $\sigma_y = 6.3$. What could be the estimated value of Y if X = 70.

Equation is $Y - 78.5 = \dfrac{0.856 \times 6.3}{8.8}(X - 72.6)$

$\therefore$ $Y - 78.5 = 0.61\ (X - 72.6)$ ... (1)

Put X = 70 in (1), then Y – 78.5 = 0.61 (70 – 72.6)
Or $Y - 78.5 = 0.61(-2.6)$
                             $Y - 78.5 = -1.586$
$\therefore$ $Y = -1.586 + 78.5 = 76.9$ (Approx.)

The value can also be obtained by drawing the graph of the line. Read the value of Y in the graph when X = 70.

Angle between the two lines of regression:

The two regression equations are

$$X - \bar{X} = r\frac{\sigma x}{\sigma y}(Y - \bar{Y})$$ ... (1)

$$Y - \bar{Y} = r\frac{\sigma y}{\sigma x}(X - \bar{X})\ 7$$ ...(2)

From (1) X $\sigma_y - \bar{X}\sigma_y - r\sigma_x(Y - \bar{Y}) = 0$

Now slope of the line = –coeff. of X / coeff. Of $Y = -\sigma_y / -r_x = \sigma_y / r\sigma_x$

From (2) Y $\sigma_x - 4Y\sigma_x - r\sigma_y(X - \bar{X}) = 0$

Slope = –coefficient of X / coefficient of $Y = -(-r\sigma_y)/\sigma_x = r\sigma_y = \sigma_x$

Let α be the acute angle between the lines

Then, $\tan \alpha = \dfrac{\dfrac{\sigma y}{r\sigma x} - \dfrac{r\sigma y}{\sigma x}}{1 + \dfrac{\sigma y}{r\sigma x} \times \dfrac{r\sigma y}{\sigma x}} = \dfrac{\sigma y - r^2 \sigma y}{r\sigma x} x \dfrac{1}{1 + \dfrac{\sigma^2 y}{\sigma^2 x}}$

$$= \frac{\left(1 - r^2\right)\sigma_y}{r\sigma_x} \times \frac{\sigma^2{}_x}{\sigma^2{}_x + \sigma^2{}_y}$$

tana = $\tan \alpha = \dfrac{1 - r^2}{r}\dfrac{\sigma_x \sigma_y}{\sigma^2{}_x + \sigma^2{}_y}$

Example: Find regression equations. Given the following details:
X = 30; $\overline{Y}$ = 25; r = 0.763 = 0.77 (app.); σ_x = 3.7; σ_y = 4

(1) Regression equation of X and Y

$$X - \overline{X} = r\frac{\sigma x}{\sigma y}\left(Y - \overline{Y}\right)$$

$$X - 30 = 0.77x\frac{3.7}{4}(Y - 25)$$

$$= 0.71(Y - 25)$$

$$= 0.71Y - 17.75$$

$$X = 0.71Y - 17.75 + 30$$

$$= 0.71Y + 12.25$$

(2) Regression equation of Y on X

$$Y - \overline{Y} = r\frac{\sigma y}{\sigma x}\left(X - \overline{X}\right)$$

$$Y - 25 = 0.77 \times \frac{4}{3.7}(X - 30)$$

$$= 0.83 \ (X - 30) = 0.83 \ X - 24.9$$

$$Y = 0.83X - 24.9 + 25 = 0.83X + 0.1$$

1) Regression equation of X on Y is X = 0.71 Y +12.25
2) Regression equation of Y on X is Y = 0.83 X + 0.1

Interpretation: (1) When r = 0, then tan α = ∞ and α = 90°, the two lines become perpendicular.

(2) When r = +1, then tan α = 0 and α = 0, then the two lines coincide.

Example: Find the acute angle between the lines of regression, given X = 30, $\overline{Y}$ = 25, r=0.77, σ_x = 3.7, σ_y = 4.

Solution: Let α be the angle between the lines

Then $\tan \alpha = \dfrac{1-r^2}{r} \times \dfrac{\sigma_x \sigma_y}{\sigma^2_x + \sigma^2_y}$

Now r = 0.77 σ_x = 3.7 σ_y = 4

$$\text{Tan } \alpha = \frac{1-r^2}{r} \times \frac{\sigma_x \sigma_y}{\sigma^2_x + \sigma^2_y}$$

Now r = 0.77, $\sigma_x = 3.7$, $\sigma_y = 4$

$$\tan \alpha = \frac{1-0.77^2}{0.77} \times \frac{3.7 \times 4}{(3.7)^2 + 4^2}$$

$$= \frac{1-0.5929}{0.77} \times \frac{14.8}{13.69+16} = \frac{0.4071}{0.77} \times \frac{14.8}{29.69}$$

$$= 0.2642$$

$$\alpha = \tan^{-1}(0.2642)$$

i.e. $\alpha = 14° - 48'$

7.7   Variation about the regression line and its significance

Considering that values of X and Y are described normally with mean given by $\bar{y} = a + bx_i$ (where $x = x_i$) and variance σ^2 measuring the variability of the measured data about the regression line and also is a measure of how well the line fits the data. Smaller the values of σ^2, the less variation is about the line and therefore, the closer is its fit to the data. Hence, it is important to have an estimate of the value of σ^2 and is given by

$$S^2 = S_{min} / (n - 2) \qquad \qquad \text{... (1)}$$

Where S_{min} is the minimum value of the sum of the squares of deviations given by

$$S = \sum_{i=1}^{n} e_i^2 = \sum_{i=1}^{n} (y_i - a - bx_i)^2 \qquad \qquad \text{... (2)}$$

Where e is the sum of squares of the e_i values [where $e_i = y_i - \bar{y}_i - (a + bx_i)$]

The values of 'a' and 'b' can be obtained by solving normal equations or deviations from real mean or assumed mean or a = $\bar{y}$ - bx

Where $b = \dfrac{\sum (x - \bar{x})(y - \bar{y})}{\sum (x - \bar{x})^2}$

(For further simplification of equation 2, the reader is advised to refer practical statistics for textile industry Part – II, GAV leaf)

Therefore,

$$S_{min} = \sum_i (y_i - \bar{y})^2 - \frac{\left[\sum_i (x_i - \bar{x})(y_i - \bar{y}) \right]^2}{\sum_i (x_i - \bar{x})^2} \qquad \text{... (3)}$$

Referring to the example number 1

$\Sigma(x - \bar{x}) = 47.71$, $\Sigma(y - \bar{y})^2 = 18.96$, $\Sigma (x - \bar{x})(y - \bar{y}) = 28.54$

Hence, equation 3 gives

$$S_{min} = 1.89$$

And this substitute in equation (1)

$$S^2 = 1.89 / 5 = 0.38$$
$$S = \sqrt{0.38} = 0.616$$

7.8   Confidence limits

It is often noticed that the dependent variable is subjected to random errors and method of least squares can be considered in such cases. If the variable are linearly related we can write

$$Y = \alpha + \beta x$$

The coefficients α and β can be assumed as the population parameters of the true regression of y on x. The values of α and β are likely to vary from one sample to another, hence, the necessity for confidence limits for mean and population are set.

The 100 $(1 - 2r)$ limits for are

$$a \pm t_{k,r} S \left\{ \frac{1}{n} + \frac{\bar{x}^2}{\sum (x - \bar{x})^2} \right\}^{y_2} , \; b \pm t_{k,r} \; S \Big/ \left\{ \sum (x - \bar{x})^2 \right\}^{y_2}$$

Where a and b represent α and β from the standard linear equation.

Note: K = n − 2 and 'S' is the S.D. about the regression line referring to the example number 1 and assuming r = 2.5%, from table $t_{5,\,2.5\%} = 2.57$, then by solving the normal equations it is shown that a = 27.18, b= 0.5982, S = 0.616 the 95% confidence limits (α) are given by

$$27.18 \pm 2.57 \times 0.615 \sqrt{\frac{1}{7} + \frac{(9.571)^2}{47.7143}}$$

$$= 27.18 \pm 2.27$$

And similarly for β

$$0.5982 \pm 0.228$$

Confidence limits for variables X and Y

It is accepted that regression is mainly used to predict the value of Y based on X. However, these Y values are subjected to error because of uncertainties in the estimation of α and β and hence, the confidence limits are found for them.

If $X = X_f$, then Y value at X_f is $Y = a + b\,X_f$

The confidence limits for 'true mean' is given by

$$a + bX_f \pm t_{k,r} \;\; S\left\{\frac{1}{n} + \frac{\left(X_f - \overline{X}\right)^2}{\sum\left(X - \overline{X}\right)^2}\right\}^{\frac{1}{2}}$$

Referring to the example 1, the estimates of the modulus when $X_f = 8$ and its limits are

$$27.2 + 0.6x8 \pm 2.57x0.615\left\{\frac{1}{7} + \frac{(8-9.571)^2}{47.7143}\right\}^2$$

$$= 32 \pm 0.70$$

The Integral with which the modulus is expected to lie is found by

$$27.2 + 0.6 \times 8 \pm 2.57 \times 0.615\left\{1 + \frac{1}{7} + \frac{(8-9.571)^2}{47.7143}\right\}^2$$

$$= 32 \pm 1.7$$

Thus it can be concluded from the above exercise, that future type cords with processing tension 8 are expected to a mean modulus lying between 31.3 and 32.7 while individual test pieces will be with moduli ranging between 30.3 and 33.7 provided the other conditions remain constant.

7.9   Tests for regression

Regression is a process of estimating the values of Y for a given value of X i.e. the value of Y obtained will depend on X. This can be tested by setting up ANOVA and such a table is shown below

Source of variation	S.S.	D.f.	M.S.S.	F
Due to regression	$\Sigma_i (Y - \overline{Y})^2$	1	M_r	
About regression (S_{min})	$\Sigma_i (Y - \overline{Y_1})^2 n - 2$		M_o	M_r / M_o
Total	$\Sigma_i (Y_i - \overline{Y})^2 n - 1$			

Note:

$\Sigma_i (Y - \overline{Y})^2$ is given by
$$\frac{\left[\sum_i \left(X_i - \overline{X}\right)\left(Y_i - \overline{Y}\right)\right]^2}{\sum_i \left(X_i - \overline{X}\right)^2}$$

And as the total sum of squares $\Sigma_i (Y_i - \overline{Y})^2$ is already calculated hence, S_{min} is found by difference.

Referring to the example 1 we can set up Anova as follows:

Source of variation	S.S.	D.f	M.S.S.	F
Due to regression	17.07	1	17.0745	
About regression	1.8941	5	0.3788	45.1
Total	18.9686	6		

As $F_{cal} >> F_{tab}$ it is concluded that the 'Y' value really do depend on X.

Fitting of $Y = \beta X$ in Regression:

If b is the least squares estimate of β its value is found by minimizing the sum of squares of deviations from $\overline{y} = bx$.

i.e. $S = \sum_i \left(y_i - \overline{y_1}\right)^2 = \sum_i \left(y_i - bx_i\right)^2$

This can be minimum only when ds/db = 0

i.e. $2 \Sigma_i (y_i - bx_i) (-x_i) = 0$

$b = \Sigma_i = x_i y_i = \Sigma_i x_i^2$

Therefore,

$S_{min} = \Sigma y_i^2 - (\Sigma_i x_i y_i)^2 / \Sigma x_i^2$ and an estimate of variance about the regression line is

$S^2 = S_{min} / (n - 1)$

Confidence limits are given by

$b \pm t_{k, r} S / \sqrt{\Sigma x^2}$

where t has k = n − 1 d.o.f. For the mean value of y when x = x_f the confidence limits are $bx_f \pm t_{kr} S x_f / \sqrt{\Sigma x^2}$ and for a future individual y value when x = x_f

$$bx_f \pm t_{k,r}S\left\{1 + x_f^2 / \sum x^2\right\}^{\frac{1}{2}}$$

Example: You are given the measurements of wet-relaxed plain knit fabric. Fit a regression through origin.

X	1.72	1.55	1.50	1.38	1.36	1.23	1.18	1.13	1.07
Y	8.61	7.38	7.00	6.92	6.71	5.86	5.92	5.5	5.09

n =10, $\sum x^2$ = 17.7736, $\sum y^2$ = 423.2012.
$\sum xy$ = 86.6974, b = 86.6974/17.7736 = 4.8779

And the line is

$$y = 4.88 \ x$$

$$S_{min} = 423.2012 - (86.6974)^2 / 17.7736$$

$$= 0.3021$$
$$S^2 = 0.3021 / 9 = 0.03357 \text{ and } S = 0.1832$$

K = n – 1 = 9, r = 0.025 for 95% confidence limits, from table at $t_{9,0.025}$ = 2.26 and the confidence limts β are

$$4.8779 \pm 2.26 \times 0.1832 / \sqrt{17.7736}$$

$$= (4.8779 \pm 0.0982)$$

$$= (4.78 , 4.98)$$

Example: The data relate the thickness loss during calendaring of a viscose needle punched fabric and the load on the calender bowl.

Load (X)	0.5	1.0	1.5	2.0	2.5	3.0
Thickness loss (%)	4	13	14	20	24	33

Fit an equation of the form y= βx. Calculate the 95% confidence limits for β and for the thickness loss when the load = 2.3.

Solution: n = 6, $\sum x^2$ = $(0.5^2 + 1^2 + 1.5^2 + 2^2 + 2.5^2 + 3^2)$
$$(0.25 + 1 + 2.25 + 4 + 6.25 + 9) = 22.75$$
$$\sum y^2 = (0.5 \times 4 + 1.0 \times 13 + 1.5 \times 14 + 20 \times 2.0 +$$
$$+ 2.5 \times 24 + 3.0 \times 33)$$
$$= (2 + 13 + 21 + 40 + 60 + 99)$$
$$= 235$$
$$b = \sum xy / \sum x^2 = 235 / 22.75 = 10.3296 \text{ and the}$$
corresponding line is
$$y = 10.33 \ x$$
$$S_{min} = \sum y^2 - (\sum xy)^2 / \sum x^2$$
$$= [2446 - (235)^2 / 22.75]$$

$$= [2466 - 2427.4725]$$
$$= 18.5275$$
$$S^2 = 18.5275 / 5$$
$$S^2 = 7.7055$$
$$S = 1.9249$$

$K = 5, r = 0.025$ for 95% confidence limits [note: r is given by $100 (1-2r)$ confidence limits for α] and from t tables $t_{5,0.025} = 2.57$ and the confidence limits

for β are

$$10.3296 \pm 2.57 \times 1.9249 / \sqrt{22.75}$$

$$10.3296 \pm 4.947 / 4.770$$

$$10.3296 \pm 1.0371$$

$$(11.3667, 9.2925)$$

If load = 2.3, the thickness loss

$$b \, x_f \pm t_{k,r} S\{ 1 + x_f^2 / \Sigma x^2\}^{1/2}$$

Where $x = x_f = 2.3$

$$10.3296 \times 2.3 \pm 2.57 - 1.9249 (1 + 5.29/22.75)^{1/2}$$

$$23.7581 \pm 4.947 (0.2592)$$

$$23.7580 \pm 1.2822$$

$$(25.0402, 22.4758)$$

8

Time series

8.1 Introduction

One of the most important tasks before economists and business man, these days is to make estimates for the future. For example, a business man is interested to forecast his sales in 1994 or as a long term planning in the year 2000, so that he could adjust the production to meet the demand. However, the first step in making the forecast consists of gathering information from the past. In this connection, one usually deals with the statistical data collected, observed or recorded at successive intervals of time.

"A series of observations of a phenomenon recorded at successive time intervals" is called time series. It is a chronological arrangement of statistical data about a phenomenon.

Consider the following time series:

Year	1981	1982	1983	1984	1985	1986	1987	1988
Sales	40	42	47	41	43	48	65	42

If we observe this series we find generally the sales have increased but there is also decline in sales. The statistician tries to analyze these forces under 4 headings.

1. Changes that have occurred as a result of general tendency of the data to increase or decrease known as "secular movements".
2. Changes that have taken place during a period of 12 months as a result of change in the climate, weather conditions, festivals, etc., such changes are known as "seasonal variations".
3. Changes that have taken place because of ups and downs in the phenomena known as "cyclical variations".
4. Changes that have taken place due to unavoidable circumstances, i.e., Natural calamities like floods, earth quakes, famine, wars, etc., are known as "irregular variations".

The above points are the main components of time series.

8.2 Utility of time series

Time series are highly useful not only to Economists, Business men but also to Scientists, Astronomists, Geologists, Sociologists, Biologists, Research workers, etc., utility of Time Series will be justified if following points are given:

1. Past behaviour can be well understood by Time series.
2. Forecasting can be done easily.
3. It helps in evaluating current accomplishments.
4. Comparison between the phenomena can be done easily through Time Series.

8.3 Components of Time Series

All types of fluctuations are of 4 types as stated below:

1. Secular trend
2. Seasonal variation
3. Cyclical variation
4. Irregular variation.

There are two models used for the indication of trend viz.:

1. Additive model
2. Multiplicative model.

Let $Y =$ be the trend, $T =$ be the secular trend, $S =$ be the seasonal variations, $C =$ be the cyclic variation and $I =$ be the irregular variation then,

$$Y = \text{Additive model} = T + S + C + I$$

$$Y = \text{Multiplicative model} = T \times S \times C \times I$$

1. Secular trend

As we know that trend is the change in the time series over a period of time. Secular trend is the change over a long period of time. Therefore, in this type of trend short-term oscillations are not included but steady movements over a period of time are observed.

Secular trend movements are attributable to factors such as population, technical progress, large scale shift in consumer tastes, etc., for example, the presence of more people means that more food, clothing and shelters are necessary. Technological changes discovery and exchange of views, exhaustion of natural sources, mass production, etc., are the causes for growth. The growth in some phenomenon is followed by decline in the other. For example, the displacement of silk by rayon the bullock-carts by other modes of transportation like tempo, trucks, etc. Similarly, better medical facilities, improved sanitation, etc., will reduce the death rate and increase birth rate.

Trends generally   1. Increase slowly.
2. Increase fast.
3. Remain relatively constant over a period of time / period of growth.
4. Decline in a reverse order.

2. Seasonal variations

These variations are those periodic changes/movements in business activity which occur regularly every year. Since, these variations repeat during a period of 12 months. Almost all types of business activities are susceptible to seasonal influence to a greater or lesser degree. Seasonal in real means is that the variations in particular period of the year, will include any kind of variation which is periodic nature and whose repeating cycles are relatively of short duration. This variation is evident when data are recorded weekly, monthly or quarterly intervals. Even though the amplitudes of these variations vary, their period is fixed being 1 year. Factors affecting seasonal variations are as follows:

Climate and weather conditions

Climate is the most important factor causing seasonal variation. Changes in climate and weather conditions such as rainfall, humidity, heat, etc., act on product and industries differently. For example, during winter there is greater demand for woolen clothes, hot drinks, etc., where as in summer cotton clothes, cool drinks have greater sale. Agriculture is very much influenced by the climate. The effect of climate is that there are generally two seasons in agriculture – the growing and the harvesting season which directly affect economic position of the farmer which in turn affects the business activity.

Customs, traditions and habits

Though nature is primarily responsible for seasonal variations in time series, customs, traditions and habits also have their impact. For example, on certain Indian festivals such as deepavali, dusserah, christmas, etc., there is big demand for sweets and also there is large demand for cash before festivals because people need for shopping and gifts. Similarly, on the 1st of every month there are heavy withdrawals and the bankers have to keep lot of cash to meet the possible demand on the basis of last month experience. To quote another example, most of the students buy books in the first few months of the opening of schools and colleges and thus sale of books, stationary, etc., shows seasonal swings.

The study and measurement of seasonal patterns constitute a very important part of analysis of a time series. Sometimes seasonal variations are themselves are of primary concern. An accurate knowledge of seasonal behaviour is an aid in mitigating and ironing out tensional movements through business policy.

3. Cyclic variation

Cyclic variations are long lasting than a year and are regular neither in amplitude nor in length.

Generally, a business activity will undergo 4 phases:

(a) Prosperity
(b) Recession / decline
(c) Depression
(d) Recovery / improvement.

Each phase changes gradually into the phase which follows it in the order given with respect to the above figure we can explain the behaviour of business.

In "prosperity" phase the public is optimistic, business is booming, prices are high and profits are easily made. There is considerable expansion of business activity which leads to an over-development. It is then difficult to secure deliveries and there is shortage of transportation facilities which has a tendency to cause large inventories to be accumulated during the time of highest prices. Wages increase and efficiency decreases. The strong demand for money causes interest rates to rise to a high level while doubt enters the bankers mind as to the advisability of granting further loans. This situation causes business man to make price concessions in order to secure necessary cash. Then follows the expectation of further reductions and the situation becomes worse instead of better. Buyers wait for lower prices and all this leads to a decline in trade. Then follows period of pessimism in trade and industry. Factories close, business fail, there is wide spread unemployment while wages and prices are low. These conditions characterize depression. After a period of rigid economy liquidation and re-organisation, money accumulates and seeks a nose. Then follows a period of increasing business activity with rising prices: a period of improvement or recovery. This improvement develops into prosperity period and thus, the "business cycle" is completed.

4. Irregular variation

Irregular variations are also called "erratic", accidental, random; referring to such variations in business activity that do not repeat in a definite pattern. Irregular movements on the other hand are considered to be largely random, being the result of chance factors which like those determining fall of a coin are wholly unpredictable.

Irregular variations are caused by such isolated special occurrences as floods, earth quakes, strikes and wars. Sudden changes in demand or very rapid technological progress. By their very nature these movements are irregular and unpredictable.

Some preliminary adjustments are necessary before analyzing time series. These adjustments are as follows:

(a)   Calendar variations
(b)   Price changes
(c)   Comparability
(d)   Population changes

8.4   Measurement of trend

Given any long term series we wish to determine and present the direction which it takes – is it growing or declining? Following are the two important reasons to study trend measurement.

1.   To find the trend characteristics in and of themselves.
     In studying trend in and of itself, we ascertain the growth factor. For example, we can compare the growth of a composite mill with
     1.   The economy as a whole (or)
     2.   With the growth in other industries (or)
     3.   In and between the composite mill(or)
     4.   Indian textiles industry with foreign
     Thus, the prediction of grow the factors helps us in predicting future trend. If the trend can be determined, the rate of change can be ascertained and tentative estimates concerning future can be made accordingly.
2.   To enable us to eliminate trend in order to study other elements.

8.4.1   Methods of trend measurement

1.   Freehand or graphic method
2.   Semi-averages method
3.   Moving averages method
4.   Method of least squares

8.5   Methods of least square

In this method a mathematical relationship is established between time and the variable. The relation may be linear (straight line) or quadratic (parabolic) or exponential. Here the relation so derived is that two conditions are satisfied.

1. Sum of the deviations of actual and computed value is zero.
2. Sum of the squared deviations of active and computed values id least.

Merits:

1. The method is mathematical and so highly efficient.
2. It can be used for predicting the future trend.
3. It can be used for deep statistical analysis.

8.6   Linear trend

In this method a relation of line $Y = a + b$ 't' is filled to the time series, where Y is the actual trend values, 't' – point of time. The constants 'a' and 'b' are obtained by solving the normal equations. Generally, the form of the equation will be:

$$Na + b\Sigma t = \Sigma y \qquad \ldots (1)$$

$$a\,\Sigma t + b\Sigma t^2 = \Sigma y\, t \qquad \ldots (2)$$

Where y = observed values, n = denotes number of observations.

$$a = \Sigma y\, /\, n$$
$$b = \Sigma y\, t\, /\, \Sigma t^2$$

By substituting the values of 't' in the Trend equation, the corresponding Trend values can be obtained.

Example: Following are the figures of production in 1000 quintals of a Blow Room.

Year	1973	1974	1975	1976	1977	1978	1979
Production	77	81	88	94	94	96	98

1. Fit a straight line trend to the data.
2. Graph the observed values and trend values.
3. Estimate the production in the year 1981.

Solution: To simplify the solution, 't' is chosen such that $\Sigma t = 0$. Here n = 7, and odd number. Therefore, middle most point of time is taken as 0 and other values (on both sides of 0 is + and − are written as −1, −2, −3, etc., and +1, +2, +3, etc.,

Year	Y	Deviations from 1976 't'	t^2	Yt	Trend Y = a + b 't'
1973	77	−3	9	−231	79.11
1974	81	−2	4	−162	82.4
1975	88	−1	1	−88	86.17
1976	94	0	0	0	89.7
1977	94	+1	1	94	93.23
1978	96	+2	4	182	96.76
1979	98	+3	9	294	100.29
	$\Sigma y = 628$	$\Sigma t = 0$	$\Sigma t^2 = 28$	$\Sigma yt = +99$	

Here 'n' is odd for middle most value i.e., 76 't' is chosen as 0.

$$a = \Sigma y / n = 628 / 7 = 89.7$$
$$b = \Sigma yt / \Sigma t^2 = 99 / 28 = 3.53$$
$$y = a + b\, t = 89.7 + 3.53 \times t$$

Example for 1973 = 89.7 − 3.53 × 3 = 79.11
values of 't' corresponding to 1981 is +5
∴ the estimated production for 1981 = 89.7 + 3.53 × 5 = 107.35

Note: The successive "trend" values can be obtained by adding 3.53 to the preceding value.

Example: Fit a straight line trend for the following series. Estimate the production in 1987.

Year	Y	Deviations from 1983 't'	t^2	Yt
1980	60	−3	9	−180
1981	72	−2	4	−144
1982	75	−1	1	−75
1983	65	0	0	0
1984	80	+1	1	80
1985	85	+2	4	170
1986	95	+3	9	285
	$\Sigma y = 532$	$\Sigma t = 0$	$\Sigma t^2 = 28$	$\Sigma Yt = 535 - 399 = 136$

Since $\Sigma t = 0$, $a = \Sigma y / n = 532 / 7 = 76$,
$B = \Sigma yt / \Sigma t^2 = 136 / 28 = 4.857$
(At 1980) y = a + bt = 76 + 4.85 × 4 = 954

Example: Below are given the figures relating to a production in (1000 quintal) of 30^s laps in a spinning mill.

Year	Production
1975	77
1977	88
1978	94
1979	85
1980	91
1981	98
1984	90

i) Fit a straight line trend.

Year	production	Deviations from 1979 't'	t^2	Yt	Trend
1975	77	−4	16	−308	83.1
1977	88	−2	4	−176	85.8
1978	94	−1	1	−94	87.24
1979	85	0	0	0	88.62
1980	91	+1	1	91	90.00
1981	98	+2	4	+196	91.38
1984	90	+5	25	+450	95.52
n = 7	Σy = 623	Σt = 1	Σt² = 51	ΣYt = 159	

$$n\,a + b\Sigma t = \Sigma y$$
$$7a + b = 623 \qquad \ldots (1)$$
$$a\Sigma t + b\Sigma t^2 = \Sigma y$$
$$a + 51b = 159 \qquad \ldots (2)$$

Solving eqs. (1) and (2)
We get a = 88.62 and hence, y = 88.62 + 1.38t

Example: The following data relate to the number of passenger cars in (million) sold from 1980 to 1987.

Year	Number
1980	6.7
1981	5.3
1982	4.3
1983	6.1
1984	5.6
1985	7.9
1986	5.8
1987	6.1

a) Fit a straight line trend to the data through 1985 only
b) Estimate the production in 1987.

Year	Y	Deviation from 1985 't'	t^2	yt
1980	6.7	−5	25	−33.5
1981	5.3	−4	16	−21.2
1982	4.3	−3	09	−12.9
1983	6.1	−2	04	−12.2
1984	5.6	−1	1	−5.6
1985	7.9	0	0	0
1986	5.8	1	1	5.8
1987	6.1	2	4	12.2
	$\Sigma y = 47.8$	$\Sigma t = -12$	$\Sigma t^2 = 60$	$\Sigma yt = -67.4$

$$\Sigma y = Na + b \Sigma t$$

(a) $47.8 = 8a - 12b$ ... (1)

$-67.4 = -24a + 120b$ ... (2)

Solving we get a = 6.122   b = 0.102

y = 6.128 + 0.102t

(b)   Production in 1987 t = 2

y = 6.128 + 0.204 = 6.322

Case – II when 'n' is even (no. observations = even)

When 'n' is 'even' consider the middle term 'n' and n / 2 + 1 terms and rate the value of 'y' as = 1 or −1 etc.

Example: Fit a straight line trend for the data given below by the method of least squares.

Year	1982	1983	1984	1985	1986	1987
Output	672	824	968	1205	1464	1758

Solution: What is the expected output in a 1991?

Year	y	Deviations from 1984 to 85 't'	t^2	yt
1982	672	−2.5	6.25	−1680
1983	824	−1.5	2.25	−1236
1984	968	−0.5	0.25	−484
1985	1205	+0.5	0.25	+602.5
1986	1464	+1.5	2.25	+2196
1987	1758	+2.5	6.25	+4395
	$\Sigma y = 6891$	$\Sigma t = 0$	$\Sigma t^2 = 17.5$	$\Sigma yt = 3797.5$

$a = \Sigma y / n = 6891 / 6 = 1148.5$

$b = \Sigma Y t / \Sigma t^2 = 3797.5 / 17.5$

$y = a + b t$

$y = 1148.5 + 279.51t$

Expected output in 1991 = t = 6.5

Y = 2965.31

Example: Fit a straight line trend by the method of least squares to the following data. Assuming that the same rate of change continues, what would be the predicted earnings for the year 1988?

Year	1979	1980	1981	1982	1983	1984	1985	1986
Earnings	38	40	65	72	69	60	87	95

Deviations are multiplied by 2 for simplification

Year	Y	Deviation' for 1982 – 85 't	T	T²	Yt
1979	38	–3.5	–7	49	–266
1980	40	–2.5	–5	25	–200
1981	65	–1.5	–3	09	–195
1982	72	–0.5	–1	1	–72
1983	69	+0.5	+1	1	69
1984	60	+1.5	+3	9	180
1985	87	+2.5	+5	25	435
1986	95	+3.5	+7	49	665
ΣY = 526				Σt² = 168	ΣyT = 616

$$a = \Sigma Y / N = 526 / 8 = 65.75$$
$$b = \Sigma XY / \Sigma X^2 = 616 / 168 = 3.667 \times 2 / 7.3 = \mathbf{7.3}$$
$$Y = 65.75 + 3.667X$$

For 1988 'X' will be +11

$$\therefore Y = 65.75 + 3.667 \times 11 = 65.75 + 7.3 \times 11 = 65.75 + 7.3 \times 11$$

8.7   Quadratic trend (parabolic trend)

Here a relation of the type $y = a + bt + ct^2$ is fitted to the time series. The constants a, b, c are obtained by solving the normal equation of the form.

$$na + b\Sigma t + c\Sigma t^2 = \Sigma y \qquad \ldots (1)$$
$$a\Sigma t + b\Sigma t^2 + c\Sigma t^3 = \Sigma yt \qquad \ldots (2)$$
$$a\Sigma t^2 + b\Sigma t^3 + c\Sigma t^4 = \Sigma yt^2 \qquad \ldots (3)$$

As in the case of linear trends here also 't' is chosen such that $\Sigma t = 0$

Example: Fit a quadratic trend for the following time series. Estimate the population in 1991.

Year	1941	1951	1961	1971	1981	1991
Population	32	36	44	55	68	?

Year	y	Deviation from 1961 / 10 't'	t^2	t^3	t^4	yt	yt^2
1941	32	−2	4	−8	16	−64	128
1951	36	−1	1	−1	1	−36	36
1961	44	0	0	0	0	0	0
1971	55	1	1	1	1	55	55
1981	68	2	4	8	16	136	272
	235		10	0	34	91	491

I $na + b\Sigma t + c\Sigma t^2 = \Sigma y$
   $5a + b \times 0 + c \times 10 = 235$
   $5a + 10c = 235$ ... (1)
II $a\Sigma t + b\Sigma t^2 + c\Sigma t^3 = \Sigma yt$
   $10b = 91$ ... (2)
III $a\Sigma t^2 + b\Sigma t^3 + c\Sigma t^4 = \Sigma yt^2$
   $10a + 0 + 34c = 491$ ... (3)
   From (2) $b = 91$

Solving Eq. (1)

$$10a + 34c = 491$$
$$5a + 10c = 235 \times 2$$

$$10a + 34c = 491$$
$$10a + 20c = 470$$
$$14c = 21$$
$$c = 21 / 14 \Rightarrow c = 1.5$$

Solving Eq. (3)

$$5a + 10c = 235$$
$$5a = 235 - 15 / 5$$
$$a = 220 / 5$$
$$a = 44$$

$y = a + bt + ct^2$
$= 44 + 91t + 1.5t^2$

In 1991 $t = +3$ ∴ Population in crores $= 44 + 27.3 + 4.5 = 75.8$ crores

Example: The prices of a commodity during 1983–88 are given below: fit a quadratic trend. Estimate the commodity price in the year 1989.

Year	Prices	Year	Prices
1983	100	1986	140
1984	107	1987	181
1985	128	1988	192

Year	y	t	t^2	t^3	t^4	ty	yt^2
1983	100	−2	4	−8	16	−200	400
1984	107	−1	1	−1	1	−107	107
1985	128	0	0	0	0	0	0
1986	140	+1	1	1	1	140	140
1987	181	+2	4	8	16	362	724
1988	192	+3	9	27	81	576	1728
	848	3	19	27	115	771	3099

I $na + b\Sigma t + c\Sigma t^2 = \Sigma y$

$\quad 6a + 3b + 19c = 848$ ... (1)

II $a\Sigma t + b\Sigma t^2 + c\Sigma t^3 = \Sigma yt$

$\quad 3a + 19b + 27c = 771$ ... (2)

III $a\Sigma t^2 + b\Sigma t^3 + c\Sigma t^4 = \Sigma yt^2$

$\quad 19a + 27b + 115c = 3099$ ... (3)

Multiplying the second equation by (2) and keeping the 1st as it is

$$6a + 3b + 19c = 848$$
$$6a + 38b + 54c = 1542$$
$$-35b - 5c = -694$$

or $\quad\quad\quad\quad 35b + 35c = 694$ ... (4)

Multiplying eq. (2) by 19 and (3) by 3, we get

$$57a + 361b + 513c = 14649$$
$$57a + 81b + 345c = 9297$$
$$280b + 168c = 5352$$ ... (5)

Multiplying eq. (4) by 8 we have

$$280b + 280c = 5552$$ ... (6)

Solving (5) and (6)

$$280b + 168c = 5352$$
$$280b + 280c = 5552$$
$$112c = 200$$
$$c = 200 / 112 \text{ or } c = 1.786$$

Substitute the value of 'c' in eq. (4) we get

$$35b + 35c = 694$$
$$35b + 35 \times 1.786 = 694$$
$$35b = 631.5 \text{ or } b = 18.042$$

Substituting the value of b and c in eq. (1) we get

$$6a + 3b + 19c = 848$$
$$6a + 3 \times 18.04 + 19 \times 1.78 = 848$$
$$6a = 759.94$$
$$a = 126.657$$
$$a = 126.657 \quad b = 18.042 \quad c = 1.786$$

$$Y = 126.657 + 18.042t + 1.786t^2$$

The trend value for 1989 the value of 't' is 4

$$\mathbf{Y} = 126.657 + 18.042 \times 4 + 1.786 + 16 = 227.41$$

8.8   Exponentional trend

Here, a relation of type $y = ab^t$ is fitted to the time series the relation can be reduced to linear form by taking log. Thus,

$$\text{Log } y = \log a + 't' \log b$$

Or $V = A + Bt$

Where, A = log a
        B = log b

The normal equations are

$$NA + B\Sigma t = \Sigma U, \quad A\Sigma t + B\Sigma t^2 = \Sigma UT$$

When $\Sigma t = 0$

$$A = \Sigma U / n \quad B = \Sigma U \, t / \Sigma t^2$$

Antilog A = a, Antilog B = b,

Example: Fit an exponential trend for the following time series.

Year	1955	1960	1965	1970	1975	1980
Y	2	3	4	6	9	13

Year	Y	Deviations from 67.5 't'	t^2	u = Log y	UT
1955	2	−12.5	156.25	0.3010	−3.76
1960	3	−7.5	56.25	0.4771	−3.57
1965	4	−2.5	6.25	0.6021	−1.50
1970	6	+2.5	6.25	0.7782	+1.94
1975	9	+7.5	56.25	0.9542	+7.15
1980	13	+12.5	156.25	1.1139	+13.92
	$\Sigma Y = 37$	$\Sigma t = 0$	$\Sigma t^2 = 437.50$	$\Sigma u = 4.2265$	$\Sigma UT = 4.18$

$$A = \Sigma U / n = 4.2265 / 6 = 0.7044$$

Antilog of A = a

$$B = \Sigma UT / \Sigma t^2 = 14.18 / 437.5 = 0.0324$$

Antilog of B = b = 1.076

$$y = 5.06 \times (1.076)^t$$

Note: If Σu is not equal to zero, then equations lane to be solved.

Example: The sales of dying company for the last 8 years is as follows:

Year	1984	1985	1986	1987	1988	1989	1990	1991
Sales Rs(000)	52	45	98	92	110	185	175	220

Estimate sales in the year 1992 using the exponential form.

Year	Y	t	t^2	u = log y	log y × t	Trend
1984	52	−3	9	1.7160	−5.1480	—
1985	45	−2	4	1.6532	−3.3064	—
1986	98	−1	1	1.9912	−1.9912	—
1987	92	0	0	1.9638	0	—
1988	110	+1	1	2.0414	+2.0414	—
1989	185	+2	4	2.2672	+4.5344	—
1990	175	+3	9	2.2430	+6.7290	—
1991	220	+4	16	2.3424	+9.3696	—

As Σt is not zero we have to solve the equations

1) $\Sigma \log y = N \log a + \log b \, \Sigma t$
2) $\Sigma (t \log y) = \log a \, \Sigma t + \log b \, \Sigma t^2$

$$8 \log a + 4 \log b = 16.2182$$
$$8 \log a + 88 \log b = 24.4576$$
$$-84 \log b = -8.2394$$
$$\log b = 0.0981$$

Substitute the value of log b in (1)

$$16.2182 = 8 \log a + 4(0.8981)$$
$$8 \log a = 16.2182 - 0.3924 = 15.8258$$
$$\log a = 1.978$$
$$\therefore \ \log y = 1.978 + 0.0981t$$

In 1992 log y = 1.978 + 0.0981 × 5

Where t = +5, log y = 2.4685
Y = Antilog of 2.4685 = 294.1

Given a relation of type $y = ab^t$ is fitted to the time series.
Taking log on both sides we get,

$$\text{Log } y = \log a + \text{'t' } \log b$$

Normal equations are as follows:

$$N \log a + \log b \Sigma t = \Sigma \log y \qquad \ldots (1)$$
$$\log a \Sigma t + \log b \Sigma t^2 = \Sigma t \log y \qquad \ldots (2)$$

Case (I) when 'n' is even and $\Sigma t = 0$

Example: Fit an exponential trend for the following time series.

Year	1955	1960	1965	1970	1975	1980
Y	2	3	4	6	9	13

Year	Y	Deviations from 67.25 (t)	t^2	log y	log y × t
1955	2	−12.5	156.25	0.3010	−3.76
1960	3	−7.5	56.25	0.4771	−3.57
1965	4	−2.5	6.25	0.6021	−1.50
1970	6	+2.5	6.25	0.7782	+1.94
1975	9	+7.5	56.25	0.9542	+7.15
1980	13	+12.5	156.25	1.1139	+13.92
	$\Sigma y = 37$	$\Sigma t = 0$	$\Sigma t^2 = 437.5$	$\Sigma\log y = 4.2265$	$\Sigma\log y \times t = 14.18$

If $\Sigma t = 0$ eq. (1) reduces to $\log a = \Sigma \log y \, / \, n = 4.2265 \, / \, 6 = 0.7044$

$$a = \text{antilog of } 0.7044 \quad a = 5.063$$

Equation (2) reduces to $\log b = \Sigma t \log y \, / \, \Sigma t^2 = 14.18 \, / \, 437.5 = 0.0324$

$$b = \text{antilog of } 0.0324 \quad b = 1.452$$

$\therefore y = 5.063 \times (1.076)^t$

Note: If $\Sigma t \neq 0$ then equations have to be solved.

Example: The sales of a dying company for the last 8 years is recorded as follows:

Year	1984	1985	1986	1987	1988	1989	1990	1991
Sales	52	45	98	92	110	185	175	220

Estimate the sales in the year 1992 using $y = ab^t$ form

Year	y	t	t^2	log y	log y × t
1984	52	−3	9	1.1160	−5.1480
1985	45	−2	4	1.6532	−3.3064
1986	98	−1	1	1.9912	−1.9912
1987	92	0	0	1.9638	0
1988	110	+1	1	2.0414	+2.0414
1989	185	+2	4	2.2672	+4.5344
1990	175	+3	9	2.2430	+6.7290
1991	220	+4	16	2.3424	+9.3696
	$\Sigma y = 977$	$\Sigma t = 4$	$\Sigma t^2 = 4$	Σlog y = 16.2182	Σlog y t = 12.2288

As $\Sigma t \neq 0$

$$N \log a + \log b \, \Sigma t = \Sigma \log y \qquad \ldots (1)$$
$$\log a \Sigma t + \log b \, \Sigma t^2 = \Sigma t \log y \qquad \ldots (2)$$

$$8 \log a + 4 \log b = 16.2182 \qquad \ldots (1)$$
$$4 \log a + 44 \log b = 12.2288 \qquad \ldots (2)$$

multiplying by 2 we get

$$8 \log a + 4 \log b = 16.2182$$
$$8 \log a + 88 \log b = 24.4576$$
$$-84 \log b = -8.2394$$

$\log b = 0.0981$

$\therefore \log a = 1.978$

$\log y = 1.9781 + 0.0981 \times t$

In 1992 t = 5 log y = 1.978 + 0.098 × 5 = 2.4685

y = antilog of 2.4685 = 294.1

Example: A wet processing unit gained profit consecutively for 5 years as follows:

Year	1988	1989	1990	1991	1992
Profit	1.6	4.5	13.8	40.2	125.0

(in Rs 000)   fit an exponential trend

Year	Y	t	logy	t^2	t log y
1988	1.6	−2	0.2041	4	−0.4082
1989	4.5	−1	0.6532	1	−0.6532
1990	13.8	0	1.1399	0	0
1991	40.2	+1	1.6042	1	+1.6042
1992	125.0	+2	2.0969	4	+4.1938
	Σlog y = 185.1	$\Sigma t = 0$	Σlog y = 5.6983	$t^2 = 10$	Σt log y = 4.7366

$$\log a = \Sigma \log y \, / \, N = 5.6983 \, / \, 5 = 1.1397$$

$$\log b = \Sigma t \log y / \Sigma t^2 = 4.7366 / 10 = 0.474$$
$$\log y = 1.1397 + 0474t$$

Example: Below are given figures relating to a ginning factory production in (kilo tones)

Year	1985	1986	1987	1988	1989	1990
Production	77	88	95	114	119	127

Fit an exponential trend.

Year production	Y	Deviations from 1987–95 ×2 't'	log y	t^2	t log y
1985	77	−5	1.8865	25	−9.4325
1986	88	−3	1.9445	9	−5.8331
1987	95	−1	1.9777	1	−1.9777
1988	114	+1	2.0569	1	+2.0569
1989	119	+3	2.0755	9	+6.2265
1990	127	+5	2.1038	25	+10.519
		$\Sigma t = 0$	$\Sigma \log y = 12.04$	$\Sigma t^2 = 70$	$\Sigma t \log y = 1.5587$

$$\log a = \Sigma \log y / N = 12.0449 / 6 = 2.0075$$

$$\log b = \Sigma t \log y / \Sigma t^2 = 1.5587 / 70 = 0.0293$$

$$\log y = 2.0075 + 0.0223t$$

8.9   Methods of semi-averages

In this method the series is split into two parts: earlier half and later half. Mean of each part is calculated. These points are plotted on a graph against the respective mid-points of time. The points are joined by a line. This line is extended both the sides. The straight line represents the trend line.

But the number of observations may be even or odd. If n is "even" entire series is divided evenly into two parts. However, if n is "odd" the middle term is left out so as to get equal parts. Hence, this method is rough estimate of trend and therefore can't be used for deep statistical analysis.

Following examples illustrates above facts.

Case (i) When 'n' is even

Procedure:

1. Divide the set of observations into two parts.
2. Centering of the year has to be chosen correctly.

Example: Fit a straight line trend of semi-averages to the data given below. Estimate the sales in 1987. If the actual sale for that year is Rs. 520 lakhs account for the difference between two figures.

				←		→			
Year	1979	1980	1981	1982	I	1983	1984	1985	1986
Sales	412	438	444	454	I	470	482	490	506

(In lakhs)

Solution: The estimated sales for 1987 is 515 lakhs, then the actual 520 lakhs. This is because time series is constructed on some assumptions. It all depends on how far these assumptions are practiced.

Example: The sale of viscose rayon in kg from a poly fiber factory is as follows:

					←		→					
Month	Jan	Feb	Mar	Apr	May	June	I July	Aug	Sept	Oct	Nov	Dec
Production:	280	300	280	280	270	240	230	230	220	200	210	200

Fit a trend line by semi-averages.

Solution: Jan to June $280 + 300 + 280 + 280 + 270 + 240 / 6$ 275

Jul to Dec $230 + 230 + 220 + 200 + 210 + 200 / 6$ 215

Example: Fit a trend line from the following data by using semi-average method.

			←		→		
Year	1983	1984	1985	I	1986	1987	1988
Profit	100	120	140	I	150	130	200

$$\text{Earlier half} = \frac{900 + 120 + 140}{3} = \frac{360}{3} = 120$$

$$\text{Later half} = \frac{150 + 130 + 208}{3} = \frac{480}{3} = 160$$

Case – II "n" is odd

Divide the series into 2 parts omitting central value

1. Fit a Trend line to the following data by the Method of averages.

			←		→		
Year	1980	1981	1982	1983	1984	1985	1986
Sales	102	105	114	110	108	116	112

(000 Rs.)

$$\text{Average of earlier half} = \frac{102 + 105 + 114}{3} = 321/3 = 107$$

Average of later half = $\dfrac{108 + 116 + 112}{3}$ = 336/3 = 112

Plot these averages at the middle year at the respective parts.

Example: Fit a trend line for the following time series.

$$\leftarrow \qquad \rightarrow$$

Year	1980	1981	1982	1983	1984	1985	1986	1987	1988	1989	1990
Price of Cotton	185	200	350	355	420	460	430	400	330	320	700

Average of Earlier part = $\dfrac{185 + 200 + 350 + 355 + 420}{5}$ = 302

Average of Later part = $\dfrac{430 + 400 + 330 + 320 + 700}{5}$ = 436

8.10   Method of moving averages

In this method the short term variations are eliminated by finding moving averages. If the time series shows the variation with period M(may be seasonal or cyclic variations), the moving averages with period M are obtained. These moving averages indicate the trend. If y_1, y_2, y_3 are observations, if m = 3 is the period. The successive moving averages are

(1) $\dfrac{y_1 + y_2 + y_3}{3}$, $\dfrac{y_2 + y_3 + y_4}{3}$, $\dfrac{y_3 + y_4 + y_5}{3}$ etc.

First moving average is the average of 1st, 2nd and 3rd observations.

Example: Calculate the 3-yearly moving averages of the production figures.

Year	Production (Y)	3-yearly total	3-yearly moving average
1973	15	–	–
1974	21	(15 + 21 + 30) 66	66 / 3 = 22.00
1975	30	(21 + 30 + 36) 87	87 / 3 = 29.00
1976	36	(30 + 36 + 42) 108	108 / 3 = 36.00
1977	42	(36 + 42 + 46) 124	124 / 3 = 41.33
1978	46	(42 + 46 + 50) 138	138 / 3 = 46.00
1979	50	(46 + 50 + 56) 152	152 / 3 = 50.66
1980	56	(50 + 56 + 63) 169	169 / 3 = 56.33
1981	63	(56 + 63 + 70) 189	189 / 3 = 63.00
1982	70	(63 + 70 + 74) 207	207 / 3 = 69.00
1983	74	(70 + 74 +82) 226	226 / 3 = 75.33
1984	82	(74 + 82 + 90) 246	246 / 3 = 82.00
1985	90	(82 + 90 + 95) 267	267 / 3 = 89.00
1986	95	(90 + 95 + 102) 287	287 / 3 = 95.33
1987	102	–	–

Example: Estimate the trend values using the data given below by taking 4-yearly moving average.

Year	value centered	4-yearly moving Total	4-yearly moving average	4-yearly moving average
1974	18	–	–	–
1975	26	–	–	–
1976	30	128	32.5	39.75
1977	54	188	47.0	54.75
1978	70	250	82.5	70.75
1979	87	316	79.0	84.75
1980	105	362	90.5	92.00
1981	100	374	93.5	90.75
1982	82	352	88.0	81.00
1983	65	296	74.0	65.75
1984	49	230	57.5	49.75
1985	34	168	42.0	34.75
1986	20	110	27.5	–
1987	07	–	–	–

Example: Calculate the trend values by 4-yearly moving averages.

Year 1988	1979	1980	1981	1982	1983	1984	1985	1986	1987	
Production 612	464	515	518	467	502	540	557	571	586	
4-yearly total	1964	2002	2027	2066	2170	2066	2170	2250	2326	–
4-yearly moving avg.	491	500.5	500.6	516.5	542.5	563.5	581.5			
4-yearly moving avg. centered	495.75	583.62	516.62	529.5	553	572.5	–	–	–	–

Control charts

9.1 Introduction

It is well known that the raw materials used to manufacture a product will be directly affecting the quality of the end product irrespective whether, the later is produced by either continuous or batch process. The ultimate decision regarding the quality of the end product depends on the quality level of the process. In other words, the percentage of defectives it contain or whether the mean value of the variable say count lies within the limits. The quality level in turn depends on the process efficiency. Thus, there arises a need to control the process.

Generally, the process control programme in a textile mill will involve the detection of changes in quality, critical examination of the causes for the changes detected and exercising the effective control over these changes. It is impossible to inspect each and every sample, the detection of deviations from the normal level can be found by "control charts". The control chart is a statistical device principally used for the study and control of the production process. The control chart is a graph in which the results of inspection of a sample of the product plotted from time to time. Control charts were first developed by Dr. Walter. A. Shewhart. He suggested that control charts serve to define the goal of the process for which the management has to strive to attain. It also serve as a means to judge whether the goal is being achieved or not.

A control chart generally consists of 3 lines drawn on a graph paper. The central line denotes the expected value of a variable like count, twist, CSP, etc., of a yarn. One line above the central line is called as upper control line and the line lying below the central line is called lower control line.

9.2 Basis of control limits

The basis of the control charts are $\pm 3\sigma$ limits with an assumption the experimental date is normally distributed. Hence, at any instant of time a process status may be interpreted as 'in control' or 'out of control'. It is necessary to detect is there any departure from the usual state of affairs. If the variable such as lea strength, lap weight, CSP, etc., is assumed as 'θ' (a parameter which can be measured or counted) then the result about the status of the process is given by setting up hypothesis as:

H_0 – the process is under/in control
H_1 – process is out of control.

If an observed value of θ is such that lower line < θ < upper line the process is assumed as under control otherwise not.

9.3   Causes of variation in quality

During the conversion of raw material to end product, variation in quality is fundamental and obvious. It is the aim of the quality inspection to keep the variations under specified limits. The sources of variation in quality may be due to chance causes and assignable causes.

9.3.1   Chance causes

The set of chance causes that produce a variation in the quality of a manufactured product is like the set of forces that causes a coil to turn head up or tail when tossed. The variation due to chance causes can be eliminated because they are due to natural variations inherent in the process.

9.3.2   Assignable causes

Besides chance variations in quality, there are variations produced by assignable causes. These are by definition, can be assigned to some specific physical element in the production process such as:

i) Errors in operation (faulty weighing in mixing of blends, misreading of a dial counter, faulty loading of top rollers in drafting system, etc.).
ii) Faulty setting (picking, beat up, beater to grid bar setting).
iii) Limitations in the design of equipment.
iv) Faulty tools such as leaf gauges, step gauges, etc.

The variation produced by chance causes follows statistical laws, for example, if 10 coins are tossed in a random manner, the relative frequencies with which 0, 1, 2, 3,......10 leads occur will tend, as the tossing is continued, to approach the frequencies of a binomial distribution. Similarly, in a random sample of 'n' units, each from a process that is affected by chance causes only, the probabilities of getting 0, 1, 2, 3....n defective units will also be given by binomial distribution. The variation produced by chance causes can thus be predicted. The knowledge of the behaviors of chance variations is the foundation on which control chart analysis based. The conditions which produce the variation due to chance causes are said to be 'under control' – if the variation in the data do not confirm to a pattern produced by chance causes, then it is concluded that one or more assignable causes are at work, and the variance is said to be "out of control".

9.4   Nature of a control chart

Suppose, samples of a given size are taken from a process at more or less regular intervals and for each sample some quality x is computed. This might be sample fraction defective, sample mean or sample range. Being a sample result, x will subject to sampling fluctuations. If no assignable causes are present, these sampling fluctuations in x will be normally distributed. If enough samples are taken, it is possible to estimate the mean and certain extreme points (usually 3σ limits) of this distribution by estimating the standard deviation.

If the vertical scale of a chart is calibrated, in units of x and the horizontal scale marked with respect to time and if horizontal lines are drawn through mean of x and through the extreme points on the upper and lower extreme points of the distribution of x, we get a control chart for x as shown in Fig. 9.1.

If sample values of x are plotted for a significant range of output, and time, and if these values are all fall within the control limits and then it can be said that the process is in a state of statistical control at the level designated with respect to the given measure of quality. In the use of control charts it is the goal of management to reduce fluctuation in a process until they are in a state of control at the level desired.

A control chart is not only a device for specifying and attaining a state

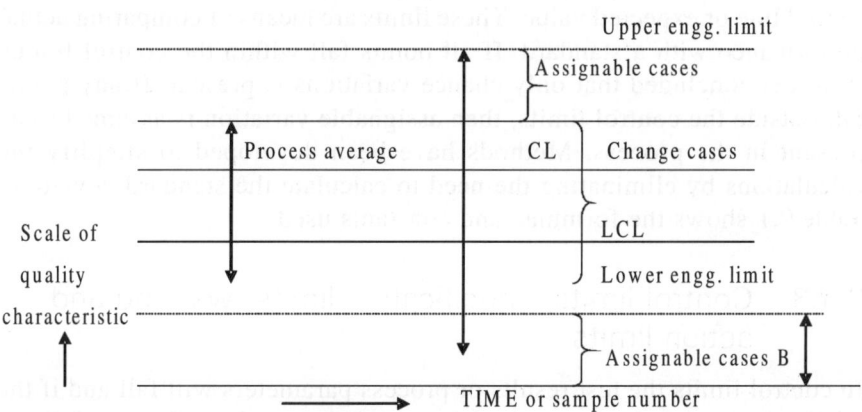

9.1 Control chart interpretation

of control but also a device for judging whether the state of control has been attained.

A = Chance variation alone can and does give rise to fluctuations in this zone.

B = Fluctuations in this zone indicate the presence of one or more assignable causes of variations which can be eliminated.

D = Effective zone.

9.4.1   Control charts for variables and attributes

Control charts based upon measurements of quality characteristics like dimensions, hardness, strength, etc., are known as control charts for variables. They are $\bar{x}$, R and σ (sigma) charts. The charts for fraction defectives are known as control charts for attributes. Attributes is the mere presence of an undesirable condition regardless of the degree to which it is present. This causes the items inspected to be classed as defective or good.

The control charts for attributes are 'p' chart and 'c' chart. Here binomial and Poisson distributions are made use of.

Defect and a defective

The term defect refers to failure to meet a specified quality standard. If the quality standard is that a water boiler be water tight, then a leak is a defective. Two leaks in a boiler would be two defects in one item.

9.4.2   Establishing control limits on control charts

Control limits are usually set at 3 sigma deviations above and below the central line or expected value. These limits are means of comparing actual performance with a standard. If all points fall within the control limits, then it is concluded that only chance variations is present. If any points fall outside the control limits, then assignable variation is assumed to be present in the process. Methods have been developed to simplify the calculations by eliminating the need to calculate the standard deviation. Table 9.1 shows the formulae and constants used.

9.4.3   Control limits, specification limits, warning and action limits

In control limits the test results or process parameters will fall and if the results do not fall the reason is to be traced, i.e., an investigation follows for initiating suitable action and hence the name action limits.

Table 9.1 Control chart limits

Chart	Central line	Lower control	Upper control limit
1. Averages, $\bar{x}$	$\bar{\bar{x}}$	$\bar{\bar{x}} - A_2 \bar{R}$	$\bar{\bar{x}} + A_2 \bar{R}$
2. Ranges, R	$\bar{R}$	$D_3 \bar{R}$	$D_4 \bar{R}$
3. Standard deviation	$\bar{\sigma}$	$B_3 \bar{\sigma}$	$B_4 \bar{\sigma}$
4. Fraction defective 'p'	$\bar{p}$	$\bar{p} - 3\sqrt{\dfrac{\bar{p}(1-\bar{p})}{n}}$	$\bar{p} + 3\sqrt{\dfrac{\bar{p}(1-\bar{p})}{n}}$
5. No. of defectives	$n\bar{p}$	$\overline{np} - 3\sqrt{\overline{np}(1-\bar{p})}$	$\overline{np} + 3\sqrt{\overline{np}(1-\bar{p})}$
6. 100 p-chart	100 P	$100\bar{p} \pm 3\sqrt{\dfrac{100\bar{p}(100-100\bar{p})}{n}}$	
7. Number of defects, per unit, 'c'	$\bar{C}$	$\bar{c} - 3\sqrt{\bar{c}}$	$\bar{c} + 3\sqrt{\bar{c}}$

Values of A_2, B_3, B_4, D_3, D_4 are given in tables on statistics.

Specification limits are the extreme points that are setup with view to determine the maximum acceptable variation in the process, i.e., these are dictated by the process requirements or performance for a particular product. On the other hand, the control limits are the actual measurements of process performance. The specification limits are within and between control limits, then only a part of the product meet the specification. Consider the limits ± 1.96σ and 3.09σ limits above and below the control limits. The Action limits = mean ± 3.09σ limits and warning limits = mean ± 1.96σ limits. (Considering α = 0.001 and 0.005, α being the level of significance chosen).

9.5   Interpretation of control charts

Generally, if the points related to process fall within upper control and lower control limits the process is said to be under control and the process is dictated by chance causes. However, if the limits fall outside UCL and LCL then the process is out of control and dictated by assignable causes. Figure 9.1 shows the various partial situations indicating the possible interpretation of control charts. It is observed in routine yarn manufacture that by eliminating the points which lay outside the upper and lower control limits the process is said to be under control. In such a situation, the fresh limits obtained by eliminating the points lying outside the UCL and LCL and reworking are called as 'future limits' and the limits in which the points lie outside the UCL and LCL are called as 'current limits'.

Table 9.2 Constants for $\bar{x}$ and R charts.

N	A₂	D₃	D₄	d₂
2	1.88	0	3.27	1.128
3	1.02	0	2.57	1.693
4	0.73	0	2.28	2.059
5	0.58	0	2.11	2.326
6	0.48	0	2.00	2.534
7	0.42	0.08	1.92	2.704
8	0.37	0.14	1.86	2.847
9	0.34	0.18	1.82	2.970
10	0.31	0.22	1.72	3.078
11	0.29	0.26	1.74	3.173
12	0.27	0.28	1.72	3.258
13	0.25	0.31	1.69	3.336
14	0.24	0.33	1.67	3.407
15	0.22	0.35	1.65	3.472

9.5.1 Construction of control charts for variables $\bar{x}$ – R charts.

Let n = subgroup size.

Sub-group no.	Observations	Mean	Range
1	$x_{11}, x_{12}, x_{13} \ldots\ldots x_{1n}$	$\bar{x}_1$	R_1
2	$x_{21}, x_{22}, x_{23} \ldots\ldots x_{2n}$	$\bar{x}_2$	R_2
3	$x_{31}, x_{32}, x_{33} \ldots\ldots x_{3n}$	$\bar{x}_3$	R_3
	: : : :	:	:
K	$x_{k1}, x_{k2}, x_{k3} \ldots.. x_{kn}$	$\bar{x}_k$	R_k
	Total	$\sum x_i$	$\sum R_i$

Central line of $\bar{x}$ chart = process average

$$\bar{\bar{x}} = \frac{\sum x_1}{k}$$

Three sigma limits are $\bar{\bar{x}} = \pm 3 \dfrac{\sigma^1}{\sqrt{n}}$ where σ^1 = population std. deviation

Central line of R chart = average range

n = sample size

$$\bar{R}_1 = \sum R_i / k$$

The estimate of $\sigma^1 = \dfrac{\bar{R}}{d_2}$ where d_2 is a constant obtained from S.Q.C.

tables which depends on sub-groups size.

$\therefore$ Control limits $= \overline{\overline{x}} \pm \dfrac{3\sigma^1}{\sqrt{n}}$

But $A_2 = \dfrac{3}{d_2\sqrt{n}}$ is tabulated in tables.

$\therefore$ U.C.L. $= \overline{\overline{x}} + A_2\overline{R}$ |

L.C.L. $= \overline{\overline{x}} - A_2\overline{R}$ | control limits for $\overline{x}$ chart.

R chart

U.C.L. $= D_4 \overline{R}$ | D_4 and D_3 are constants obtained in tables.
L.C.L. $= D_3 R$ |

$\overline{x}$ chart shows weather process average is stable. R chart shows weather process variability is stable.

Process spread $= \overline{\overline{x}} - 3\sigma^1$ ro $\overline{\overline{x}} + 3\sigma^1$
Process capability $= 6\sigma^1$

Estimate of σ^1 the universe standard deviation

I *method*:

$$\sigma^1 = \frac{\overline{R}}{d_2}$$

II *method*:

$$\sigma^1 = \frac{\overline{\sigma}}{c_2} \text{ where } \overline{\sigma} = \frac{\Sigma\sigma}{k}$$

c_2 = constant obtained in tables.

9.5.2 Making the control charts

1. Find the control limits (Trial control limits)

$$\text{U.C.L.} = \overline{\overline{x}} + 3\overline{\sigma x} \quad \text{U.C.L.} = \overline{\overline{x}} - A_2\overline{x}$$

Or

$$\text{L.C.L.} = \overline{\overline{x}} - 3\overline{x} \quad \text{L.C.L.} = \overline{\overline{x}} - A_2\overline{R}$$

Where $\sigma\,\overline{x} = \dfrac{\sigma^1}{\sqrt{n}}$ and $\sigma^1 = \dfrac{\overline{R}}{d_2}$

$$\text{U.C.L.} = D_4\overline{R} \qquad \text{L.C.L.} = D_3\overline{R}$$

2. While drawing the control charts, it is to be kept in mind that first R chart is to be drawn. If the data for R chart is within control (when all points fall within U.C.L. and L.C.L.) then proceed for $\bar{x}$ chart, otherwise it is not worthwhile. The reason being that R stands for range and the variability in one sub group size is not within control, individual data must be out of control. If the range is in control, probably $\bar{x}$ data may also be in control or can be brought under control. But the reverse is not true. If the points fall outside the control limits on R chart, then eliminate those values and find again the control limits for R chart. When R chart is within control then proceed for $\bar{x}$ chart. The control limits obtained before eliminating the out of control points are known as trial control limits and the control limits obtained after eliminating the out of control points are known as revised control limits. The same procedure is followed for $\bar{x}$ in first determining the trial control limits then obtaining the revised control limits.

These revised control limits can be used for future production.

Problem 1: The mean GSM of 4 samples of 1 meter length cotton duck fabric each measured and the ranges over 20 sub-groups is as follows:

Sub-group no.	Mean weight (g)	Range
1	452	3
2	456	6
3	452	5
4	453	6
5	455	4
6	454	4
7	458	1
8	456	5
9	455	0
10	455	7
11	452	4
12	453	0
13	456	4
14	457	5
15	457	2
16	453	7
17	452	5
18	461	9
19	456	3
20	454	0
	$\Sigma \bar{x} = 9097$	$\Sigma R = 80$

a) Construct $\bar{x}$ – R charts for the data.
b) Do you think the weaving activity is operating under assignable causes? If so, what is the influence the assignable cause is having on wt. of the fabric?

$$R \text{ chart } \bar{R} = \frac{\Sigma R}{20} = \frac{80}{20} = 4$$

$$UCL_R = D_4 \bar{R} = 2.282 \times 4 = 9.128$$
$$LCL_R = D_3 \bar{R} = 0 \times 4 = 0$$

The process is under control, because all points fall within U.C.L. and L.C.L.

$\bar{x}$ chart:

$$\bar{\bar{x}} = \frac{\Sigma \bar{x}}{20} = \frac{9097}{20} = 454.85$$

$$\text{U.C.L} = \bar{\bar{x}} + A_2 \bar{R} = 454.85 + 0.729 * 4 = 457.76$$

$$\text{L.C.L} = \bar{\bar{x}} - A_2 \bar{R} = 454.85 - 0.729 * 4 = 451.93$$

b) The weaving activity is operating under assignable causes as 2 points on the X chart fall out the U.C.L. The influence of the assignable cause is towards increasing the weight of the fabric.

Problem 2: The values of $\Sigma \bar{x}, \Sigma \bar{R}$ for a process for 20 sub-groups of 5 samples are 3569.2 and 196 respectively. Specification limits for process are 171 ± 11.

a) Determine the control limits for $\bar{X}$ and R charts.
b) Sub-groups 1 and 3 have R value of 25 and 20. As these are very much out, may be discarded. Determine new control limits new.
c) The waste is very costly and as such it should be avoided. How the process should be changed for achieving this and
d) What will be new control limits?

Sol. a) $\Sigma x = 3569.2$, $\Sigma R = 196$, $n = 5$. $N = 20$, $\bar{\bar{x}} = 3569.2 / 20 = 178.46$, $\bar{R} = 196 / 20 = 9.8$

$$UCL \bar{x} = 178.46 + A_2 \bar{R} = 178.46 + 0.58 \times 9.8$$
$$= 178.46 + 5.69 = 184.15$$
$$LCL \bar{x} = 178.46 - 5.69 = 172.77$$
$$UCL_R = D_4 \bar{R} = 2.11 \times 9.8 = 20.7, LCL_R = 0 \times 9.8 = 0$$

b) Now control limits of R-chart:

Sub-groups 1 and 3 are out of control. Eliminating them, ΣR for 18 groups = 196 – 45 = 151.

$\therefore$
$$\bar{R} = 151 / 18 = 8.4$$
$$UCL_R = 2.11 \times 8.4 = 17.724, LCL_R = 0$$

All values lie within control limits, so R chart is in control at a centering of 8.4.

New $\bar{x}$ – chart limits will be:

$$\text{UCL } \bar{x} = 178.46 + 8.4 \times 0.58 = 178.46 + 4.875 = 183.335$$
$$\text{LCL } \bar{x} = 178.48 - 4.875 = 173.605$$

c) Specification limits = 171 ± 11, LSL = 160, USL = 182

As waste is costly, we keep LSLS = LCL and just centering
Accordingly, $\bar{X} = \text{LCL} + 3 \sigma^1 = 160 + 10.83 = 170.83$

e) UCL $\bar{X} = 170.83 + 4.875 = 175.705$
   LCL $\bar{x} = 170.83 - 4.875 = 165.955$
∴ $\bar{R} = 8.4$, $\text{UCL}_R = 17.124$, $\text{LCL}_R = 0$

Problem 3: A blow room is working to a specification of 12.58 ± 0.05 in kg processing 100 % shrinkable acrylic fibres. A study of 50 consecutive pieces shows the following measurements put into 10 groups of 5 each.

1	2	3	4	5	6	7	8	9	10
12.62	12.63	12.62	12.61	12.59	12.57	12.57	12.58	12.61	12.56
12.60	12.56	12.56	12.66	12.58	12.63	12.56	12.57	12.60	12.59
12.62	12.60	12.57	12.62	12.57	12.60	12.61	12.60	12.62	12.62
12.61	12.59	12.58	12.61	12.59	12.60	12.59	12.60	12.60	12.58
12.65	12.60	12.63	12.60	12.56	12.59	12.59	12.61	12.65	12.54

i)   Determine the process capability.
ii) Determine the 3 sigma limits for $\bar{x}$–chart.
iii) Does it appear that the machine is capable of meeting the specification requirements?
iv) Calculate the percent defective, if any.
v)   Suggest possible ways by which the percent defective can be reduced.

Assume: 1. Normal distribution 2. d_2 for sub-group size 5 is 2.326

Solution: Values of $\bar{x}$ and R for the 10 groups from the given data are the following:

Group		$\bar{x}$	R
1.	63.20 / 5	12.64	0.05
2.	62.98 / 5	12.60	0.07
3.	62.96 / 5	12.59	0.07
4.	63.10 / 5	12.62	0.06
5.	62.89 / 5	12.58	0.03
6.	62.99 / 5	12.60	0.06
7.	62.92 / 5	12.58	0.05
8.	63.08 / 5	12.59	0.04
9.	63.08 / 5	12.62	0.05
10.	62.99 / 5	12.60	0.06

$\therefore \ \bar{x} = 126.02 / 10 = 12.602$

And $\bar{R} = 0.54 / 10 = 0.054$

Now σ^1 = population standard deviation = $\dfrac{\bar{R}}{d_2} = \dfrac{0.054}{2.326} = 0.0232$

(i) Process capability is the minimum spread of the measurement variation which includes 99.73% of the measurements from given process, i.e., 6 σ^1.

$\therefore$ Process capability = 6 × 0.0232 = 0.1392 mm.

(ii) 3 σ limits for $\bar{x}$– chart, $3\sigma \ \bar{x} = \dfrac{3\sigma^1}{\sqrt{5}} = \dfrac{3 \times 0.0232}{2.236} = 0.0311.$

$\therefore$ UCL $\bar{x} = \bar{x} + 3 \ \sigma \ \bar{x} = 12.602 + 0.0311 = 12.6331$ kg

Or   LCL $\bar{x} = \bar{x} - 3\sigma \ \bar{x} = 12.602 - 0.0311 = 12.5709$ kg

iii)   It will be noted that first point of $\bar{x}$ lies outside the upper control limit, indicating thereby the process is not in control. However, assuming that process in future will be in control and therefore, eliminating this point.

Revised $\bar{x}$ = 113.38 / 9 = 12.598 and R= 0.49 / 9 = 0.0544

$\therefore$ $\sigma^1 = \dfrac{3 \times 0.0232}{2.236} = 0.0233$

Now process is centered at 12.598 with 3 σ^1 spread of 3 × 0.0233 = 0.0699 kg.

$\therefore$ Maximum and minimum points can fall up to 12.598 + 0.0699 = 12.6679

       12.598 – 0.0699 = 12.5281

Whereas, specification limits are 12.58 ± 0.05, i.e., 12.63 and 12.53 kg.

Obviously the process capability being more than tolerance values, rejects will be there.

iv)   Percent defective will correspond to area between the lines for dimensions 12.6679 and 12.63 on upper side, and 12.5281 and 12.53 on lower side.

Area beyond dimension 12.63 mm corresponds to $\dfrac{12.63 - 12.598}{\sigma^1}$

       Z = 0.032 / 0.0233 = 1.37 limits.

       = 0.9147 (from table at area under normal curve)

$\therefore$ Percent defective in shaded area = 1 – 0.9147

       = 0.0853 OR 8.53%

The percent defective on lower side is negligible and may be ignored.

$\therefore$ Percent defective = 8.4%

v) Actually the process is not capable of meeting the specification limits.

However, 0.4% defective can be reduced further by changing the machine setting to 12.58 kg.

Problem 4: a) Control chart of $\overline{X}$ is to be prepared for a dimension of ring. The sub-group size is 4. After 20 sub-groups it is found that $\Sigma \overline{x} = 825.60$ mm and $\Sigma R = 5.60$.

Compute the central line and the control limits for X chart.

d_2 for sub-group size 4 is equal to 2.059.

b) If the specified dimension is 41.0 ± 0.40 mm and the above process is in control is normally distributed, can it meet the specification requirement? If not, determine the percentage of rejections.

Sol. a) $\Sigma \overline{x} = 825.60$

$$\therefore \qquad \overline{\overline{x}} = \frac{\Sigma \overline{x}}{20} = \frac{825.60}{20} = 41.28$$

$\therefore$ Central line = 41.28 mm

$$\overline{R} = \frac{\Sigma R}{20} = \frac{5.60}{20} = 0.28 \text{ mm}$$

σ^1 = population standard deviation.

$$\sigma^1 = \frac{\overline{R}}{d_2} = \frac{0.28}{2.059} = 0.136$$

$$3 \sigma \overline{x} = \frac{3\sigma^1}{\sqrt{n}} = \frac{3 \times 0.136}{\sqrt{4}} = 0.2$$

$\therefore \qquad UCL_X = 41.28 + 0.2 = 41.48$

And $LCL_X = 41.28 - 0.2 = 41.08$

$\therefore$ Control limits on X chart are 41.48 and 41.08 mm.

c)   Specified dimension = 41.0 ± 0.40 mm is between = 41.4 and 40.6 mm.

Central line = 41.28 and $3 \sigma^1 = 3 \times 0.136 = 0.4$

$\therefore$ For this process, the dimensions can vary from 41.28 = 0.4, i.e., 40.88

41.28 + 0.4 = 41.68 mm.

Obviously, the process variability (0.8 mm) being equal to the specification limits (0.8 mm), it can meet the specification limits.

But since centering is not properly done, rejects will be expected.

$$\text{Area up to 41.4 is } Z = \frac{41.4 - 41.28}{0.136} = 0.88$$

From tables area up to 41.4 = 0.8106

Area beyond 41.4 = 1 − 0.8106 = 0.19

∴ Percentage number of defectives = 19%

Problem 5: The following table gives the coded measurements obtained from 20

Subgroups no.	Statistics		R
1	−1, 2, 1, 0, 1	0.6	3
2	2, 0, 1, 0, 1	0.8	2
3	1, 1, 0, 0, 1	0.6	1
4	2, 1, 0, −1, 0	0.4	3
5	1, −1, 0, 0, −1 −0.2	2	
6	1, −1, 2, 0, −2	0.0	4
7	−1, −1, 0, −2,1	−0.6	3
8	1, 1, 2, −1, 0.	0.6	3
9	2, 1, −1, 0, 0	0.4	3
10	−2, 1, −2, 2, 1	0.0	4
11	0, 1, -3, 2, 1	0.2	5
12	2, 1, −1, 0, 0	0.4	3
13	0, 1, −3, 2, 1	0.2	5
14	0, 0, −1, 0, 1	0.0	2
15	−1, 2, 1, 1, 2	1.0	3
16	1, −1, 2, 0, −2	0.0	4
17	2, 1, −1, 0, 0	0.4	3
18	2, 0, 1, 0, 1	0.8	2
19	0, 1, 1, −1, 1	0.4	2
20	3, −3, 1, 1, 1	0.6	6

a) Construct the $\overline{X}$ and R charts and plot the points on the charts.

b) What will be the control limits on $\overline{X}$ and R charts for immediate future use?

c) Estimate the value of σ^1.

Solution: $$\overline{X} = \frac{0.6 + 0.8 + ... + 0.6}{20} = \frac{6.6}{20} = 0.33$$

$$\overline{R} = \frac{3 + 1 + ... + 6}{20} = \frac{62}{20} = 3.1$$

$$\text{UCL}_{\overline{x}} = \overline{x} + A_2 \overline{R} = 0.33 + (0.58 \times 3.1) = 2.13$$

$$\text{LCL}_{\overline{x}} = 0.33 - (0.58 \times 3.1) = -1.47$$

$$\text{UCL}_R = D_4 \overline{R} = 2.11 \times 3.1 = 6.54$$

$$\text{LCL}_R = D_3 \overline{R} = 0 \times 3.1 = 0$$

a) Control charts for X and R are shown in Fig. 9.1.
b) Since no point on either chart falls beyond control limits. The process is in the state of control and hence, there is no change in control limits for immediate future.
c) $\sigma^1 = \overline{R}/d_2 = 3.1 / 2.326 = 1.33$

Problem 6: A Reed manufacturing company produces all metal reed wires.

The following are the $\overline{X}$ and R values for sub-groups of 5 readings.
The specifications for this product characteristic are 0.4037 ± 0.0010.
The values given are the last two figures of the dimension reading, i.e., 31.6 should be 0.40316.

Subgroups	X̄	R	Subgroups	X̄	R
1	34.0	4	11	35.8	4
2	31.6	4	12	38.4	4
3	30.8	2	13	34.0	14
4	33.0	3	14	35.0	4
5	35.0	5	15	33.8	7
6	32.2	2	16	31.6	5
7	33.0	5	17	33.0	5
8	32.6	13	18	28.2	3
9	33.8	19	19	31.8	9
10	37.8	6	20	35.6	6

a) Determine the control limits for $\overline{X}$ and R charts for future use, elimination all the out of control points.
b) Will the process be able to meet the specification?
c) Will you recommend shifting of the process centering?

Solution: $\overline{x} = \dfrac{\Sigma \overline{x}}{20} = \dfrac{34.0+...35.6}{20} = \dfrac{671}{20} = 33.6 = 33.6$

$\overline{R} = \dfrac{\Sigma \overline{R}}{20} = \dfrac{4+...+35.6}{20} = \dfrac{124}{20} = 6.20$

Trial control limits on $\overline{x}$ and R charts.

$$\text{UCL}_{\overline{x}} = \overline{x} + A_2 \overline{R} = 33.6 + (0.58 \times 6.20) = 37.20$$
$$\text{LCL}_{\overline{x}} = \overline{x} ....A_2 \overline{R} = 33.6 - (0.58 \times 6.20) = 30.00$$
$$\text{UCL}_R = D_4 \overline{R} = 2.11 \times 6.20 = 13.08$$
$$\text{LCL}_R = D_3 \overline{R} = 0 \times 6.20 = 0$$

On plotting the control charts it will be noticed that subgroups 10, 12 fall above UCL and sub-groups 18 falls below LCL and hence, the process is out of control. Since, assignable causes are known for out of control points, eliminating these points.

$$\overline{\overline{x}}(revised) = \frac{671.0 - (37.8 + 38.4 + 28.2)}{(20 - 3)} = \frac{566.6}{17} = 33.3$$

On plotting the R chart, it will be noticed that subgroups 9 and 14 fall above UCL_R. Since, assignable causes for this are also known, eliminating these points.

$$\text{R (revised)} = \frac{124}{20} - \frac{(19 + 14)}{-2} = \frac{91}{18} = 5.06$$

a) Control limits for future use:

$$UCL_{\overline{x}} = \overline{x} + A_2 \overline{R} = 33.3 + (0.5 \times 5.06) = 33.3 + 2.93 = 36.23$$
$$LCL_{\overline{x}} = \overline{x} - A_2 \overline{R} = 33.30 - 2.93 = 30.37$$
$$UCL_R = D_4 \overline{R} = 2.11 \times 5.00 = 10.67$$
$$LCL_R = D_3 \overline{R} = 0 \times 5.06 = 0$$

b) $\sigma^1 = \overline{R} / d_2 = 5.06 / 2.3726 = 2.175$

Upper natural specification limits = $\overline{x} + 3\sigma^1 = 33.3 + 3(2.175) = 39.825$
Lower natural specification limits = $\overline{x} - 3\sigma^1 = 33.3 - 3(2.175) = 26.775$
Since the specification limits are 0.4047 and 0.4027. It is evident that the process will be able to meet the specifications.

c) Since the process is able to meet its specification. It is not advisable to shift the process centering, provided the process remains in control at the above level i.e.,0.4033.

Problem 7: a) A spinning machinery manufacturing company is currently producing Saphier travelers.

b) Control charts of $\overline{x}$ and R are to be established at a work station. The analysis begins by estimating the magnitude $\overline{x}$ and R. Twenty five groups of 5 samples each are as follows (dimension measurement is in mg).

Group no.	Sample average $\overline{x}$ in	Sample range R in
1	3.5492	0.005
2	3.5546	0.004
3	3.5488	0.009
4	3.5464	0.008
5	3.5516	0.015
6	3.5496	0.006
7	3.5496	0.007
8	3.5544	0.010
9	3.5506	0.003
10	3.5470	0.005

(Contd.)

Group no.	Sample average $\bar{x}$ in	Sample range R in
11	3.5534	0.008
12	3.5526	0.012
13	3.5468	0.020
14	3.5480	0.004
15	3.5488	0.008
16	3.5506	0.007
17	3.5534	0.009
18	3.5470	0.010
19	3.5608	0.011
20	3.5540	0.023
21	3.5506	0.005
22	3.5498	0.011
23	3.5476	0.006
24	3.5320	0.010
25	3.5514	0.006

i) Compute the values of the $\pm 3\sigma$ limits and the central line for the $\bar{x}$ and R charts.

ii) What are the natural tolerances of their process if the individual terms are normally distributed?

iii) The specifications for the dimension under consideration are 3.5500 $\pm$ 0.0076. If the individual items are normally distributed, what percentage defectives can be expected if the process remains in control at present level? (Take $A_2 = 0.58$, $D_4 = 2.11$, $D_3 = 0$, $d_2 = 2.326$)

Solution:

a) Natural tolerances – Any production process has a natural inherent variation in producing identical parts. This is due to technological reasons and the variations are due to chance causes only. The extent of natural tolerances can be determined by finding $\pm 3\sigma^1$ value using the formula $\sigma^1 = \bar{R} / d_2$.

b) i) $\bar{x}$ and R charts

$$\bar{x} = \frac{\Sigma \bar{x}}{25} = \frac{88.77}{25} = 3.5507$$

$$\bar{R} = \Sigma R / 25 = 0.222 / 25 = 0.0088$$
$$\sigma^1 = \bar{R} / d_2 = 0.0088 / 2.326 = 0.00378$$
$$\text{UCL} = \bar{x} + A_2 \bar{R} = 3.5507 + 0.58 \times 0.0088$$
$$\text{LCL}_x = \bar{x} - A_2 \bar{R} = 3.5507 - 0.58 \times 0.0088$$
$$\text{UCL}_R = D_4 \bar{R} = 2.11 \times 0.0088$$
$$\text{LCL}_R = D_3 \bar{R} = 0 \times 0.0088 = 0$$

ii) Natural tolerances

Upper natural tolerance limit = $\bar{x} + 3\sigma^1$

$$= 3.5507 + 3 \times 0.00378$$
$$= 3.5620$$

Lower natural tolerance limit $= \bar{x} - 3\sigma^1$

$$= 3.5507 - 3 \times 0.00378 = 3.5393$$

iii)   Upper specification limit $= 3.5500 + 0.0076 = 3.5576$

Lower specification limit $= 3.5500 - 0.0076 = 3.5424$

Percentage of defectives is shown:

From tables, area up to $z_1 = 0.0143$ or 1.43%

From tables, area up to $z_2 = 0.9656$

Area beyond $z_2 = 1 - 0.9656 = 0.0344$ or 3.44%

$\therefore$ Total percentage of defectives $= 1.43 + 3.44 = 4.87\%$

Problem 8: A preparatory shed in a composite mill consists of RJK cone winders. 34^s cones were produced using Atira-Arvind slub catcher. The details of weight of the cone produced over 10 spindles and the range of weight in kg for 5 observations of samples are as follows. Draw the control chart and examine whether the process is under control.

Spindle no.	1	2	3	4	5	6	7	8	9	10
Mean weight in kg.	2	2.10	2.15	2.19	2.04	2.05	2.0	2.15	2.17	2.1
Range in kg.	0.2	0.25	0.3	0.2	0.2	0.25	0.2	0.3	0.25	0.15

$$\bar{X} = \Sigma \ \bar{x}/N = 20.85/10 = 2.085$$

$$\bar{R} = \Sigma \ \bar{R}/N = 2.3/10 = 0.23$$

9.6   First construct of $\bar{R}$ chart

$\bar{R}$ $= 0.23$, $D_3 = 0$, $D_4 = 2.11$ (for sample subgroup 5)

$\text{UCL} = D_4 \ \bar{R} = 2.11 \times 0.23 = 0.4853$, $\text{LCL} = 0$

Since, all the points are within control limits, hence proceed to $\bar{x}$ chart.

$\bar{X}$ $= 2.085$, $A_2 = 0.58$ (for sample subgroup 5)

$\text{UCL} = \bar{X} + A_2 \ \bar{R} = 2.085 = (0.58 \times 0.23) = 2.2184$

$\text{LCL} = \bar{X} - A_2 \ \bar{R} = 2.085 - (0.58 \times 0.23) = 1.9516$

Since, all the points are within the control limit the process is under control. It is to be noted that the process is centered above the control line.

Problem 9: A scutcher is producing laps of the following lap weighs:

Time	1	2	3	4	5	6	7	8	9	10
	20	18	24	21	22	20	16	20	22	20
Lap weight	22	21	21	25	24	22	14	21	20	18
	18	24	22	24	19	20	13	22	22	20
	24	20	20	18	20	21	12	22	20	22

Examine whether the process is under control or not?

Solution:

i) For $\overline{R}$ chart
    CL = 4.2, UCL = 9.58, LCL = 0, As the process range is within the limits, hence, proceed to $\overline{x}$ chart.
ii) For $\overline{x}$ chart
    UCL = 23.40, LCL = 17.28, CL = 20.34

But it is clear that 7th period observations are below LCL. Hence, process mean has shifted and the process is out of control.

Problem 10: An investigation included the measurement of tpi of 2 / 20 s yarn production at ring doubler frame. Mean and range for the sample of size 5 each as follows:

Sample	1	2	3	4	5	6	7	8	9	10
Mean $\overline{x}$	11.2	11.8	10.8	11.6	11.0	9.6	10.4	9.6	10.6	10.0
Range R	7	4	8	5	7	4	8	4	7	9

Examine about the process condition.

Solution:

$\Sigma \overline{X} = 106.6$, $\Sigma R = 63$, $\overline{X} = 10.66$, $\overline{R} = 6.3$, $A_2 = 0.57$
For $\overline{R}$ chart: UCL= 13.32, LCL= 0.
As the points lie within control limits. Hence, proceed to $\overline{x}$ chart.

For $\overline{x}$ chart:

LCL = 7.02 UCL = 14.29
The points are within the limits. Hence, the process is under control.

Problems for practice

1. A synthetic fibre producer produces 1.4 Dx 42 mm staple length polyester staple fibres. The staple length was checked for different batches of production with a sample size of 5 per batch:

Batch no.	1	2	3	4	5	6	7	8	9	10
$\overline{X}$ (in mm)	43	49	37	44	45	37	51	46	43	47
R	5	6	5	7	7	4	8	6	4	6

Construct the suitable chart and pass your comments.

2. An investigation was carried out to know whether the pickspacing in a 7 wheel take up mechanism is under control or not by collecting 3 sorts produced on a loom for different periods.

Period no.	Observations		
1	32	37	42
2	28	32	40
3	39	52	28
4	50	42	31
5	42	45	34
6	50	29	21
7	44	52	35
8	22	35	44

Do you conclude that take up motion is faulty in its working?

3. A R and D manager examines the GSM of the fabric samples produced in the weaving section.

Sample no.	1	2	3	4	5	6	7	8	9	10
	104	101	105	112	101	98	105	104	106	114
	109	107	99	100	99	96	102	99	107	102
	105	105	104	113	107	99	102	102	101	100
	106	100	103	106	103	96	102	100	102	103

Examine whether the process is with control limits.

4. In a sweater manufacturing unit the length of the sweaters were measured for 10 days. The expected length was 57 inches.

Day	1	2	3	4	5	6	7	8	9	10
length	57.7	57.2	57.7	57.9	56.1	56.4	56.1	55.4	56.9	58.2
(inches)	57.4	57.9	55.8	56.1	55.6	57.7	57.4	56.6	55.6	58.4
	56.9	56.1	55.6	55.4	56.6	58.2	58.2	57.7	57.7	56.1
	56.1	55.9	56.6	55.4	57.2	56.1	58.4	56.9	56.4	57.2

Compute the control limits.

Define process capability and state the different courses of action possible when:

i) Process capability is much smaller compared to tolerance range.

    ii)   Process capability is approximately equal to tolerance range.

    iii)   Process capability is much larger compared to tolerance range.

For the case of two-sided specifications.

II.   PC < TR (process capability < tolerance range)
1. Job can be shifted to a less costly m/c.
2. Sp. tolerance can be squeezed if it is economical
3. Inspection interval can be increased and 100% inspection is dispersed with.
4. Products can be accepted on the basis of control chart.
5. Process average can be set at any economical level closer to U.C.L. or L.C.L.

  ii)   Action possible PC = TR
1. Process average to be maintained at sp. average.
2. Set the m/c. at the most economical level at the risk of allowing some scrap or rework.
3. Investigate the possibility of reducing process variability.

  iii)   PC > TR
1. Scrap and rework are inevitable (cannot be avoided)
2. Resort to min. m/c adjustment
3. 100% inspection must be done.
4. Change the job to a better and costly m/c.

9.7   Type I and Type II errors

When we establish U.C.L. and L.C.L. for $\bar{x}$ chart, if a point falls outside these limits, it may be due to change in the process average or it may be due to assignable cause. If we find there are no assignable causes, then certainly the process average has changed, i.e., the universe has changed. This change may be true or may not be true. We are making a judgment based on the evidence of $\bar{x}$ of a small sample. Sometimes, this judgment will be correct sometimes it will be incorrect.

If we conclude that the universe has changed when it really is unchanged, this conclusion is described as Type I error. If we conclude that the universe has not change when it really has changed, this conclusion is described as Type II error.

1. With limits on $\bar{x}$ chart and $\bar{X} \pm 3\sigma\ \bar{X}$ it is evident that Type I errors will be infrequent.
2. An increase in sub-group size reduces the frequency of Type II errors of judgements.

Process capability:

Process capability is defined as the minimum spread of a specific measurement variation which will include 99.73% of the measurements from the given process. In other words, it is equal to 6 σ^1 where σ^1 is estimated by R / d_2. Process capability studies are done on the machines to find out the capability of individual m/cs. It is an estimation of natural variation of inherent with the machine under study when all extraneous factors (assignable causes) are minimized.

The process capability study requires 50 to 100 or more observations for computing the std. variation. When a process shows that it is incapable of producing the majority of the units within specification requirements the following alternatives are the courses of action to be taken.

1. Use a different process or m/c.
2. Change the specified limits.
3. Conduct 100% inspection to remove defective items.

9.8   The σ chart

For large samples chart in sometimes used. The construction of such a chart is given below.

First step: Calculate the (the central line) from the individual std. deviations.

i.e., $$\bar{\sigma} = \frac{\sigma_1 + \sigma_2 + \sigma_3 + ...\sigma_k}{K}$$

Second step:

$$U.C.L. = B_4 \, \bar{\sigma}$$

$$L.C.L. = B_3 \, \bar{\sigma}$$

Third step:

Estimate the value of σ^1 (the population std. deviation) by $\sigma^1 = \bar{\sigma} / c_2$

Problem 1: Control charts for $\bar{x}$ and σ are maintained for the resistance in ohms of certain electrical parts used on fully automatic loom. The sub-groups are 25. The values of $\bar{x}$ and σ are computed for each sub group. After 20 sub groups $\Sigma \bar{x} = 1612.9$ and $\Sigma\sigma = 71.4$

Compute the values for a 3σ limits for $\bar{x}$ and σ charts and estimate the value of on the assumption that the process is under statistical control.

($A_1 = 0.62$, $B_3 = 0.56$, $B_4 = 1.44$ and $C_2 = 0.9696$.)

$\overline{x}$ *chart*

$$\text{U.C.L.} = \overline{X} + A_2 \, \overline{R} \; (1) \quad \overline{X} = 1612.9 \, / \, 20 = 80.645$$

$$\text{L.C.L.} = \overline{X} - A_2 \, \overline{R}$$

$$\text{U.C.L.} = \overline{X} + 3\sigma \, \overline{x}$$

$$\text{L.C.L.} = \overline{X} - 3\sigma \, \overline{X}$$

$$3\sigma \, \overline{X} = 3 \, \sigma^1 \, / \, \sqrt{n} = 3 \times 3.725 \, / \, \sqrt{25} = 2.12$$

$$\sigma^1 = \overline{\sigma} \, / \, d_2 = 3.57 \, / \, 0.9696 = 3.725$$

σ *chart*

$$\text{U.C.L.} = B_4 \, \overline{\sigma}$$

$$\text{L.C.L.} = B_B \, \overline{\sigma} \qquad\qquad \overline{\sigma} = 71.4 \, / \, 20 = 3.57$$

$$\text{U.C.L.} = 1.44 \times 3.57 = 5.15$$

$$\text{L.C.L.} = 0.36 \times 3.57 = 1.999$$

$\overline{x}$ *chart*

$$\text{U.C.L.} _{\overline{x}}= 80.645 + 2.12 = 82.765$$

$$\text{L.C.L.} _{\overline{x}}= 80.645 - 2.12 = 78.525$$

Problem 2: In order to meet govt. regulations, the contained wt. of a product must at least equal the labeled weight 98% of the time. Control charts for $\overline{x}$ and is maintained on the wt-in ounces of the contents using a sub group size of 10. After 20 sub groups $\sum \overline{x} = 731.4$ and $\sum \sigma = 9.16$. Compute 3σ control limits for $\overline{x}$ and σ and estimate the value of σ^1 assessing the process is in statistical control, if the labeled weight is 36.0 ounce and assuming the process generate a normal distribution, does it meet federal requirement?

$C_2 = 0.9227$	$D_3 = 0.22$	$A_1 = 1.03$	$B_3 = 0.28$
$d_2 = 3.072$	$D_4 = 1.78$	$A_2 = 0.31$	$B_4 = 1.72$

Solution:

σ chart

$$\overline{\sigma} = \sum\sigma \, / \, 20 = 9.16 \, / \, 20 = 0.458$$

$$\text{U.C.L.} = B_4 \, \overline{\sigma} = 1.72 \times 0.458 = 0.787$$

$$\text{L.C.L.} = B_3 \, \overline{\sigma} = 0.28 \times 0.458 = 0.128$$

$\overline{X}$ chart

$$\overline{x} = \sum \overline{x} / 20 = 731.4 / 20 = 36.57$$

$$\text{U.C.L.} = \overline{x} + 3\sigma \overline{x} \qquad\qquad \sigma \overline{x} = \sigma^1 / \sqrt{n}$$

$$\text{L.C.L.} = \overline{x} - 3\sigma \overline{x} \quad \sigma^1 = \sigma^1 / c_2 = 0.458 / 0.9227 = 0.496$$

$$\text{U.C.L.} = 36.57 + 3 \times 0.1569 \qquad \left[\quad \sigma \overline{x} = 0.496 / \sqrt{10} \right.$$

$$= 36.57 + 0.47 = 37.04 \quad \left\lfloor = 0.496 / 3.16 = 0.1569 \right.$$

$$\text{L.C.L.} = 36.57 - 0.47 = 36.10$$

This will meet the federal requirements if the process is centered at 36.00.

Problem 3: Control charts are maintained for $\overline{x}$ and σ on the weight in grams of the contents of a dye in the pack. The size of the sub-group is 10. After 18 sub-groups $\sum \overline{x} = 5958$ and $\Sigma\sigma = 8.24$. Assuming the process to be under control find σ^1 and 3 σ limits for $\overline{x}$ and σ charts.

Solution: $\overline{x}$ charts.

$$\overline{x} = \sum \overline{x} / 18 = 5958 / 18 = 331 \text{ and}$$
$$\overline{\sigma} = \Sigma\sigma / 18 = 8.24 / 18 = 0.4577$$
$$\sigma^1 = \overline{\sigma} / c_2 = 0.4577 / 0.9227 = 0.496$$
$$\text{UCL} = \overline{x} + 3\sigma \overline{x} = 331 + 3X\sigma^1 / \sqrt{n} = 331 + 3 \times 0.496/\sqrt{10} = 331.47$$
$$\text{LCL} = \overline{x} - 3\sigma \overline{x} = 331 - 3 \times (0.496/\sqrt{n}) = 330.5$$

Chart

$$\text{UCL} = B_4 \overline{\sigma} = 1.72 \times 0.4577 = 0.7872$$
$$\text{LCL} = B_3 \overline{\sigma} = 0.28 \times 0.4577 = 0.1281$$

9.9   Charts for attributes

Control charts for fraction defectives and for number of defects/unit.

These charts are used when the completeness of the product is important and not the dimensional accuracy and where the products are subjected to a qualitative assessment like 'Good' or 'Bad'.

(Ex: Water tank – leaks or not

Soldered joint – Makes electrical contact or not
Explosives – Either Fires or not
Weft pirns checked by ('Go' or 'No go' gauges)

Control in such cases is achieved on the basis of the proportion of pieces found defective. They are known as 'P' charts.

Similarly, there are products where the no. of defects per piece may be important, and acceptable if controlled below certain limit.

Example: Blow holes in castings, air bubbles in glass sheets / bottles, knots and other defects in yarn, scratches and bubbles on painted surface, defective rivets in air plane wing, etc.

In such products control is maintained on the basis of the number of defects / piece. They are known as 'c' charts.

9.9.1 'p' chart

The 'p' chart shows the variation in the fraction defectives of output. It is also known as control chart for 'GO' and 'NO GO' data. During the course of inspection, a unit is recognized as simply meeting the design specifications or not. Fraction defective is defined as the value obtained by dividing number of defectives obtained from the total number of units inspected. It is usually represented by a fraction such as 5 / 100, 9 / 20 or in decimals like 0.2, 0.03, etc.

$\overline{p}$ = Defective units in the lot / total no. of units in the lot

If $\overline{p}$ = average of fraction defectives, remains constant, then the proportion of defectives 'p' in each sample will vary from sample to sample and will from a binomial distribution having the following properties.

Mean proportion defective = $\overline{p}$ (central line of 'p' chart) the average of fraction defectives of the universe.

$\overline{p}$ = Standard deviation of fraction defectives
n = Number of units in the sample (sample size)

Therefore, control limits are given by:

$$\sigma p = \sqrt{\overline{p}\frac{(1-\overline{p})}{n}}$$

$$\text{UCL} = \overline{p} + 3\sigma p = p + 3\sqrt{\frac{\overline{p}(1-\overline{p})}{n}}$$

$$\text{LCL} = \overline{p} + 3\sigma p = p - 3\sqrt{\frac{\overline{p}(1-\overline{p})}{n}}$$

In case of 'p' charts, lower limits are only of interest in so far as any significant decrease in proportion of defective is very welcome and steps are taken to consolidate the improvement. Therefore, it is usual to plot only upper limits.

In controlling dimensions we have two charts $\bar{x}$ and p. But in controlling fraction defective we have only one chart, i.e., 'p' control charts for proportion defectives may be based on either on the proportion of defectives over the output of a shift or a day. Or on the proportion of defectives found in samples from the output takes at regular intervals. In the former case the effective sample size will vary, while in the latter case it should be constant.

Case 1: When the value of 'n' (sample size) is constant
Case 2: When the value of 'n' is variable .

When n is constant, the chart for actual number of defectives may be used. Such a chart is called a 'np' chart.
The control limits for 'np' chart are given by

$$UCL = n\bar{p} + 3\sqrt{n\bar{p}(1-\bar{p})}$$

$$LCL = n\bar{p} - 3\sqrt{n\bar{p}(1-\bar{p})}$$

Whenever, the value of n is variable, the control chart must show the fraction defective rather than the actual number of defectives. In such a case a 'p' chart may be used.

100 p chart or percent defective chart:

Some times 100 p or percent defectives charts are also plotted to serve some specific purpose. Control limits for such a chart are given by:

$$UCL = 100\bar{p} + 3\sqrt{\frac{100\bar{p}(100 - 100\bar{p})}{n}}$$

$$LCL = 100\bar{p} - 3\sqrt{\frac{100\bar{p}(100 - 100\bar{p})}{n}}$$

9.9.2 Comparison of $\bar{x}$– R charts with 'p' chart

	x – R charts		p. chart
1.	These are control charts for variables.	1.	These are control charts for attributes.
2.	Cost of collecting data is high	2.	Cost of collecting data is less.

(Contd.)

	x – R charts			p. chart
3.	Accurate measurement is required.		3.	Separation of defectives from good ones are enough.
4.	Separate $\bar{x}$ – R charts are required for each quality characteristic.		4.	Number of quality characteristics can be observed for one article.
5.	Very sensitive and disclose causes of variation.		5.	Not so sensitive.
6.	Used for improvement of one quality characteristic.		6.	Used for overall improvement of quality.
7.	Sample size is smaller.		7.	Sample size is large
8.	Assumes normal distribution.		8.	Assumes binomial distribution.
9.	Not sensitive in detecting a shift.		9.	Very sensitive in detecting a shift.
10.	Variation in sample size influences control limits.		10.	Very little variation is observed when Sample size is varied.
11.	Not gained good popularity.		11.	Gained popularity among shop personnel and management.

$$LCL = 100\bar{p} - 3\sqrt{\frac{100\bar{p}(100 - 100\bar{p})}{n}}$$

Problem 1: Using each days production as the day's sample, draw a control chart for fraction defectives, on the basis of the proportion of defective castings produced in a carding machine manufacturing unit for 10 days tabulated below:

Day	No. of castings produced	No. of castings found defective	$\bar{p}$
1	154	4	4 /154=0.0259
2	152	2	2/152=0.0131
3	158	2	0.0135
4	150	4	0.0266
5	154	3	0.0194
6	145	4	0.0277
7	151	2	0.0132
8	154	2	0.0129
9	150	1	0.0066
10	153	4	0.0261

Total no. of defectives = 28
Total no. of casting inspected = 1511

$$\therefore \bar{p} = 28 / 1511 = 0.0185$$
$$(1 - \bar{p}) = 1 - 0.0185 = 0.9815$$
$$n = 1511 / 10 = 151.1$$

$$UCL = \bar{p} + 3\sqrt{\frac{\bar{p}(1-\bar{p})}{n}} = 0.0185 + 3\sqrt{\frac{0.0185 \times 0.9815}{151}} = 0.0513$$

$$UCL = \bar{p} - 3\sqrt{\frac{\bar{p}(1-\bar{p})}{n}} = 0.0185 - 3\sqrt{\frac{0.0185 \times 0.9815}{151}} = 0.0143$$

It is seen that all the points fall within the control limits. Therefore, the process is under control.

Problem 2: The management is interested to know the quality level of loom frame blocks cast continuously in a foundry shop. A random sample of 50 blocks is taken from each day production and inspected. This is continued for 30 days. The observations are given in the table below. Determine the control limits for use in future production.

Date	No. of rejections	Date	No. of rejections	Date	No. of rejections
1	5	11	26	21	16
2	10	12	19	22	10
3	12	13	13	23	9
4	14	14	5	24	16
5	31	15	4	25	17
6	27	16	12	26	4
7	14	17	9	27	7
8	9	18	15	28	9
9	24	19	21	29	4
10	33	20	24	30	11

Solution: Total no. of defectives = 430
Total no. of items inspected = 30 × 50 = 1500
Here, the sample size = 50 and is constant for all days.
Therefore, 'np' chart can be conveniently used.

$$\bar{p} = 430 / 1500 = 0.2866$$
$$n\,\bar{p} = 0.2856 \times 50 = 14.33$$

Trial control limits for np chart:

$$UCL = n\bar{p} + 3\sqrt{n\bar{p}(1-\bar{p})} = 14.33 + 3\sqrt{14.33 \times 0.7134} = 14.33 + 9.59 = 23.92$$

$$LCL = n\bar{p} - 3\sqrt{n\bar{p}(1-\bar{p})} = 14.33 - 3\sqrt{14.33 \times 0.7134} = 14.33 - 9.59 = 4.74$$

It is seen that the fraction defective of days 5, 6, 9, 10, 11, and 20 fall beyond UCL and for the days 15.25 and 29 fall outside the L.C.L.
Eliminating these values, the centre line n $\bar{p}$ is revised.

$$\text{Revised } \bar{p} = \frac{430 - 177}{21 \times 50} = 0.24$$

$$\bar{n}p = 50 \times 0.24 = 12.$$

Now all the points are within the limits. These can be used for future production.

Note: In case of a 'p' chart, if any point falls below the LCL it is not a bad sign. It means that the fraction defective has a tendency to become zero. Hence, it is a good sign. But it does not mean we should not have lower control limits at all. Any point below the LCL can only be obtained by chance, and cannot be a usual feature of the process. Therefore, while calculating the revised limits, those points which are outside the LCL are also eliminated.

Problem 3: A 'p' chart is to be used to analyze the september record for 100% inspection of a certain electronic tubes in an uster classimat unit. The total number inspected during the month was 2196 and the total number of defectives was 158. Compute $\bar{p}$.

Compute individual 3σ control limits for the following three days and state whether the fraction defectives fell within control limits for each day.

Day	No. of units inspected	No. of defectives
Sept. 14	54	8
Sept. 15	162	24
Sept. 16	213	3

Solution: $\bar{p}$ = Total no. of defectives / Total no. inspected = 158 / 2196

Sept. 14: 3 sigma limits

$$UCL = \bar{p} + 3\sqrt{\frac{\bar{p}(1-\bar{p})}{n}} = 0.07 + 3\sqrt{\frac{(0.07)(0.93)}{54}} = 0.07 + 0.10 = 0.17$$

$$LCL = \bar{p} - 3\sqrt{\frac{\bar{p}(1-\bar{p})}{n}} = 0.07 - 3\sqrt{\frac{(0.07)(0.93)}{54}} = 0.07 - 0.10 = 0$$

Sept. 15: 3 sigma limits

$$UCL = \bar{p} + 3\sqrt{\frac{\bar{p}(1-\bar{p})}{n}} = 0.07 + 3\sqrt{\frac{(0.07)(0.93)}{162}} = 0.07 + 0.06 = 0.13$$

$$LCL = \bar{p} - 3\sqrt{\frac{\bar{p}(1-\bar{p})}{n}} = 0.07 + 3\sqrt{\frac{(0.07)(0.93)}{162}} = 0.07 - 0.06 = 0.01$$

Sept. 16: 3 sigma limits

$$UCL = \overline{p} + 3\sqrt{\frac{\overline{p}(1-\overline{p})}{n}} = 0.07 + 3\sqrt{\frac{(0.07)(0.93)}{213}} = 0.07 + 0.017 = 0.087$$

$$LCL = \overline{p} - 3\sqrt{\frac{\overline{p}(1-\overline{p})}{n}} = 0.07 - 3\sqrt{\frac{(0.07)(0.93)}{213}} = 0.07 - 0.017 = 0.053$$

Date	No. inspected	No. of defects	P	UCL	LCL	Remarks
Sept. 14	54	8	0.148	0.17	0	within control limits
Sept. 15	162	24	0.148	0.13	0.01	falls outside UCL (process out of control)
Sept. 16	213	3	0.014	0.087	0.053	falls below LCL (Process shows good sign)

Problem 4: The following data refer to the production and no. of defectives for 15 consecutive days. Each day 400 units were inspected.

Day	No. of defectives
1	2
2	5
3	0
4	
5	3
6	0
7	1
8	0
9	
10	8
11	6
12	0
13	3
14	0
15	6
	66

Plot 100 or percent defective chart and find what control limits you adopt for future production.

Ans: $\overline{P} = 66 / (400 \times 15) = 66 / 6000 = 0.011$

$100 \, \overline{p} = 1.1.$

$$UCL = 100\overline{p} + 3\sqrt{\frac{100\overline{p}(100 - 100\overline{p})}{n}} = 1.1 + 3\sqrt{\frac{1.1(100 - 1.1)}{400}}$$

$$= 1.1 + 3 \times 0.53 = 2.7$$

LCL = 1.1 – 1.6 = 0

A verification shows that 4th day 9th day points cross the upper units. Eliminating those, we get the revised control units for future production.

$$\text{Revised } 100 \ \overline{p} = \frac{100(66 - 32)}{600 - 800} = \frac{3400}{5200} = \frac{2}{3} = 0.66$$

$$UCL = 0.66 + 3\sqrt{\frac{0.66(100 - 0.66)}{400}} = 0.66 + 3\sqrt{\frac{0.66 \times 99.34}{400}} = 1.87$$

LCL = 0 – 0.553 = 0.

Problem 5: a) The following table gives the results of a daily inspection of knitting needles. The standard value of fraction defective 'p' established at the start or the month was 0.04. The estimated daily average production was 1600 needles. Draw the control chart for fraction defective. What are your comments?

S. no.	No. inspected	No. of defectives	Fraction defective
1	531	25	0.0471
2	2000	58	0.0290
3	2150	89	0.0414
4	1422	61	0.0428
5	2330	75	0.0322
6	1500	73	0.0487
7	2417	115	0.0476
8	850	27	0.0318
9	1948	41	0.0210

Ans: $p^1 = 0.04$

$$UCL = p^1 + 3\sqrt{\frac{p^1(1 - p^1)}{n}} = 0.04 + 3\sqrt{\frac{0.04 \times 0.96}{1600}} = 0.04 + 3 \times 0.0049 = 0.0547$$

$$LCL = p^1 - 3\sqrt{\frac{p^1(1 - p^1)}{n}} = 0.04 - 3\sqrt{\frac{0.04 \times 0.96}{1600}} = 0.04 - 3 \times 0.0049 = 0.0253$$

Sl. no. 9 Fall outside L.C.L. But it must be determined whether this pt. is really out of control. Computing UCL and LCL for solution number 9 for which n = 1948, we get,

$$UCL = p^1 + 3\sqrt{\frac{p^1(1-p^1)}{n}} = 0.04 + 3\sqrt{\frac{0.04 \times 0.96}{1948}} = 0.0535$$

The above results show that this point is definitely out of control.

Problem 6: A P chart indicates that the current average is 0.02. If 50 items are inspected each day, what is the probability of catching a shift in process average to 0.04 on the first day after the shift? By the end of the third day after the shift?

Solution: The present process average is 0.02 or 2% that is 2 out of every 100 are defectives or 1 defective for every 50 items. When the process average shifts to 0.04.

$$\overline{n}p = 50 \times 0.04 = 2$$

This means that for every 50 items 2 are defectives.

Probability of getting 2 defectives in a sample of 50 = probability of getting 0, 1 or defectives – probability of getting 0 or 1 defective.

(2) = p (up to 2) – p (up to 1)

= 0.677 – 0.406 (from table G)

= 0.271

∴ Probability of detecting a shift on first day = 0.271

Probability of detecting a shift on 3rd day = (0.406) (0.406) (0.271) = 0.0446

Problem 7: An item is made in lots of 200 each. The lots are given 100% inspection. The record sheet for the first 25 lots inspected showed that a total of 75 items were defective.

i)   Determine the trial control limits for an np chart showing number of defectives in each lot.
ii)   What is your estimate of process average fraction defective?
iii) If p remains unchanged what is the probability that the 26th lot will contain exactly 7 defectives that will contain 7 or more defectives?

Solution:

$$\overline{p} =$$
$$\overline{n}p = 200 \times 0.015 = 3$$

i)   Trial control limits for np chart.

$$UCL = n\overline{p} + 3\sqrt{n\overline{p}(1-\overline{p})} = 3 + 3\sqrt{3 \times 0.985} = 3 + 5.15 = 8.15$$

$$LCL = n\overline{p} - 3\sqrt{n\overline{p}(1-\overline{p})} = 3 - 3\sqrt{3 \times 0.985} = 3 - 5.15 = -ve = 0$$

ii)   The estimate of process average fraction defective p' = 0.015
iii) Probability that the 25th lot contain exactly 7 defectives is obtained
      from using table G (Poisson approximation) for which p = 0.015 and
      np = 200 × 0.015 = 3, against column c = 7
      Probability of no. of defectives up to 7 = 0.988
      Probability of no. of defectives up to 6 = 0.966
      ∴Probability of exactly 7 defectives = 0.988 – 0.966 = 0.022

   Probability that the sample contain 7 or more defectives PC ≥ 1 –
Probability (≤ 6) = 1 – 0.966 = 0.34).

Problems for practice

1. A blow room record shows the following details about lower grade
    cotton processing. Comment about the statistical quality control of
    the process.

    Solution:

	1	2	3	4	5	6	7	8	9	10	11	12	13	14
No. of laps delivered	42,	52,	51,	48,	30,	61,	72,	77,	70,	54,	42,	51,	36,	71
Laps rejected after checking weight	6,	18,	16,	15,	3,	15,	22,	20,	20,	19,	10,	7,	17,	14

2. A garment export house undertaking the inspection of a finished
    dressed material for 10 days run. Construct the percent defective
    chart assuming that the average no. of cuts inspected per day is equal
    to 504 and pass your comments about the statistical quality control.

Cuts	500	510	513	493	497	503	505	498	509	512
No. of seconds	25	27	13	22	26	25	27	30	12	19

3. A large number of warp cones were tested for quality for 10 days
    nearly 200 cones were selected at random from each day production.
    Results are as follows:

Day	1	2	3	4	5	6	7	8	9	10
No. of defective cones	8	11	5	4	7	11	23	12	10	5

    Construct a suitable chart and comment on the process control.

4. Draw a control chart for the following data and state your conclusion.

Sample no. (each of 100)	1	2	3	4	5	6	7	8	9	10
No. of defectives	12	10	6	8	9	9	7	10	11	8

(Hint: $\bar{p} = 90/100 = 0.09$,

$$UCL = \bar{p} + 3\sqrt{\frac{(1-\bar{p})}{n}} = 0.1758$$

LCL = 0.0042, process under control)

5. Construct a suitable control chart for the following spinning ring cop CSP test problem.

Sample no. of 100	1	2	3	4	5	6	7	8	9	10
No. of defectives	12	10	6	8	9	9	7	11	11	9

[Hint. $\bar{p} = 92 / 1000 = 0.092$, $\bar{np} = 100 \times 0.092 = 9.2$

[Hint: $LCL = 0.1537 - 3\sqrt{\dfrac{0.1537(1-0.1537)}{2000}} = 0.12952$ or zero]

LCL = 0.53]

6. If the average fraction defective of a large sample of products is 0.1537. Compute the control limits (given sub group size as 2000).

9.9.3 "C" Chart

This is known as control chart for defects/unit. We know that a defective may contain more than one defect. Example of data used on 'c' chart may be such things as surface defects/unit area. Number of faults/unit length of cloth, insulation defects/unit length of wire, etc., the sample may consist of 5 square yards, 1000 meters of wire length, or 5 test specimens. The defects to be counted may be blow holes in castings, scratches in glass piece, pin holes in tanks, surface irregularities, etc. In such products it is desirable to take into account how much bad each defective item is.

If p represents the number of defects/unit (this must not exceed 0.10) and N no. of units, then P N or most commonly designated as "c" will represent the number of defects in the unit.

9.10   Determining the control limits

It is found reasonable to assume that the distribution of variation in the number of defects/unit follows very closely the Poisson distribution. This is because, the number of defects/unit can be considered as

(1) fraction defectives / place – p which is small.
(2) No. of units – n

Then C = Number of defects / unit = p.n.
C = Average number of defects / unit for the universe.

In case of Poisson distribution:

Average = variance = (standard deviation)^2 $\sigma = \sqrt{c^1}$
If the universe remains the same, $c^1 = \overline{C}$
Hence 3 control units are

U.C.L. = $\overline{c} + 3 \sqrt{\overline{c}}$
L.C.L. = $\overline{c} - 3 \sqrt{\overline{c}}$

Problem 1: (a) A set of travelers were subjected to inspection. A set consists of 5 travelers and there are 20 sub-groups. The inspection data obtained is as follows:

Group no.   1, 2, 3, 4, 5, 6, 7, 8, 9, 10, 11, 12, 13, 14, 15, 16, 17, 18, 19, 20

No. of defects 77, 64, 75, 93, 45, 61, 49, 65, 45, 77, 59, 54, 41, 87, 40, 22, 92, 89, 55, 25

Total = 1215

$\overline{C}$ = No. of defects in the inspected lot / No. of units submitted for inspection.

= 1215 / 20 = 60.75

U.C.L. = $\overline{c} + 3 \sqrt{\overline{c}}$ = 60.75 + 3

= 60.75+23.4 = 84.15

L.C.L. = $\overline{c} - 3\sqrt{\overline{c}}$ = 60.75 – 23.4 = 37.35   [Where $\overline{c}$ = centre line].

These are trial control limits. It is seen that values pertaining to group no. 4, 14, 17, 18, 16 and 20 fall outside the control limits. Hence, these points should be eliminated and revised control limits are computed for the remaining points.

$$\overline{c} = \frac{1215 - 408}{20 - 6} = \frac{807}{14} = 57.6$$

UCL = $\overline{c} + 3\sqrt{\overline{c}}$ = 57.6 + 3 $\sqrt{57.6}$ = 80.4
LCL = $\overline{c} - 3\sqrt{\overline{c}}$ = 57.6 – 22.8 = 34.8
Centre line = $\overline{c}$ = 57.6

Now all points are within the control limits. Hence, these limits can be used as control chart limits.

Prepare a $\bar{c}$ chart based on the evidence of the cloth length given below:

100 m. cloth length N   1, 2, 3, 4, 5, 6, 7, 8, 9, 10
No. of minor defects found on inspection 2, 3, 1, 4, 4, 0, 2, 1, 4, 2

Ans.: Total no. of defects = 23
No. of lengths   = 10
$\bar{c}$ = 23 / 10 = 2.3
U.C.L.   = $\bar{c} + 3\sqrt{\bar{c}} = 2.3 + 3\sqrt{2.3} = 6.9$
L.C.L   = $c - 3\sqrt{\bar{c}} = 2.3 - 4.6 = 0$

Here all points fall within the control limits. Therefore, the process is under control.

(b) The following table gives the number of defects noted in extruded (POY) polyester spools of 1.5 m diameter each at final inspection, for 24 units. Find $\bar{c}$. compute trial control limits and plot control chart for c what value of $\bar{c}$ would you suggest for the subsequent period?

Lot no.	No. of defects	Lot no.	No. of defects
1	33	13	28
2	27	14	33
3	17	15	36
4	22	16	
5	19	17	28
6	28	18	30
7	31	19	20
8	38	20	17
9	24	21	23
10	12	22	27
11	23	12	
12	18	24	15
	310		312

$\bar{c} = 622 / 24 = 25.91$

9.10.1 Trial control limits

UCL = $\bar{c} + 3\sqrt{\bar{c}} = 25.91 + 3\ 25.91 = 41.18$
LCL = $c - 3\sqrt{\bar{c}} = 25.91 - 3\ 25.91 = 10.64$

It is seen that lot number 11 and 16 fall outside the limits. Eliminating these two, we get,

$\bar{c}_R$ = 528 / 22 = 24.45
U.C.L. = $\bar{c} + 3\sqrt{\bar{c}} = 24.45 + 3\sqrt{24.95} = 39.28$
L.C.L. = $\bar{c} - 3\sqrt{\bar{c}} = 24.45 - 3\sqrt{24.45} = 19.62$

Problem 2: The following table refers to the number of missing stitches noted during the inspection in a big garment manufacturing company.

Garment no.	No. of missing stitches	Garment no.	No. of missing stitches
1	08	14	25
2	15	15	15
3	15	16	10
4	19	17	10
5	09	18	12
6	15	19	15
7	09	20	09
8	12	21	10
9	21	22	22
10	13	23	08
11	23	24	27
12	16	25	09
13	09		

Find $\bar{c}$. Compute trail control limits and plot the control chart for c. what value of C can be suggested for the subsequent period?

Solution: Total No. of missing stitches = 356

$$\bar{c} = 366 / 25 = 14.24$$

Trial control limits

U.C.L. = $c + 3\sqrt{\bar{c}}$ = 14.24 + 3 $\sqrt{14.24}$ = 14.24 + 11.32 = 25.56
L.C.L. = $\bar{c} - 3\sqrt{\bar{c}}$ = 14.24 – 11.32 = 2.92

It is seen that one point pertaining to garment number 24 fall above UCL. Eliminating this value, the revised control limits are determined

Revised $\bar{c} = (356 – 27) / 24 = 13.7$
Revised U.C.L. = $\bar{c} + 3\sqrt{\bar{c}} = 13.7 + 3\sqrt{13.7} = 13.7 + 11.1 = 24.8$
Revised L.C.L. = $\bar{c} - 3\sqrt{\bar{c}} = 13.7 – 3\sqrt{13.7} = 13.7 – 11.1 = 2.6$
These are used for the subsequent period.

Problems for practice:

1. In grading fabric a mill decides after investigation and establishment of this system that the maximum number of points acceptable for first quality fabric is 80, beyond an 80 point total, the fabric is downgraded to second quality what must be the average number of points per piece of first quality fabric in order that the mill can be assured that practically all the fabric will be first quality.
    [Hint: Given UCL = 80, UCL = $\bar{c} + 3\sqrt{\bar{c}}$, $\bar{c} + 3\sqrt{\bar{c}} – 80 = 0$ is a quadratic equation and taking positive root $\bar{c} = 57.30$. If control limit = 57.30, LCL = 34.6]

2. M/s XYZ automatic loom works manufactures 50″ reed space all metal reeds. The number of defective reeds as shown by R and D was as follows:

12, 6, 18, 4, 5, 2, 4, 7, 12, 14, 8, 11, 14, 21, 21, 10, 12, 9, 13, 10

Comment on the state of control. [Hint: use $\bar{c}$ chart]

3. In a certain sampling inspection, the number of defectives in 10 samples of 100 each are as given below:

16, 18, 11, 18, 21, 10, 20, 18, 17 and 21.

Do these indicate that the quality characteristic under inspection is under statistical control?

4. The following are the number defects noted in the final inspection of 10 bales of woolen cloth. 0, 3, 1, 4, 2, 2, 1, 3, 5 and 2. Construct the chart and pass your comments.

5. The following table gives the number of defects observed in 7 woolen carpets. Construct a suitable control chart. 2, 1, 4, 7, 6, 5, 3

6. 10 pieces of cloth out of different rolls of equal length contained the following number of defects = 1, 3, 5, 0, 6, 0, 9, 4, 4, 3

construct a control chart and state whether the process confirms a state of statistical control.

7. 15 pieces of 2m × 2m polyester cloth was checked for defects and the following data was available. 7, 12, 3, 20, 21, 5, 4, 3, 10, 8, 0, 9, 6, 7, 20. Draw a suitable control chart pertaining to snarls and foreign (gout) matters.

8. In a spinning mill the numbers of imperfections in 1000 m lengths of 30^s yarn was recorded as follows:

Sample no.	Thin places	No. of thick places	Neps
1	20	74	55
2	20	86	42
3	25	87	36
4	24	83	45
5	22	64	41
6	30	75	43
7	22	63	43
8	14	78	43
9	22	92	29
10	19	75	39

Construct a suitable chart.

[Hint: Draw separate charts for each imperfection]

Adoption of 'c' chart to variations in the area of opportunity for defect.

The quantity 'c' is the number of defects observed in some specified inspection. Sometimes, this inspection may be of a single unit of product like a radio set, a coil of wire in airplane etc., in such a case 'c' is both the number of defects / unit and the total number of defects. The units should be alike in size and in the apparent likelihood of the existence of a defect; so that the area of opportunity for a defect be constant from unit to unit. However, for the control chart purposes, it is really not necessary that a sub group be a single unit of product. The sub group may be 10 product units, or 100 yards or any convenient number. Total defects for each subgroup may be plotted just as if the sub group were a single unit of product.

Whenever for some reason, there is an evident change in the area of opportunity for occurrence of a defect from subgroup to subgroup, the conventional 'c' chart showing total number of defects is not necessary. In such cases, the control limit on the chart as well as the control limits would have to change from one sub group to another. This would make the chart confusing and difficult to read.

A way out of this difficulty is to divide the defects 'c' by units 'n'. The n c / n is called by the symbol 'u'. The control line on a 'u' chart will be standard defects per unit u_0^1 limits lines on such a chart will vary with sub group size, just as control limits vary with sub group size of 'p' chart. The formulae for control limits on such a chart are

$$UCL = U_0^1 + 3\sqrt{\frac{u_0^1}{n}}$$

$$LCL = U_0^1 - 3\sqrt{\frac{u_0^1}{n}}$$

These formulae assume that a value has been established for standard defects / unit u_0^1. For control limits this standard value may be estimated as equal to the average number of defects/unit, i.e., the total number of observed defects/total number of units.

Problem 1:

a) Give the procedure the drawing 'c' chart. What changes are necessary when the area of opportunity for defects vary?

b) A control chart for defects / unit 'u' uses probability limits corresponding to probabilities of 0.975 and 0.025. The central line of the control chart is at u^1=2.0 vary with 'n'. Determine the UCL and LCL when n = 5.

$$c^1 = nu^1 = 5 \times 2.0 = 10$$

From table G (Poisson tables) for c^1 = 10 the following cumulative probabilities are obtained.

c	Probability
3	0.010
4	0.029
16	0.973
17	0.986

Interpolating for 0.025 and 0.975 in the above table we get the limits 3.79 and 16.15 respectively. Therefore for 'u' chart the limits are 3.79/5 and 16.15/5, i.e., 0.76 and 3.23.

Problem 2: The following tables shows the No. of defects recorded in 10 lots containing different no. of units. Plot a suitable control chart.

Lot no.	Units	Defects	Defects/unit
1	46	118	2.56
2	43	96	2.23
3	49	125	2.55
4	45	87	1.93
5	45	90	2.20
6	47	123	2.61
7	44	104	2.36
8	46	123	2.67
9	45	112	2.49
10	42	98	2.33
Total	452	1085	

$\bar{u}$ = 1085 / 452 = 2.40

n = 452 / 10 = 45.2

$$\text{UCL of 'u' chart} = \bar{u} + 3\sqrt{\frac{\bar{u}}{n}} = 2.40 + 3\sqrt{\frac{2.4}{45.2}} = 3.00$$

$$\text{LCL of 'u' chart} = \bar{u} - 3\sqrt{\frac{\bar{u}}{n}} = 2.40 - 3\sqrt{\frac{2.4}{45.2}} = 1.71$$

Problems for practice

Problem: Set up control charts for average and range of weights of 5 m wrapings of draw frame sliver, 25 sets of wrappings of size 6 each have been taken over a continuous period of time and the results are presented in table given below:

Sub-group no.	Weight in grams					
	1	2	3	4	5	6
1	16.10	15.67	16.12	16.26	15.77	15.91
2	15.76	16.24	15.71	16.01	15.77	16.26
3	15.67	16.21	15.92	15.73	15.89	16.30
4	15.68	16.26	16.12	15.83	15.95	16.31
5	16.12	16.05	16.02	15.82	16.27	16.09
6	15.98	16.02	15.83	15.90	16.35	15.98
7	16.08	15.84	15.83	16.02	16.17	15.68
8	16.18	15.93	16.21	15.94	15.70	16.25
9	16.01	15.84	16.11	15.97	15.80	15.92
10	15.74	15.80	16.08	15.83	16.08	15.04
11	15.93	15.65	16.25	16.13	15.83	16.22
12	15.95	16.15	15.94	16.25	15.72	15.92
13	16.06	15.85	16.35	15.96	16.26	16.01
14	16.20	15.69	15.94	15.73	16.06	15.67
15	16.00	15.58	15.67	15.68	16.30	15.90
16	16.02	15.73	15.81	16.26	16.33	16.01
17	16.29	16.31	15.91	16.38	16.30	16.26
18	16.08	16.05	16.08	15.69	16.03	15.92
19	16.00	16.11	15.67	15.65	15.84	16.05
20	16.25	16.24	15.87	16.23	16.18	16.27
21	15.85	16.07	15.86	16.08	16.29	16.11
22	15.65	15.69	16.09	15.92	15.77	15.74
23	16.00	16.33	16.33	16.02	15.82	15.68
24	15.63	15.72	16.30	16.06	16.13	15.79
25	15.77	16.19	15.86	16.00	15.98	16.10

Problem: The number of defective cones while inspecting 250 nos. in each sample are tabulated below. Draw suitable chart and pass your comments.

Number of defective cones out of 250 inspected in each case.

Sample no.	Defectives	Sample no.	Defectives	Sample no.	Defectives
1	3	11	2	21	1
2	2	12	1	27	0
3	6	13	1	23	0
4	9	14	1	24	2
5	5	15	9	25	2
6	1	16	5	26	3
7	0	17	4	27	2
8	0	18	2	28	1
9	12	19	6	29	6
10	3	20	3	30	4

10

Tests of significance

10.1 Introduction

William S. Gosset who wrote under the pseudonym 'student' has given a more refined technique known as t-test. Sampling distribution of the statistics t is called student's distribution or t-distribution.

In a sampling distribution, t is the ratio of a deviation from the mean or other parameter to the standard error of the sample statistic.

$$t = \frac{\text{Deviation from the population mean}}{\text{Standard error of the sample mean}}$$

This test is based on what is known as null-hypothesis.

Null-hypothesis. We would illustrate the concept with an example. We know that the sum of deviations of individual values from the mean value is equal to zero. The problem in the case of small samples is to test whether the deviation of sample mean from population mean is significantly different from zero. Significance means significantly different from zero. Our working hypothesis is that there is a null amount of deviation. It is a hypothesis of no difference and is based on the assumption that whenever observations are measured or estimated, nothing but laws of chance are operating in a free manner. It is this assumption of reasoning that this testing technique is to nullify or support.

In case of two samples, the principle of null-hypothesis postulates that no significant difference exists between the samples and the existence of a difference if there is any, is due to random sampling error. The t-test is designed to verify the correctness or otherwise of this supposition, i.e. we have to test whether such a difference is significantly different from zero.

Under the above noted assumptions, fisher computed in a table form certain critical values of t at different levels of significance for various degrees of freedom. Fisher has also provided several formulae for calculation of t.

If the calculated value of t is greater than the table value of t for appropriate degrees of freedom, then the difference is significant.

i) t-test of a sample mean

t is a measure of the deviation of a sample mean from the population mean and is equal to the ratio deviation (difference) of a sample mean from the population mean to the standard error of the sample mean.

$$t = \frac{\text{Deviation from the population mean}}{\text{Standard error of the sample mean}}$$

or

$$t = \frac{M_s - M}{\dfrac{\sigma_s}{\sqrt{n}}} = \frac{(M_s - M) \times \sqrt{n}}{\sigma_s}$$

Where M is the sample mean, M_s the population mean, σ is the standard deviation (SD) of the sample and is equal to

$$\sqrt{\frac{\Sigma d^2}{n-1}} \, or \sqrt{\frac{\Sigma\left(x - \bar{x}\right)^2}{n-1}}$$

The number of degrees of freedom = n – 1

Important notes

a) If SD of sample has been computed by using the

Formula $\sigma_s = \sqrt{\dfrac{\Sigma d^2}{n}}$ then $t = \dfrac{(M_s - M)}{\sigma_s} \times \sqrt{n-1}$

b) If M = 0 then t = $\dfrac{M_s}{\sigma_s} \times \sqrt{n}$ where $\sigma_s = \sqrt{\dfrac{\Sigma d^2}{n-1}}$

Or   t = $\dfrac{M_s}{\sigma_s} \times \sqrt{n-1}$ where $\sigma_s = \sqrt{\dfrac{\Sigma d^2}{n}}$

The number of degrees of freedom = (n – 1)

Example 1: The data to the static tensile strength of samples of paper made from a particular mechanical pulp:

It is desired to test whether the mean strength deviates from 4.0.

Data: 4.1, 4.35, 4, 4.1, 4.3, 4.3, 3.85, 4.3, 3.9.

The table value of t for 8 df at 5 percent level of significance is 2.306.

Solution:

n = 9M = 4.0

	Strength	d (deviation from mean 4.13)	d²
1	4.10	−0.03	0.0009
2	4.35	0.22	0.0484
3	4.00	0.13	0.0169
4	4.10	−0.03	0.0009
5	4.30	0.17	0.0289
6	4.30	0.17	0.289
7	3.85	−0.28	0.0784
8	4.30	0.17	0.0289
9	3.90	−0.23	0.0529
Total = 37.20			Σd² = 0.2851

Find mean and SD of the sample.
Mean i.e. M_s = 37.20 / 9 = 4.13.

Use the formula $\sigma_s = \sqrt{\dfrac{\Sigma d^2}{n-1}}$

$$\sigma_s = \sqrt{\frac{\Sigma d^2}{n-1}} = \sqrt{\frac{0.2851}{8}} = \sqrt{0.0356} = 0.189$$

Degrees of freedom = 8.

$$t = \frac{\left(M_s - M\right)}{\sigma_s} \times \sqrt{n}$$

$$= \frac{4.13 - 4.0}{0.189} \times \sqrt{9} = \frac{0.13}{0.189} \times 3 = \frac{0.39}{0.189} = 2.06$$

Value of r at 5 percent level for 8 df = 2.306
The calculated value of t (2.06) is less than the table value of t (2.306). Therefore, the mean strength is not significantly different at 5 percent level.

Example 2: The yield of two types of cottons gave the single yarn with following yarn number. What comments would you make on differences in the mean counts? You may assume that if there be five degrees freedom and P = 0.02, t is approximately = 1.476.

Replication	Jayadhar 1 (J₁)	Jayadhar 2 (J₂)
1	20.50	24.86
2	24.60	26.39
3	23.06	28.19
4	29.98	30.75
5	30.37	29.97
6	23.83	22.04

Replication	J1	J2	Differences	d from mean i.e.1.64	d²
1	20.50	24.86	+4.36	2.72	7.3984
2	24.60	26.39	+1.79	0.15	0.225
3	23.06	28.19	+5.13	3.49	12.180
4	29.98	30.75	+0.77	−0.87	0.7559
5	30.37	29.97	−0.40	−2.04	4.1616
6	23.83	22.04	−1.79	−3.43	11.764
Total	9.86				Σd^2 = 36.2844

n = 6 Degrees of freedom = n – 1 = 6 – 1 = 5

Mean of the differences i.e. M_s = 9.86 / 6 = 1.64 (Approx.)

$$\sigma_s = \sqrt{\frac{\Sigma d^2}{n-1}} = \sqrt{\frac{36.2844}{6-1}} = \sqrt{\frac{36.2844}{5}}$$

$$\sqrt{7.2569} = 2.69$$

The problem is whether their mean differences in count is significantly different from zero (M = 0)

$$t = \frac{M_s - M}{\sigma_s} \times \sqrt{n}$$

$$= \frac{1.64 - 0}{2.69} \times \sqrt{6} = \frac{1.64}{2.69} \times 2.4495$$

$$= \frac{4.01718}{2.69} = 1.493$$

As the calculated value of t (1.493) is greater than table value of t (1.476) at 2 percent level. Therefore, at this level, there is difference in counts.

ii) t – test for difference between two sample means

t is an index to represent the relationship between the difference of two sample means and the standard error of this difference.

$$t = \frac{\text{Difference between the means}}{\text{Standard error of the difference}}$$

$$= \frac{M_1 - M_2}{s\sqrt{\dfrac{1}{n_1} + \dfrac{1}{n_2}}}$$

(s is the estimate of SD obtained from samples).

Where $\quad s = \sqrt{\dfrac{\sum d_1^2 + \sum d_2^2}{(n_1 - 1)(n_2 - 1)}}$

$$= \sqrt{\dfrac{\sum(x_1 - M_1)^2 + \sum(x_2 - M_2)^2}{n_1 + n_2 - 2}}$$

Degrees of freedom = $(n_1 - 1) + (n_2 - 1) = n_1 + n_2 - 2$.

Note: If σ_1 and σ_2 are the SDs of two samples respectively then,

$$s = \sqrt{\dfrac{n_1\sigma_1^2 + n_2\sigma_2^2}{n_1 + n_2 - 2}}$$

Example 3: Two groups of spinning centers, one group X of new employees having followed a different training scheme from the other group Y of existing employees were tested. For piecing rate (in hundredths of a second)

Group X	56	62	63	54	60	51	67	69	58	62
Group Y	70	71	62	60	56	75	64	72	68	66

Test whether the piecing rates of group X are significantly shorter than those of group Y.

Solution: Find M_1, M_2 and s using the formula

$$s = \sqrt{\dfrac{\sum d_1^2 + \sum d_2^2}{n_1 + n_2 - 2}}; \qquad n_1 = 9, \; n_2 = 11;$$

Degrees of freedom $= (n_1 - 1) + (n_2 - 1) = (9 - 1) + (11 - 1)$
$$= 8 + 10 = 18.$$

Group X X_1	d_1 $(X_1 - M_1)$	d_1^2	Group Y X_2	d_2 $(X_2 - M_2)$	d_2^2
56	−4	16	62	−4	16
62	+2	4	70	+4	16
63	+3	9	71	+5	25
54	−6	36	62	−4	16
60	0	0	60	−6	36
51	−9	81	56	−10	100
67	+7	49	75	+9	81
69	+9	81	64	−2	4
58	−2	4	72	+6	36
			68	+2	4
			66	0	0
540		$\sum d_1^2 = 280$	726		$\sum d_2^2 = 334$

$M_1 = \Sigma x_1 / n_1 = 540 / 9 = 60,$

$M_2 = \Sigma x_2 / n_2 = 726 / 11 = 66$

$$s = \sqrt{\frac{\Sigma d_1^2 + \Sigma d_2^2}{n_1 + n_2 - 2}}$$

$$= \sqrt{\frac{280 + 334}{9 + 11 - 2}} = \sqrt{\frac{614}{18}} = \sqrt{34.11} = 5.84$$

$$t = \frac{|M_1 - M_2|}{s\sqrt{\frac{1}{n_1} + \frac{1}{n_2}}} = \frac{|60 - 66|}{5.84\sqrt{\frac{1}{9} + \frac{1}{11}}} = \frac{6}{5.84 \times \sqrt{\frac{20}{99}}}$$

or

$$t = \frac{6}{5.84 \times \sqrt{0.202}} = \frac{6}{5.84 \times 0.45} = 2.281$$

The table value of t for 18 df at 5 percent level is 2.101. The calculated value of t (2.281) is greater than the table value of (2.101). The difference is significant.

Therefore, the piecing rate of group X are significantly shorter than those of group Y.

Example 4: A set of 15 observations in lea strength measurement gives mean = 68.57 kg, SD = 2.40 kg, another of seven observations gives mean = 64.14 kg, SD = 2.70 kg.

Use the t-test to find whether two sets of data were drawn from populations with the same mean.

Solution: Given $n_1 = 15$, $M_1 = 68.57$, $\sigma_1 = 240$

$$N_2 = 7, \ M_2 = 64.14, \sigma_2 = 2.70$$

$$s = \sqrt{\frac{n_1 \sigma_1^2 + n_2 \sigma_2^2}{n_1 + n_2 - 2}} = \sqrt{\frac{15 \times (2.4)^2 + 7(2.7)^2}{15 + 7 - 2}}$$

$$= \sqrt{\frac{15 \times 5.76 + 7 \times 7.29}{20}} = \sqrt{\frac{86.40 + 51.03}{20}}$$

$$= \sqrt{\frac{137.43}{20}} = \sqrt{6.8715} = 2.62$$

$$t = \frac{|M_1 - M_2|}{s\sqrt{\dfrac{1}{n_1} + \dfrac{1}{n_2}}} = \frac{|68.57 - 64.14|}{2.62 \times \sqrt{\dfrac{1}{15} + \dfrac{1}{7}}} = \frac{4.43}{2.62 \times \sqrt{0.209524}}$$

or $\qquad t = \dfrac{4.43}{2.62 \times 0.457} = \dfrac{4.43}{1.197} = 3.7$

df = $n_1 + n_2 - 2 = 15 + 7 - 2 = 20$

The table value of t for 20 df at 5 percent level is 2.086
The calculated value of t (3.7) is greater than the table value (2.086).
Therefore, there is a significant different and the data were drawn from populations with different means.

iii) t – test of coefficient correlation

In testing the null-hypothesis for a coefficient of correlation t is given by the formula

$$t = r\sqrt{\frac{n-2}{1-r^2}}, \text{ where n is the number of pairs of observations.}$$

The degrees of freedom = n – 2.

Example 5: Given r = 0.02 and n = 10 find t and test the significance of the correlation coefficient.

Solution: The degrees of freedom = n – 2 = 10 – 2 = 8

$$t = r\sqrt{\frac{n-2}{1-r^2}}$$

Or $\qquad t = 0.02 \times \sqrt{\dfrac{10-2}{1-(0.02)^2}} = 0.02 \times \sqrt{\dfrac{8}{1-0.0004}}$

Or $\qquad t = 0.02 \times \sqrt{\dfrac{8}{0.9996}} = 0.02 \times 2.83 = 0.566$

The table value of t for 8 df at 5 percent level is 2.306.
The calculated value (0.0566) is much less than 2.306.
Therefore, it is quite insignificant.

10.2   Z-Test of significance of coefficient of correlation

Another method for testing the significance of coefficient of correlation is z-test. Fisher has developed another statistic called z. First of all the value of coefficient of correlation, i.e. r is converted into the value of z. The following formula is used to transform r into z.

$$z = \frac{1}{2}\log\frac{1+r}{1-r}$$

$$= 1/2\ [\log\ (1 + r) - \log\ (1 - r)]$$
$$= 1.1513\ [\log_{10}\ (1 + r) - \log_{10}\ (1 - r)]$$

For example, if r = 0.6.

Then $z = 1.1513[\log_{10}\ (1 + 0.6) - \log_{10}(1 - 0.6)]$
$$= 1.1513[(\log_{10}\ 1.6 - \log_{10}(1 - 0.6)]$$
$$= 1.1513(0.2041 - 160.21)]$$
$$= 1.1513(1.2041 - 0.6021) = 1.1513 \times 0.6020 = 0.693$$

For general practice, Fisher has developed a table for the transformation of r into z and z into r. We can find the value of z corresponding to a given value of r and vice-versa from this table.

10.2.1 Advantages of z

The statistic z has two great advantages.

1) Its distribution is approximately normal even for small samples and its standard error can be calculated.
2) Its standard error does not depend upon the unknown population value. It takes the size of the sample into consideration.

Standard error of z – Standard error of z is estimated by the following formula

$$\text{Standard error of z i.e. } \sigma_z = \frac{1}{\sqrt{n-3}}$$

The same procedure is used to obtain the confidence limits. The standard error of z is interpreted like any other statistic that has a normal distribution. The confidence limits in terms of z can be transformed into limits in terms of r.

10.3 Test of significance of difference between two coefficients of correlation

First of all the coefficients of correlation, i.e. r_1 and r_2 are transformed into z_1 and z_2. Then we are required to test the significance of difference between two z's i.e. between z_1 and z_2 .

i) Standard error of difference between z's (i.e. $\sigma\, z_1 - z_2$)

The formula is $\sigma_{z_1 - z_2} = \sqrt{\dfrac{1}{n_1 - 3} + \dfrac{1}{n_2 - 3}}$

If the difference between the values of z_1 and z_2 is greater than twice the standard error, the difference is significant.

ii) t-test – t-test can also be applied to test the significance of difference between two coefficients of correlation.

The coefficients of correlation are transformed into z's. i.e., z_1 and z_2.

Then $\qquad t = \dfrac{1}{\sqrt{\dfrac{1}{n_1 - 3} + \dfrac{1}{n_2 - 3}}}$

Degrees of freedom = $(n_1 - 3) + (n_2 - 3) = n_1 + n_2 - 6$.

Example 6(a): Test the significance of the correlation r = 0.5 from a sample of size 8 against hypothesis correlation ρ = 0.7.

Solution: We have to test the hypothesis that correlation in the population is 0.7.
Applying Z-transformation

$$Z = \frac{1}{2}\log\frac{1+r}{1-r} = 1.1513\log_{10}\left(\frac{1+0.05}{1-0.05}\right)$$

$$= 1.1513 \log 3$$
$$= 1.1513 \times 0.4771 = 0.549$$

$$\xi = \log_{10}\frac{1+p}{1-p} \times 1.1513$$

$$= \log_{10}\frac{1+0.3}{1-0.3} \times 1.1513$$

$$= \log 1.857 \times 1.1513$$

$$= 0.2688 \times 1.1513 = 0.309$$

$$(Z - \xi) = 0.549 - 0.309 = 0.24$$

$$S.E._s = \frac{1}{\sqrt{n-3}} = \frac{1}{\sqrt{16}} = 0.25$$

$$\frac{\text{Difference}}{\text{S.E.}} = \frac{0.24}{0.25} = 0.96$$

Since, the difference between Z and ξ is less than 2.58 S.E. (1% level), the difference could have arisen due to fluctuations of sampling. Hence, the given correlation coefficient is not significantly different from 0.3.

$$Z = \frac{Z_1 - Z_2}{\sqrt{\dfrac{1}{n_1 - 3} + \dfrac{1}{n_2 - 3}}}$$

where $Z_1 = \dfrac{1}{2}\log\left(\dfrac{1+r_1}{1-r_1}\right)$ or $1.1513\log_{10}\dfrac{1+r_1}{1-r_1}$

and $Z_2 = \dfrac{1}{2}\log\left(\dfrac{1+r_2}{1-r_2}\right)$ or $1.1513\log_{10}\left(\dfrac{1+r_2}{1-r_2}\right)$

$$S.E._{(Z_1 - Z_2)} = \sqrt{\frac{1}{n_1 - 3} + \frac{1}{n_2 - 3}}$$

If the absolute value of this statistic is greater than 1.96 the difference will be significant at 5% level. The following examples illustrate the application to this test.

Example 6(b): The following data give sample sizes and correlation coefficients. Test the significance of the difference between two values using Fisher's Z-transformation.

Sample size	Value of r
5	0.870
12	0.560

Solution: Applying Z-test

$$Z = \frac{Z_1 - Z_2}{\sqrt{\dfrac{1}{n_1 - 3} + \dfrac{1}{n_2 - 3}}}$$

$$Z_1 = \frac{1}{2}\log\left(\frac{1 + r_1}{1 - r_1}\right) \quad or \quad 1.1513\log_{10}\frac{1 + r_1}{1 - r_1}$$

Here $r_1 = 0.87$,

$$Z_1 = 1.1513 \log \frac{1 + 0.87}{1 - 0.87}$$

$$= 1.1513 \log \frac{1.87}{0.13}$$

$$= 1.1513 \log 14.385$$

$$= 1.1513 \times 1.1579 = 1.333$$

$$Z_2 = \frac{1}{2}\log\left(\frac{1 + r_2}{1 - r_2}\right) \quad or \quad 1.1513\log_{10}\left(\frac{1 + r_2}{1 - r_2}\right)$$

$$= 1.1513 \log_{10} \frac{1 + 0.56}{1 - 0.56}$$

$$= 1.1513 \log \frac{1.56}{0.44}$$

$$= 1.1513 \log 3.545$$

$$= 1.1513 \times 0.5496 = 0.633$$

$$Z_1 - Z_2 = 1.333 - 0.633 = 0.7$$

$$S.E._{(Z_1 - Z_2)} = \sqrt{\frac{1}{n_1 - 3} + \frac{1}{n_2 - 3}}$$

$$= \sqrt{\frac{1}{5 - 3} + \frac{1}{12 - 3}} = 0.782$$

$$\frac{Z_1 - Z_2}{S.E.} = \frac{0.7}{0.782} = 0.895$$

Since the difference is less than 2.58 S.E. (1% level) the experiment provides no evidence against the hypothesis that the samples are drawn from the same population.

Example 6(c): Find the confidence limits for population coefficient of correlation with confidence coefficient of 0.95. Given r = 0.65 in a sample of 40 cases.

Solution: We have to find confidence limits for population coefficient of correlation, i.e., for r with confidence coefficient of 0.95 i.e., 95 percent.

r = 0.65   n = 40

Transform r into z

$$z = 1.1513 \, (\log_{10}(1 + r) - \log_{10}(1 - r)$$
$$= 1.1513 \, (\log_{10} 1.65 - \log_{10} 0.35)$$
$$= 1.1513 \, (0.2175 - 1.5441)$$
$$= 1.1513 \, (1.2175 - 0.5441)$$
$$= 1.1513 \times 0.6734 = 0.7753 = 0.78 \text{ (Approx.)}$$

If r = 0.65   z = 0.78.

Note: We can read the value of z corresponding to r, direct from Fisher's table.

Standard error of z i.e., $\sigma_z = \dfrac{1}{\sqrt{n-3}} = \dfrac{1}{\sqrt{40-3}} = \dfrac{1}{\sqrt{37}}$

$$= \sqrt{0.027} = 0.164$$

95 percent confidence limits are given by z ± 1.96 standard error

i.e.,   0.78 ± 1.96 × 1.64 or 0.78 ± 0.32
or   (0.78 − 0.32) to (0.78 + 0.32)
or   0.46 to 1.10.

Find the values of r corresponding to z from the table.

If z = 0.46   r = 0.43
If z = 1.10   r = 0.80

These confidence limits are 0.43 to 0.8.

Example 7: The correlation coefficient between yarn forming and textile fibres aptitude tests for a group of 20 boys is 0.42. For a group of 25 girls the correlation is 0.75. Is the difference significant?

Solution: Given $r_1 = 0.42$, $r_2 = 0.75$, $n_1 = 20$, $n_2 = 25$

Transform r_1 and r_2 into z_1 and z_2 by using the formula

$z = 1.1513 [\log_{10}(1+r) - \log_{10}(1-r)]$ or by reading from the table.

$$r_1 = 0.42 \qquad z_1 = 0.45 \qquad n_1 = 20$$
$$r_2 = 0.75 \qquad z_2 = 0.97 \qquad n_2 = 25$$

Standard error of difference between z_1 and z_2:

$$\sigma_{z1-z2} = \sqrt{\frac{1}{n_1-3} + \frac{1}{n_2-3}}$$

$$= \sqrt{\frac{1}{20-3} + \frac{1}{25-3}} = \sqrt{\frac{1}{17} + \frac{1}{22}}$$

$$= \sqrt{0.0588 + 0.454} = \sqrt{0.1042} = 0.32$$

The difference between z1 and z2 = 0.97 – 0.45 = 0.52
The difference (0.52) is less than twice standard error (2 × 0.32 i.e. 0.64)
Therefore, the difference is not significant.

Application of t-test:

We can apply t-test also

$$t = \frac{|z_1 - z_2|}{\sqrt{\frac{1}{n_1-3} + \frac{1}{n_2-3}}} = \frac{|0.45 - 0.97|}{\sqrt{\frac{1}{17} + \frac{1}{22}}} = \frac{0.52}{0.32}$$

$$= 1.625$$

Degrees of freedom = $n_1 + n_2 - 6 = 20 + 25 - 6 = 39$
$F_{cal} < F_{tab}$; hence, difference is not significant.

Example 8: Twelve ring cops are tested for count and the mean found to be 94.2^s. The SD of the twelve observations is 2.2 counts. If the nominal count is 92's is the machine spinning too fine?

Given: u = 92's, s = 2.2 x = 94.2's, n = 12

$$t = \frac{|(\bar{x} - u)|}{s/\sqrt{n}} = \frac{192 - 94.2}{2.2/\sqrt{12}} = 34.7$$

$t_{cal} > t_{tab}$. Hence, machine is spinning too fine.

Example 9: A breaking strength test on 6 nylon ropes showed a mean breaking strength of 7,750 lb with a S.D. of 145 lbs. But the company claims a mean breaking strength of 8,000 lb. Can the company's claim be supported?

Given : U = 8000 lb., $\bar{x}$ = 7750 lb., S = 145 lb., n = 6.

$$t = \frac{|7750 - 8000|}{145\sqrt{6}} = 4.22$$

Therefore, $t_{cal} > t_{tab}$. Hence, company claim can be admitted.

Example 10: Same yarn treated with two different sizes gave the following values for breaking load:

Test no.	Breaking load in grams.	
	Starch A	Starch B
1	22	23
2	19	20
3	19	17
4	18	19
5	20	20
6	17	17
7	16	18
8	20	21
9	18	17
10	15	18

Test the results and state whether the starches are effective.

	Starch A	Starch B
Mean	18	19
S.D.	2.30	2.0
Number of tests	10	10

$$t = \frac{|(\bar{x}_1 - \bar{x}_2)|}{S\sqrt{\dfrac{i}{n_i} + \dfrac{i}{n_2}}}$$

$$S = \sqrt{\left[\frac{9(2.30)^2 + 9(2)^2}{18}\right]} = 2.15$$

$$t = \frac{|(19 - 18)|}{2.15\sqrt{\dfrac{1}{10} + \dfrac{1}{10}}} = 1.04$$

$t_{cal} < t_{tab}$ Hence, sizes are not effective.

Example 11: Two yarns, each of 32's cotton count, were tested for strength.

	32ˢ (Station A)	32ˢ (Station B)
Number of tests	30	30
Mean strength (lb)	58	65
Standard deviation	7.8	82

Do the strength differ?

$$Z = \frac{\left(\overline{x}_1 - \overline{x}_2\right)}{\sqrt{\dfrac{S_1}{n_1} + \dfrac{S_2^2}{n_2}}} = \frac{(58 - 65)}{\sqrt{\dfrac{(7.8)^2}{30} + \dfrac{(8.2)^2}{30}}} = 3.4$$

Calculated value is greater than table value hence, the lea strength do differ.

Example 12: Following are the lea strength values in pounds of 20's hosiery yarn, spun on the same frame from 'flexible card' processed roving and 'Metallic cord' processed roving (the average count of both were same).

Flexible				Metallic				
63	67	71	70	65	56	62	68	64
69	66	77	77	54	65	61	66	66
56	66	65	66	74	64	62	62	61
54	67	76	76	61	66	70	62	67
54	66	60	70	75	58	56	65	70

Is there any reason, to believe that material processed through metallic cards will have significantly lower lea strength.

	Mean	Standard deviation	Number of tests
Flexible	66.48	6.39	25
Metallic	64.00	5.16	25

$$Z = \frac{\left(\overline{x} - \overline{x}_2\right)}{\sqrt{\dfrac{S_1^2}{n_1} + \dfrac{S_2^2}{n_2}}}$$

$$Z = \frac{(66.48 - 64)}{\sqrt{\dfrac{(6.39)^2}{25} + \dfrac{(5.16)^2}{25}}} = 1.51$$

As calculated value is less than table value hence, material processed through metallic card will have same strength as that of flexible.

Example 13: A typical polyester furnishing fabric was subjected to deweighting process. The effect of the process was studied through change in tensile strength. Do you feel that the process is in favour of the fabric?

	Control fabric	Deweighted fabric
Number of tests	25	25
Mean strength	48	44
Standard deviation (units)	4	7

$$Z = \frac{\left(\overline{x} - \overline{x_2}\right)}{\sqrt{\dfrac{S_1^2}{n_1} + \dfrac{S_2^2}{n_2}}}$$

$$Z = \frac{(48 - 44)}{\sqrt{\dfrac{4^2}{25} + \dfrac{7^2}{25}}} = 2.48$$

As $t_{cal} < t_{tab}$ the process is not in favor of the fabric.

Example 14: Two yarns were tested for strength and the following is results:

	Waxy yarn	Regular yarn
Number of tests	32	32
Mean strength	58	65
Standard deviation	7.2	8.4

Do you conclude that regular yarn is better than waxy yarn?

$$Z = \frac{(S_1 - S_2)}{SF_{1-2}} = \frac{(S_1 - S_2)}{\sqrt{\dfrac{S_1^2}{2n_1} + \dfrac{S_2^2}{2n_2}}}$$

$$Z = \frac{(17.2 - 8.4)}{\sqrt{\dfrac{(7.2)^2}{64} + \dfrac{(8.4)^2}{64}}} = 0.87$$

As t_{cal} is less than table value the yarns do not differ.

Example 15: The life time of a traveler for a random sample of 10 from a spinning shed gave the following data:

Item:	1	2	3	4	5	6	7	8	9	10
Failure rate:	4.2	4.6	3.9	4.1	5.2	3.8	3.9	4.3	4.4	5.6

Can we accept the hypothesis that the failure rate is significant?

Solution: Let us take the hypothesis that there is no significant difference in the sample mean and the hypothetical population mean. Applying the t-test

$$t = \frac{\overline{X} - \mu}{S} \sqrt{n}$$

Calculation of $\overline{X}$ and S

X	$(X - \overline{X})$	$(X - \overline{X})^2$
4.2	−0.2	0.04
4.6	+0.2	0.04
3.9	−0.5	0.25
4.1	−0.3	0.09
5.2	+0.8	0.64
3.8	−0.6	0.36
3.9	−0.5	0.25
4.3	−0.1	0.01
4.4	0	0
5.6	+1.2	1.44
$\Sigma X = 44$		$\Sigma(X - \overline{X})^2 = 3.12$

$$S = \sqrt{\frac{\Sigma(X - \overline{X})^2}{n-1}} = \sqrt{\frac{3.12}{9}} = 0.589$$

$$t = \frac{4.4 - 4}{0.589}\sqrt{10} = \frac{0.4 \times 3.126}{0.589} = 2.123$$

$v = n - 1 = 10 - 1 = 9$; For $v = 9$, $t_{0.05} = 2.26$

The calculated value of t is less than the table value. The hypothesis is accepted. The average failure rate of traveler is significant.

Example 16: Two types of slub catchers were used on 5 and 7 winders for clearing the yarn.

Clearer A was imported and clearer B indigenous. The decrease in the imperfectives after clearer yarns is as follows:

Clearer A:	10	12	13	11	14		
Clearer B:	8	9	12	14	15	10	9

Is there is significant difference in the efficacy of the two clearings? (For $v = 10$, $t_{0.05} = 2.223$)

Solution: Let us take the hypothesis that there is no significant difference in the efficacy of the two clearers. Applying t-test.

$$t = \frac{\overline{X_1} - \overline{X_2}}{S} \sqrt{\frac{n_1 n_2}{n_1 + n_2}}$$

X_1	$(X_1 - \overline{X_2})$	$(X_1 - \overline{X_1})^2$	X_2	$(X_2 - \overline{X_2})$	$(X_2 - \overline{X_2})^2$
10	−2	4	8	−3	9
12	0	0	9	−2	4
13	+1	1	12	+1	1
11	−1	1	14	+3	9
14	+2	4	15	+4	16
10	−1	1			
9	+2	4			
$\Sigma X_1 = 60$	$\Sigma(X_1-X_1)^2 = 10$		$\Sigma X_2 = 77$		$\Sigma(X_2 - X_2)^2 = 44$

*If the bias correction due to small sample is ignored, pooled estimate of the SD can be obtained by:

$$S = \sqrt{\frac{n_1 S_1^2 + n_2 S_2^2}{n_1 + n_2}}$$

However, it is advisable to take account of bias.

$$\overline{X_1} = \frac{\Sigma X_1}{n_1} = \frac{60}{5} = 12; \quad \overline{X_2} = \frac{\Sigma X_2}{n_2} = \frac{77}{7} = 11$$

$$S = \sqrt{\frac{\Sigma(X_1 - \overline{X_1})^2 + \Sigma(X_2 - \overline{X_2})^2}{n_1 + n_2 - 2}} = \sqrt{\frac{10 + 44}{5 + 7 - 2}} = \sqrt{\frac{54}{10}} = 2.324$$

$$t = \frac{\overline{X_1} - \overline{X_2}}{S} \sqrt{\frac{n_1 n_2}{n_1 + n_2}} = \frac{12 - 11}{2.324} \sqrt{\frac{5 \times 7}{5 + 7}} = \frac{1.708}{2.324} = 0.735$$

$$v = n_1 + n_2 - 2 = 5 + 7 - 2 = 10.$$

For $v = 10$, $t_{0.05} = 2.228$

$t_{cal} < t_{tab}$. Hence, both clearers do not differ.

Example 17: For a random sample of 10 sewing threads (A), usage on sewing machines.

| 10 | 6 | 16 | 17 | 13 | 12 | 8 | 14 | 15 | 9 |

For another random sample of 12 threads the usage is

| 7 | 13 | 22 | 15 | 12 | 14 | 18 | 8 | 21 | 23 | 10 | 17 |

Test whether the sewing threads (B) differ significantly as regards their usage is concerned.

Given the following:

Degree of freedom	19	20	21	22	23
Value of t.a. 5% level.	2.09	2.09	2.08	2.07	2.07

Solution: Let us take the null hypothesis that threads do not differ significantly with regard to their usage. Applying t-test:

$$t = \frac{\overline{X}_1 - \overline{X}_2}{S} \sqrt{\frac{n_1 n_2}{n_1 + n_2}}$$

$$S = \sqrt{\frac{\Sigma(X_1 - \overline{X}_1)^2 + \Sigma(X_2 - \overline{X}_2)^2}{n_1 + n_2 - 2}}$$

Calculating the required values:

A			B		
Usage deviations from mean 12	$(X_1 - \overline{X}_1)$	$(X_1 - \overline{X}_1)^2$	Usage deviations from actual mean 15	$(X_2 - \overline{X}_2)$	$(X_2 - \overline{X}_2)^2$
10	−2	4	7	−8	64
6	−6	36	13	−2	4
16	+4	16	22	+7	49
17	+5	25	15	0	0
13	+1	1	12	−3	9
12	0	0	14	−1	1
8	−4	16	18	+3	9
14	+2	4	8	−7	49
15	+3	9	21	+6	36
9	−3	9	23	+8	64
10	−5	25			
17	+2	4			

$\Sigma X_1 = 120$, $\Sigma(X_1 - \overline{X}_1) = $, $\Sigma(X_1 - \overline{X}_1)^2 = 120$, $\Sigma X_2 = 180$, $\Sigma(X_2 - \overline{X}_2) = 0$, $\Sigma(X_2 - \overline{X}_2)^2 = 314$

Usage of 10 threads

$$\overline{X}_1 = \frac{\Sigma X_1}{n_1} = \frac{120}{10} = 12 \ pounds$$

Usage of 12 threads

$$\overline{X}_2 = \frac{\Sigma X_2}{n_2} = \frac{180}{12} = 15 \ pounds$$

$$S = \sqrt{\frac{\Sigma(X_1 - X_1)^2 + \Sigma(X_2 - X_2)^2}{n_1 + n_2 - 2}} = \sqrt{\frac{120 + 314}{10 + 12 - 2}} = \sqrt{\frac{434}{20}} = 4.66$$

$X_1 = 12$, $X_2 = 15$, $n_1 = 10$, $n_2 = 12$, $S = 4.66$. Substituting the values in the above formula:

$$t = \frac{12 - 15}{4.66} \times \sqrt{\frac{10x12}{10 + 12}} = \frac{3}{4.66} \times 2.34 = 1.51$$

$$v = n_1 + n_2 - 2 = 10 + 12 - 2 = 20.$$

$t_{cal} < t_{tab}$, Hence, threads A and B do not differ.

Example 18: Two laboratories A and B carry out independent estimates of cupper content in a tarpaulin. A sample is taken from each batch, halved, and the separate halves sent to the two laboratories. The copper content obtained by the laboratories is recorded below:

Batch no.	1	2	3	4	5	6	7	8	9	10
Lab A	9	8	7	3	8	6	9	4	7	8
Lab B	9	8	8	4	7	7	9	6	6	6

Is there a significant difference between the mean copper content obtained by the two laboratories, A and B?

You may use the following extracts from t table in answering the questions:

Degrees of freedom:	6	7	8	9	10	16	18	20
t at 5% level:		1.45	2.36	2.31	2.26	2.23	2.12	2.10	2.09

Solution: Let us take the hypothesis that there is no significant difference between the mean copper content obtained by the two laboratories A and B. Applying t-test:

$$t = \frac{\overline{X}_1 - \overline{X}_2}{S} \sqrt{\frac{n_1 n_2}{n_1 + n_2}}$$

Since, the actual means are in fractions, we shall take deviations from the assumed means.

Batch no.	Lab A			Lab B		
	X_1	$(X_1 - A_1)$ $A_1 = 6$	$(X_1 - A_1)^2$	X_2	$(X_2 - A_2)$ $A_2 = 7$	$(X_2 - A_2)^2$
1	7	+1	1	9	+2	4
2	8	+2	4	8	+1	1
3	7	+1	1	8	+1	1
4	3	−3	9	4	−3	9
5	8	+2	4	7	0	0
6	6	0	0	7	0	0
7	9	+3	9	9	+2	4
8	4	−2	4	6	−1	1
9	7	+1	1	6	−1	1
10	8	+2	4	6	−1	1

$\Sigma X_1 = 67 \quad \Sigma(X_1 - A_1) = 0 \quad \Sigma(X_1 - A_1)^2 = 37 \quad \Sigma X_2 = 70 \quad \Sigma(X_2 - A_2) = 0 \quad \Sigma(X_2 - A_2)^2 = 22$

$X_1 = 67 / 10 = 6.7, X_2 = 70 / 10 = 7.0.$

$$S = \sqrt{\frac{\Sigma(X_1 - A_1)^2 + \Sigma(X_2 - A_2)^2 - n_1(X_1 - A_1)^2 - n_2(X_2 - A_2)^2}{n_1 + n_2 - 2}}$$

$$= \sqrt{\frac{37 + 22 - 10(6.7 - 6)^2 - 10(7 - 7)^2}{10 + 10 - 2}} = \sqrt{\frac{59 - 4.9}{18}} = \sqrt{\frac{54.1}{18}} = 1.734$$

$$t = \frac{6.7 - 7}{1.734} \times \sqrt{\frac{10 \times 10}{10 + 10}} = \frac{0.3}{1.734} \times 2.236 = 0.387$$

$v = n_1 + n_2 - 2 = 18$, For $v = 18$, $t_{0.05} = 2.10$.

$t_{cal} < t_{tab}$. Hence, the mean copper contents obtained by two laboratories A and B do not differ significantly.

Example 19: The mean life of a sample of 10 voltaic cells in ERM cleaner was found to be 1,456 hours with SD of 423 hours. A second sample of 17 cells chosen from a different batch showed a mean life of 1,280 hours with SD of 398 hours. Is there a significant difference between the means of the two batches?

Solution: Let us take the hypothesis that the means of the two batches do not differ significantly. Applying t-test

$$t = \frac{\overline{X}_1 - \overline{X}_2}{S} \sqrt{\frac{n_1 n_2}{n_1 + n_2}}$$

$X_1 = 1456$, $n_1 = 10$, $S_1 = 423$, $X_2 = 1280$, $n_2 = 17$, $S_2 = 398$.

$$S = \sqrt{\frac{(n_1 - 1)S_1^2 + (n_2 - 1)S_2^2}{n_1 + n_2 - 2}} = \sqrt{\frac{9(423)^2 + 16(398)^2}{10 + 17 - 2}}$$

$$= \sqrt{\frac{1610361 + 2534464}{25}} = \sqrt{165793} = 407.18$$

$$t = \frac{1456 - 1280}{407.18} \sqrt{\frac{10 \times 17}{10 + 17}} = \frac{176}{407.18} \times 2.51 = 1.085$$

$\nu = 10 + 17 - 2 = 25$, For $\nu = 25$, $t_{0.05} = 2.06$

$t_{cal} < t_{tab}$, we, therefore, conclude that the means of the two batches do not differ significantly.

Example 20: In a test, bear sorter for two groups of cottons gave the length parameter details as follows:

First cotton: 18   20   36   50   49   36   34   49   41
Second cotton: 29   28   26   35   30   44   46

Examine the significance of difference between the arithmetic mean of two cotton samples.

(The value of t at 5% level of significance for $\nu = 14$, is 2.14.)

Solution: Let us take the hypothesis that there is no significant difference in the arithmetic mean of the cottons. Applying t-test

$$t = \frac{\overline{X}_1 - \overline{X}_2}{S} \sqrt{\frac{n_1 n_2}{n_1 + n_2}}$$

Group I X_1	$(x_1 - \overline{X}_1)$ X_1	$(x_1 - \overline{X}_1)^2$ $\overline{X}_1 = 37$	Group II X_2	$(X_2 - \overline{X}_2)$ $\overline{X}_2 = 34$	$(X_2 - \overline{X}_2)^2$
38	−19	361	29	−5	25
20	−17	289	28	−6	36
36	−1	1	26	−8	64
50	+13	169	35	+1	1
49	+12	144	30	−4	16
36	−1	1	44	+10	100
34	−3	9	46	+12	144
49	+12	144			
41	+4	16			
$\Sigma X_1 = 333$	$\Sigma(X_1 - \overline{X}_1) = 0$	$\Sigma(X_1 - \overline{X}_1)^2 = 1,134$	$\Sigma X_2 = 238$	$\Sigma(X_2 - \overline{X}_2) = 0$	$\Sigma(X_2 - \overline{X}_2)^2 = 386$

$$\overline{X_1} = \frac{\Sigma X_1}{n_1} = \frac{333}{9} = 37; \quad \overline{X2} = \frac{\Sigma X_2}{n2} = \frac{238}{7} = 34;$$

$$S = \sqrt{\frac{\Sigma(X_1 - X_1)^2 + \Sigma(X_2 - X_2)^2}{n_1 + n_2 - 2}} = \sqrt{\frac{1134 + 386}{9 + 7 - 2}} = 10.42$$

$$t = \frac{37 - 34}{10.42}\sqrt{\frac{9 \times 7}{9 + 7}} = \frac{3}{10.42} \times 1.984 = 0.571$$

$v = n_1 + n_2 - 2 = 9 + 7 - 2 = 14$, For $v = 14$, $t_{0.05} = 2.14$
$t_{cal} < t_{tab}$. Hence, two cottons do not differ.

10.4   Testing difference between means of two samples

10.4.1 Dependent samples or paired observations

In the previous test it was assumed that the two samples were independent, i.e. the values of observations in one sample don't depend on the other. However, there are many situations in which this condition does not hold true, i.e. we have dependent (or paired) samples. Two samples are said to be dependent when the elements in one sample are related to those in the other in any significant or meaningful manner. In fact, the two samples may consist of pairs of observations made on the same object, individual, or more generally, on the same selected population elements. When samples are dependent they compromise the same number of elementary units. We may carry out some experiment, say, to find out the affect of training on some employees, find out the efficacy of a coaching class or determine whether there is a significant difference in the efficacy of two drugs – one made within the country and another imported. Often the use of dependent or paired samples will enable us to perform a more precise analysis, because they will allow us to control the extraneous factors. The t-test based on paired observations is defined by the following formula:

$$t = \frac{\overline{d} - 0}{S} \times \sqrt{n} \quad or \quad t = \frac{\overline{d}\sqrt{n}}{S}$$

where $\overline{d}$ = the mean of the differences
S = the SD of the differences.

The value of S is calculated as follows:

$$S = \sqrt{\frac{\Sigma(d-\bar{d})^2}{n-1}} \quad or \quad \sqrt{\frac{\Sigma d^2 - n(\bar{d})^2}{n-1}}$$

It should be noted that t is based on n − 1 degrees of freedom.

The following examples will illustrate the application of difference test.

Example 21: A finishing treatment was given to 10 sorts and change in thread spacing were recorded as 3, 6, −2, 4, −3, 4, 6, 0, 0, 2. Do you conclude that finishing is effective (Given $t_{0.05}$ = 9df = 2.26)?

Solution: Let us take the hypothesis that the treatment has no effect on thread spacing. Applying the difference test:

$$t = \frac{\bar{d}\sqrt{n}}{S}$$

d	d²
3	9
6	36
−2	4
4	16
−3	9
4	16
6	36
0	0
0	0
2	4
Σd = 20	Σd² = 130

$$\bar{d} = \frac{\Sigma d}{n} = \frac{20}{10} = 2$$

$$S = \sqrt{\frac{\Sigma d^2 - n(\bar{d})^2}{n-1}}$$

$$= \sqrt{\frac{130 - 10(2)^2}{10-1}} = 3.162$$

$$t = \frac{2 \times 3.162}{62} = 2$$

$v = n - 1 = 10 - 1 = 9$, For $v = 9$, $t_{0.05} = 2.26$

The calculated value of t is less than the table value. The hypothesis is accepted. Thus, it is concluded that finishing has no effect on thread spacing.

10.5   Testing the significance of an observed correlation coefficient:

Given a random sample from a bivariate normal population. If we are to test the hypothesis that the correlation coefficient of the population is zero, i.e., the variables in the population are uncorrelated, we have to apply the following test:

$$t = \frac{r}{\sqrt{1-r^2}} \times \sqrt{n-2}$$

here t is based on (n – 2) degrees of freedom.

If the calculated value of 't' exceeds $t_{0.05}$ for (n – 2) df, we say that the value of r is significant at 5% level. If $t < t_{0.05}$ the data are consistent with the hypothesis of an uncorrelated population.

The following examples will illustrate the test.

Example 22: A study of the length of 18 pairs of shuttles in a factory shows that the coefficient correlation is 0.52. Apply t-test to find whether correlation is significant.

(For 16 degrees of freedom at 5% level of significance, the table value of t = 2.12.)

Solution: Let us take the hypothesis that there is no significant differences in the sample correlation and correlation in the population. Applying t-test:

$$t = \frac{r}{\sqrt{1-r^2}} \times \sqrt{n-2}$$

r = 0.52, n = 18.

$$t = \frac{0.52}{\sqrt{1-0.52^2}} \times \sqrt{18-2} = \frac{0.52 \times 4}{0.854} = 2.44$$

$v = (n - 2) = (18 - 2) = 16$
For $v = 16$, $t_{0.05} = 2.12$.

The calculated value of t is greater than the table value. The hypothesis is rejected. The given value of r is significant.

Example 23: How many pairs of observations must be included in a sample in order that an observed correlation coefficient of value 0.42 shall have a calculated value of t greater than 2.72?

Solution:

$$t = \frac{r}{\sqrt{1 - r^2}} \times \sqrt{n - 2}$$

We are given the value of t and r and we have to find out n

$$2.72 = \frac{0.42}{0.908} \times \sqrt{n - 2}$$

$$\sqrt{n - 2} \times 0.42 = 2.72 \times 0.908$$

$$\sqrt{n - 2} = \frac{2.47}{0.42}$$

$$\sqrt{n - 2} = 5.88 \Rightarrow n - 2 = (5.88)^2$$

n = 34.57 + 2 = 36.57 or 37.

Hence, we should include 37 pairs of observations.

Example 24: The following table gives the ends/cm and picks/cm of 10 sorts. Compute the correlation coefficient and test for its significance.

Ends/cm :	23	27	28	29	30	31	33	35	36	39
Picks/cm:	18	22	23	24	25	26	28	29	30	32

Solution: We set up the hypothesis that there is no correlation in the population.

Applying t-test.

$$t = \frac{r}{\sqrt{1 - r^2}} \times \sqrt{n - 2}$$

$$= \frac{0.939}{\sqrt{1 - (0.939)^2}} \times \sqrt{10 - 2}$$

$$= \frac{0.939}{\sqrt{1 - 0.882}} \times 2.8284 = \frac{0.939}{0.344} \times 2.8284 = 7.72$$

v = n − 2 = (10 − 2) = 8.

For v = 8, $t_{0.05}$ = 2.310

The calculated value being much higher than the table value, the correlation is significant.

Example 25: Is a correlation coefficient of 0.5 significant if obtained from a random sample of 11 pairs of values from a normal population? Use t-test.

Solution: We have to test the significance of the observed correlation coefficient.

$$t = \frac{r}{\sqrt{1 - r^2}} \times \sqrt{n - 2}$$

r = 0.5, n = 11

$$t = \frac{0.5}{\sqrt{\left(1 - (0.5)^2\right)}} \times \sqrt{11 - 2}$$

$$= \frac{0.5}{\sqrt{1 - 0.25}} \times \sqrt{9} = \frac{0.5}{0.87} \times 3 = 1.724$$

$\nu = 11 - 2 = 9$

For $\nu = 9$, $t_{0.05} = 2.26$

The calculated value of t is less than the table value and hence, the given correlation coefficient is not significant.

Example 26: Find the least value of r in a sample of 27 pairs from a bivariate normal population significant at 5% level.

Solution:

$$t = \frac{r}{\sqrt{1 - r^2}} \times \sqrt{n - 2}$$

$\therefore \qquad t = \frac{r}{\sqrt{1 - r^2}} \times \sqrt{27 - 2} = \frac{5r}{\sqrt{1 - r^2}}$

Now for 'r' to be significant at 5% level calculated value of t should be greater than the table value. At 5% level for 25 degrees of freedom the table value is zero.

$\therefore \qquad t = \frac{5r}{\sqrt{1 - r^2}} > 2.06$

$25r^2 > 4.2436 \, (1 - r^2)$

$29.2436 \, r^2 > 4.2436$

$\therefore \qquad |r| > \sqrt{\frac{4.2436}{29.2436}} = 0.381$

Hence, the required least value of r in a sample of 27 pairs to be significant at 5% level should be 0.381.

Example 27: Ten spools are taken at random from a batch of tyre cord line. The mean net weight of the spool is 11.8 kg and the standard deviation is 0.15 kg. Does the sample mean differ significantly from the intended weight of 12 kg (Given for $v = 9$, $t_{0.05} = 2.26$).

Solution: Let us take the hypothesis that the sample mean does not differ significantly from the intended weight of 12 kg.

$$t = \frac{|\bar{X} - \mu|}{S}\sqrt{n}$$

$\bar{X} = 11.8$, $\mu = 12$, $S = 0.15$, $n = 10$

$$\therefore \quad t = \frac{|11.8 - 12|}{0.15} \times \sqrt{10} = \frac{0.2 \times 3.162}{0.15} = 4.216$$

For $v = 9$, $t_{0.05} = 2.26$

$t_{cal} > t_{tab}$.

Example 28: Two working designs are under consideration for adoption in a plant. A time and motion study shows that 12 workers using design A have a mean assembly time of 300 seconds with a SD of 12 seconds and that 15 workers using design B have a mean assembly time of 335 seconds with a SD of 15 seconds. Is the difference in the mean assembly time between the two working design significant at one percent level of significance? The following table gives some t-values which may be used:

Level of significance	Degrees of freedom		
	25	26	27
pr = 0.05	2.06	2.06	2.05
pr = 0.01	2.79	2.78	2.77

Solution: Let us take the hypothesis that the difference between the two designs A and B in respect of mean assembly time is not significant. Applying t-test

$$t = \frac{\bar{X}_1 - \bar{X}_2}{S}\sqrt{\frac{n_1 n_2}{n_1 + n_2}}$$

$\bar{X}_1 = 300$, $S_1 = 12$, $n_1 = 12$
$\bar{X}_2 = 335$, $S_2 = 15$, $n_2 = 15$

$$S = \sqrt{\frac{(n_1 - 1)S_1^2 + (n_2 - 1)S_2^2}{n_1 + n_2 - 2}}$$

$$= \sqrt{\frac{11(12)^2 + 14(15)^2}{12 + 15 - 2}} = \sqrt{\frac{5.103}{25}} = 13.8$$

$$t = \frac{300 - 335}{13.8} \times \sqrt{\frac{12 \times 15}{12 + 15}}$$

$$= \frac{35}{13.8} \times 2.582 = 6.55$$

$v = n_1 + n_2 - 2 = 12 + 15 - 2 = 25$

For $v = 25$, $t_{0.05} = 2.79$

The calculated value of t is greater than the table value. Hence, the hypothesis does not hold true. We therefore, conclude that the difference in the mean assembly time between the two working designs is significant at 1 percent level.

Example 29: 10^s and 12^s beams prepared on jupiter warper were weighed and the values in kg are

10^s: 66   67   75   76   82   84   88   90   92
12^s: 64   66   74   78   82   85   87   92   93   95   97

Test whether the two counts have the same variance at the 5% level of significance. (F = 3.11 at 5% level for $v_1 = 8$ and $v_2 = 10$)

Solution: Let us take the hypothesis that the two populations have the same variance.

Applying F-test:

$$F = \frac{S_1^2}{S_2^2}$$

A X_1	$(X_1 - \bar{X}_1)$ x_1	x_1^2 X_2	B	$(X_2 - \bar{X}_2)$ x_2	x_2^2
66	−14	196	64	−19	361
67	−13	169	66	−17	289
75	−5	25	74	−9	81
76	−4	16	78	−5	25
82	+2	4	82	−1	1

(Contd.)

A X_1	$(X_1 - \bar{X}_1)$ x_1	x_1^2 X_2	B	$(X_2 - \bar{X}_2)$ x_2	x_2^2
84	+4	16	85	+2	4
88	+8	61	87	+4	16
90	+10	100	92	+9	81
92	+12	144	93	+10	100
95	+12	144			
97	+14	196			
$\Sigma X_1 = 720$	Σx_1	$\Sigma x_1^2 = 734$	$\Sigma X_2 = 913$	$\Sigma x_2 = 0$	$\Sigma x_2^2 = 1298$

$$X_1 = \frac{\Sigma X_1}{n_1} = \frac{720}{9} = 80; \quad X_2 = \frac{\Sigma X_2}{n_2} = \frac{913}{11} = 83$$

$$S_1^2 = \frac{\Sigma x_1^2}{n_1 - 1} = \frac{734}{9 - 1} = 91.75 .$$

$$S_2^2 = \frac{\Sigma x_2^2}{n_2 - 1} = \frac{1298}{11 - 1} = 129.8$$

$$F = \frac{S_1^2}{S_2^2} = \frac{129.8}{91.75} = 1.415$$

$$F_{cal} < F_{tab}$$

For $v_1 = 8$ and $v_2 = 19$, $F_{0.01} = 3.11$ (given)

Hence, it may be concluded that the two counts have the same variance.

Example 30: In measuring the crease recovery of casement fabrics the sample of 8 observations, the sum of squared deviations of items from the mean was 94.5. In another sample of 10 observations, the value was found to be 101.7. Test whether the difference is significant at 5% level.

Solution: Given $n_1 = 8$, $\Sigma(X_1 - X_1)^2 = 94.5$, $N_1 = 10$, $\Sigma(X_2 - X_2)^2 = 101.7$

$$F = \frac{S_1^2}{S_2^2}$$

$$S_1^2 = \frac{\Sigma(X_2 - X_2)^2}{n_1 - 1} = \frac{94.5}{7} = 13.5$$

$$S_2^2 = \frac{\Sigma(X_2 - X_2)^2}{n_2 - 1} = \frac{101.7}{9} = 11.3$$

$$F = \frac{13.5}{11.3} = 1.195$$

$F_{cal} < F_{tab}$; hence, it is concluded that the difference in the variances of two samples is not significant at 5% level.

Example 31: The mean (GSM) population of a random sample of 400 G10 Tarpaulins 'w' factory was found to be 400 with a SD of 12. The mean(GMS) population of a random sample of 400 G30 Tarpaulins 'y' factory was found to be 395 with a SD of 15. Is the difference between the two means statistically significant?

Solution: The mean GSM of 400 samples of G10 Tarpaulins was 400 with S.D. 12. On the other hand, the mean values of 400 G30 paulins was 395 with S.D. 15 Test. For the difference between the means

$$S.E._{(X_1 - X_2)} = \sqrt{\frac{\sigma_1^2}{n_1} + \frac{\sigma_2^2}{n_2}}$$

$\sigma_1 = 12$, $n_1 = 400$, $\sigma_2 = 15$, $n_2 = 400$

$$S.E. = \sqrt{\frac{12^2}{400} + \frac{15^2}{400}} = \sqrt{\frac{144}{400} + \frac{225}{400}} = 0.96$$

$$X_1 - X_2 = 400 - 395 = 5$$

$$\frac{\text{Difference}}{\text{S.E.}} = \frac{5}{0.96} = 5.21$$

As difference is greater than table value, the mean GSM is statistically significant.

Example 32: Twelve sorts were produced on looms which were repaired and maintained. The production rates are given below. Do you find any difference between the conditions?

No. of sorts: 1, 2, 3, 4, 5, 6, 7, 8, 9, 10, 11, 12
Spares replaced: 50, 42, 51, 26, 35, 42, 60, 41, 70, 55, 62, 38
New parts inserted: 62, 40, 61, 35, 30, 52, 68, 51, 84, 63, 72, 50

(the value of 't' for 11 degrees of freedom at 5% level of significance is 2.20)

Solution: Let us take the hypothesis that there is no difference in repairs and maintenance. Applying t-test

$$t = \frac{\overline{d}\sqrt{n}}{S}$$

| No. of sorts | Production rates of looms | | Difference | |
	Repaired	Maintained	d	d²
1	50	62	+12	144
2	42	40	−2	4
3	51	61	+10	100
4	26	35	+9	81
5	35	30	−5	25
6	42	52	+10	100
7	60	68	+8	64
8	41	51	+10	100
9	70	84	+14	196
10	55	63	+8	64
11	62	72	+10	100
12	38	50	+12	144
			$\Sigma d = 96$	$\Sigma d^2 = 1122$

$$\bar{d} = \frac{\Sigma d}{n} = \frac{96}{12} = 8$$

$$S = \sqrt{\frac{\Sigma d^2 - n(\bar{d})^2}{n-1}} = \sqrt{\frac{1122 - 12(8)^2}{12-1}} = 5.673$$

$$t = \frac{8\sqrt{12}}{5.673} = 4.885$$

$t_{cal} > t_{tab}$; hence, the performance of loom differs.

Example 33: The following data were collected from two mills as regards the starting stipend paid to new management trainees of a textile mill.

Do the data give evidence that the stipend paid in mill B is significantly more than that in city A?

Test at a significance level of 1%.

Mill	Monthly stipend (mean)	Sample SD	Sample size
A	Rs.1,400	Rs.80	200
B	Rs.1,600	Rs.120	175

Solution: Let us take the hypothesis that there is no significant difference in the stipend paid in the two mills 'A' and 'B'. Applying large sample test of difference of means

$$S.E._{(x_1 - x_2)} = \sqrt{\frac{\sigma_1^2}{n_1} + \frac{\sigma_2^2}{n_2}}$$

$\sigma_1 = 80$, $n_1 = 210$, $n_2 = 120$, $n_2 = 175$

$$S.E. = \sqrt{\frac{80^2}{200} + \frac{120}{175}} = \sqrt{32 + 82.286} = 10.69$$

$$\frac{\text{Difference}}{\text{S.E.}} = \frac{|1400 - 1600|}{11.69} = 14.29$$

We can conclude that mills differ in stipend payment.

Example 34: Two samples of 6 and 5 items, respectively, gave the following data:

Mean of 1st sample	40
Standard deviation of 1st sample	8
Mean of the second sample	50
Standard deviation of the 2nd sample	10

Is the difference of means significant? The value of t for 9 degrees of freedom at 5% level is 2.26.

Solution: Let us take the hypothesis that there is no significant difference in the means of two samples. Applying t-test:

$$t = \frac{\overline{X_1} - \overline{X_2}}{S} \sqrt{\frac{n_1 n_2}{n_1 + n_2}}$$

$\overline{X_1} = 40$, $X_2 = 50$, $n_1 = 6$, $n_2 = 5$

$$S = \sqrt{\frac{(n_1 - 1)S_1^2 + (n_2 - 1)S_2^2}{n_1 + n_2 - 2}}$$

$$= \sqrt{\frac{5(8)^2 + 4(10)^2}{6 + 5 - 2}} = \sqrt{\frac{320 + 400}{9}} = 8.944$$

$$t = \frac{40 - 50}{8.944} \sqrt{\frac{6 \times 5}{6 + 5}} = \frac{10}{8.944} \times 1.651 = 1.846$$

$v = 6 + 5 \times 2 = 9$

For $v = 9$, $t_{0.05} = 2.26$

$t_{cal} < t_{tab}$. Hence, two samples do not differ.

Example 35: Two salesmen A and B are working in a certain district. From a sample survey conducted by the head office, the following results were obtained. State whether there is any significant difference in the average sales between the two salesmen.

	A	B
No. of sales	10	18
Average sales (in Rs.)	170	205
Standard deviation (in Rs.)	20	25

Solution: Let us take the hypothesis that there is no significant difference in the average sales of the two salesmen.

Applying t-test,

$$t = \frac{\overline{X}_1 - \overline{X}_2}{S}\sqrt{\frac{n_1 n_2}{n_1 + n_2}}$$

$\overline{X}_1 = 170$, $\overline{X}_2 = 205$, $n_1 = 10$, $n_2 = 18$, $S_1 = 20$, $S_2 = 25$.

$$S = \sqrt{\frac{(n_1 - 1)S_1^2 + (n_2 - 1)S_2^2}{n_1 + n_2 - 2}}$$

$$= \sqrt{\frac{(10-1)400 + (18-1)625}{10+18-2}} = \sqrt{\frac{3600 + 10625}{26}}$$

$$= \sqrt{547.115} = 23.39$$

$$t = \frac{170 - 205}{23.39}\sqrt{\frac{10 \times 18}{10 + 18}} = 3.79$$

$v = n_1 + n_2 - 2 = 10 + 18 - 2 = 26$

For $v = 26$, $t_{0.05} = 2.056$.

$t_{cal} > t_{tab}$

Hence, sales man differ in sales.

Problems for practice

Problem 1: The supplier of cots claims that the average shore hardness of this supply is 80°.

a) with the standard deviation 1°
b) no mention of standard deviation

A sample of 9 cots are tested and the results are:
78, 81.5, 78.5, 78, 80, 79.5, 80.5, 77.0, 79.0.
Test whether the claim of the supplier could be accepted.

Problem 2: A mill produces 80s p/c yarn on two makes of machines A and B. The mill wants to find out whether machines of make B produce more hairy yarns compared to machines of make A. Twenty random samples of yarn from each group of machines have been tested for hairiness. The number of hairs per 1000 M (average of 20 readings) and the SDs estimated from the samples are

A: Mean number of hairs per 1000 M – 8000, S.D. – 2400
B: Mean number of hairs per 1000 M – 10000, S.D. – 4000

Do you conclude 'B give more hairy yarns'?

Problem 3: Two samples of 10 and 15 leas have been taken and weighed. The sample averages are 9.8 g and 9.2 g. The sample standard deviations are 0.3 g and 0.4 g, respectively. The population standard deviations are also not known. Test whether the two samples could be from the same population.

Problem 4: The standard deviation of twist tested on yarn from two spindles are as follows:

Spindle – A – S_1 = 1.31 n_1 = 50
Spindle – B – S_2 = 2.85 n_2 = 60.

Test whether the twist variation is more on spindle B.

Problem 5: The variation in the incidence of neps in 1000 M of yarn has been studied from random samples of yarns produced by machines A and B.

Machine – A: n_1 = 14 S_1^2 = 510
Machine – B: n_2 = 10 S_2^2 = 240

Test whether the machines differ in performance.

Problem 6: A sample of 250 cones has been inspected and 4% of the cones are found defective. Find whether the incidence of defectives in the population is 2%.

10.6   Test of goodness of fit

The χ^2 distribution discussed earlier can be used for testing the actual frequency of occurrence of an event with the expected frequency. The test can be applied to data like and breaks in different groups of spindles, nep count in cards, defects in cloth etc. If O_1, O_2, ..., O_p are the observed frequencies and E_1, E_2,.........E_p are the respective expected frequencies, then the statistic

$$\chi^2 = \sum_{1}^{p} (O_1 - E_i)^2 \Big/ E_i$$

is distributed like χ^2 with (p – 1) df. If the actual $\chi^2 > \chi^2_{0.05}$, then the observed frequencies differ from the expected as per the test results.

Where only two cells are involved, say with observations O_1 and O_2 with a common sample size, the statistic simplifies to:

$$\chi^2 = \frac{(O_1 - O_2)^2}{(O_1 + O_2)}$$

Example 36: Four ring frames have been observed for end breaks and the results are shown below:

Machine	Duration of observations (Spindle hours)	No. of breaks (O)
A	500	50
B	1000	120
C	1000	150
D	800	105

Is there any evidence to conclude that breakages rates differ between machines?

Formulate the null hypothesis that, in the population, the breakage rates do not differ between the machines. If B_1, B_2, B_3, B_4 are the breakages rates on the four machines A,B,C,D respectively then Ho: $B_1 = B_2 = B_3 = B_4$. H_1 : B_1 to B_4 are not same. Under the null hypothesis, the expected number of breaks for the period of observation on the four machines are 64, 129, 129 and 103 then

$$\chi^2 = \frac{(50 - 64)^2}{64} + ... + \frac{(105 - 103)^2}{103.} = 7.15$$

$\chi^2_{0.05}$ for 3 df being the range 0.48 to 11.19, the null hypothesis is accepted.

While applying the χ^2 test, it should be ensured that adjusted data is not utilized. The actual observed values only have to be used if the conclusions are to be correct. For example, let us convert the observations in example 36 to 2000 spindle hours in each case even though the observations have been for different periods. Then we have

Machine	End breaks
A	200
B	240
C	300
D	262.5

then $\chi^2 = 21.0$. Therefore, the conclusion is that, the breakage rates differ from machine to machine. This factor has to be kept in mind while using the χ^2 distribution for any test.

Example 37: Warp breaks were observed for a period of 40 loom hours in an auto loom shed. The total number of warp breaks during observations was 60. To test whether the breakage rate has increased from the earlier figure of 1.0 per loom hour.

H_o: Breaks per loom hour b = 1.0
H_1 : b > 1.0 (one sided test)

Under null hypothesis total breaks for 40 loom hours = 40. Therefore,

$$\chi^2 = \frac{(60-40)^2}{40} = 10 \text{ for 1 degree of freedom, using upper tail } \chi^2_{0.05}$$

critical value = 3.84
Thus, the null hypothesis is rejected.

Example 38: Lea strength is to be tested to ensure that a higher strength of 1.5kg from the present level of 40 kg will be accepted 90% of the times. The standard deviation of the strength is known to be 2.8. What should be the sample size?

Analysis of variance

11.1   Introduction

Statistical methods are the techniques for studying variation in nature. Analysis of variance is a useful practical method of testing the significance. It has a wider application as compared to t-test, another important method of testing reliability of data. With the help of t-test we can compare two samples. The t-test generally determines the significance of difference between two means. When more than two samples are to be compared, the technique used for the purpose is analysis of variance. It is a technique to test the homogeneity of means; to test the hypothesis that means do not differ significantly. In fact, it is a method for testing the difference between variances.

How these variances arise and how they are related are the important problems to be discussed in this technique.

Variability may arise due to a large number of causes, and the amount of variation in the data may be the sum total of small deviations produced by these factors and causes forming a homogeneous system. The variation in data may also arise due to other random causes such as lack of homogeneity of some raw material or error or chance fluctuations. For example, the yield of wheat depends upon many factors such as fertility of soil, quality of seeds, amount of manure, fertilizers applied, weather conditions, etc. Each factor makes it own contribution towards yield. The component variations due to these factors and other random causes form the overall variability in the data of the sample. Analysis of variance is a method to estimate the contribution made by each factor to the total variation.

Analysis of variance is thus a procedure to split up the total variability into component variations ascribable to different sources of causes. It determines how much of variance is due to one group of causes and how much of it is due to other group of causes.

It is known that variance is the mean of the sum of squares of deviations of items from the general mean. The sum of squared deviations or simply the sum of squares is equal to $\Sigma d^2 \, or \, \Sigma x^2 - \dfrac{(\Sigma x)^2}{n}$.

Suppose we have yields per acre of eight plots of cotton. Four plots are of variety A and four plots are of variety B.

Variety	Plots	Total	Mean					
A	33	41	42	44	=	160	40
B	34	50	44	48	=	176	44

$$\text{General mean} = \frac{\sum x}{n} = \frac{336}{8} = 42$$

(a) Total sum of squares $= \sum d^2$

$$= (33 - 42)^2 + (41 - 42)^2 + (42 - 42)^2 + (44 - 42)^2 + (34 - 42)^2 + (50 - 42)^2 + (44 - 42)^2 + (48 - 42)^2$$

$$= 81 + 1 + 0 + 4 + 64 + 64 + 4 + 36 = 254$$

or by using the formula $\sum x^2 - \dfrac{(\sum x)^2}{n}$

Sum of squares $= [33^2 + 41^2 + 42^2 + 44^2 + 34^2 + 50^2 +$

$$44^2 + 48^2] - (336^2/8)$$
$$= [1089 + 1681 + 1764 + 1936 + 1156 + 2500$$
$$+ 1936 + 2304] - 336 \times 336/8$$
$$= 14366 - 14112 = 254$$

(b) The respective means of varieties are 40 and 44. Each variety is sown in four plots.

The sum of squared deviations between the varieties

$$= 4(40 - 42)^2 + 4(44 - 42)^2 = (4 \times 4) + (4 \times 4) = 32$$

We can also find the above sum by using the formula

$$\sum \left[\frac{X^2}{V} \right] - \frac{(\sum x)^2}{n}$$

where X is the sum of values of observations in each variety, i.e., the sample total, and V is the number of observations (values) in each variety.

$$\text{Sum of squares} = \left[\frac{(160)^2}{4} + \frac{(176)^2}{4} \right] - \frac{336^2}{8}$$

$$= 6400 + 7744 - 14112$$
$$= 14144 - 14112 = 32$$

(c)   The sum of the squared deviations within varieties
    (i)   Within variety A
$$(33 - 40)^2 + (41 - 40)^2 + (42 - 40)^2 + (44 - 40)^2$$
$$= 49 + 1 + 4 + 16 = 70$$
    (ii)   Within variety B
$$(34 - 44)^2 + (50 - 44)^2 + (44 - 44)^2 + (48 - 44)^2$$
$$= 100 + 36 + 0 + 16 = 152$$
Total sum of squares within varieties = 70 + 152 = 222
or sum of squares within varieties

$$= \text{Total sum of squares} - \text{Sum of squares between varieties}$$
$$= 254 - 32 = 222$$

Therefore, total sum of squares = Sum of squares between varieties + Sum of squares within varieties

Thus, there are two types of variations:

(i)   Variations between samples
(ii) Variations within samples

The overall variance is due to differences between the samples and differences within the samples and the first essential thing is to resolve the resultant variance into these parts, i.e. into the part that is due to "between sample differences" and the part that is due to "differences within the samples".

11.2   Variance ratio

As it is shown later, variance due to between sample differences is very high as compared to that due to within sample differences. The analysis of variance is thus a technique to find out the relationship of the variation between the sample differences and the variation within the sample differences. The analysis of variance gives us a test to determine the significance of the difference between these two variances. To find the relationship between these variances, we are required to find the variance ratio denoted by F.

$$\text{The variance ratio (F)} = \frac{\text{Larger variance estimate}}{\text{Smaller variance estimate}}$$

or

$$F = \frac{\text{Variance for between the variables (samples)}}{\text{Variance for within the variables (samples)}}$$

Fisher and Yates have formulated a table giving values of variance ratio at different levels of significance for different combinations of degrees of freedom.

Snedecor has also given us a table for the values of F at 1 percent and 5 percent levels corresponding to different degrees of freedom. The degrees at the top of the table refer to larger variance while those at the side refer to smaller variance.

Assumptions

The analysis of variance test (variance-ratio or F-test) is based on certain assumptions. The following assumptions must be satisfied for the validity of this test.

  (i)   *Additivity of treatment effects*. The contributions made by different sources of variance in the total sum must be additive.
 (ii)   *Random sampling*. The practice of free and random sampling must be followed within the sets, i.e. the observations within samples should be mutually independent and laws of chance should be allowed to operate freely.
(iii)   *Normality of distribution*. The variations within experimentally homogeneous sets should be from normal population. To test the homogeneity of the estimates of variance, it is necessary that the population is normally distributed.
(iv)   The variances within homogeneous sets must be approximately equal. We assume that experimental errors have a common variance.

Basis of classification

Data can be classified according to different criteria or factors. In a one-way classification, there is one reason for segregating data into sets. The same general character is possessed by several samples. In a two-way classification, there are two distinct bases of classification. Data may be classified according to two different criteria, e.g. into different classes and different groups.

11.3   Calculation of variance ratio or F

One-way classification

The value of variance ratio or F can be computed as follows:

  (a)   Find the sum of squared deviations (total sum of squares) using the formula $\sum x^2 - \dfrac{(\sum x)^2}{n}$.

We are required to split the sum of squares into two parts.

(i)   Sum of squares due to 'variation between samples'. This sum can be obtained by using the formula

$$\Sigma\left[\frac{X^2}{V}\right] - \frac{(\Sigma x)^2}{n}$$

where X is the sum of observations in each sample (i.e. sum total) and V is the number of observations (values) in each sample.

(ii) Sum of squares due to variation within samples, i.e., sum of squares within samples

= Total sum of squares – Sum of squares between samples.

$$= \left[\Sigma x^2 - \frac{(\Sigma x)^2}{n}\right] - \Sigma\left[\frac{X^2}{V}\right] - \frac{(\Sigma x)^2}{n}$$

$$= \Sigma x^2 - \Sigma\left[\frac{X^2}{V}\right]$$

(b) Variance for each part is obtained by dividing the sum of the squares by the respective degrees of freedom.

Total number of df = Total number of items – 1 = n – 1.

(i)   df for between samples = number of samples – 1 = N – 1

(ii) df for within samples   = Total df – df for between samples =

= (n – 1) – (N – 1) = n – N.

An analysis of variance table is set up as follows:

Source of variation	Sum of squares	df	Variance
(a) Between samples	$\Sigma\left[\dfrac{X^2}{V}\right] - \dfrac{(\Sigma x)^2}{n}$	N – 1	$\dfrac{\Sigma\left[\dfrac{X^2}{V}\right] - \dfrac{(\Sigma x)^2}{n}}{N-1} = v_2$
(b) Within samples	$\Sigma x^2 - \Sigma\left[\dfrac{X^2}{V}\right]$	n – N	$\dfrac{\Sigma x^2 - \Sigma\left[\dfrac{X^2}{V}\right]}{n-N} = v_1$

The variance for within samples is known as error variance also.

The variance ratio or $F = v_2 / v_1$

11.4   Interpretation of F

If the calculated value of variance ratio (F) is greater than its table value for n1 and n2 degrees of freedom, then the differences between samples are significant. The variance ratio table is used for testing the homogeneity of the estimates of population variance. We start from the null-hypothesis with the presumption that the difference between the samples and within the samples is insignificant. Variance ratio is obtained as illustrated in the following examples.

Illustration 11.1 In order to compare the mileage yields of three kinds of nylon tyres, several tests were run and the following results were obtained:

A	B	C
19	23	20
21	20	17
20	22	21
18	20	19
21	24	20
21	23	17

Calculate F and assume that the necessary assumptions can be met, test at a level of significance of 0.05 whether the observed differences between the means obtained for the three kinds of nylon tyres may be attributed to chance.

Solution: *First method*:

(1) Find total sum of squares by using the formula

$$\sum x^2 - \frac{\left(\sum x\right)^2}{n}$$

Here n = 18 (there are 18 items)

	x			x^2	
A	B	C	A	B	C
19	23	20	361	529	400
21	20	17	441	400	289
20	22	21	400	484	441
18	20	19	324	400	361
21	24	20	441	576	400
21	23	17	441	529	289
120	132	114	2408	2918	2180
$\sum x = 120 + 132 + 114 = 366$			$\sum x^2 = 2408 + 2918 + 2180 = 7506$		

$$\text{Total sum of squares} = \sum x^2 - \frac{\left(\sum x\right)^2}{n}$$

$$= 7506 - \frac{366^2}{18} = 7506 - 7442 = 64$$

Total df $= n - 1 = 18 - 1 = 17$

(2) Find sum of squares for between the varieties. There are three kinds and there are 6 values in each kind, i.e. N = 3, V = 6. Sum of squares for between varieties

$$\Sigma \left[\frac{X^2}{V} \right] - \frac{(\Sigma x)^2}{n} = \frac{120^2}{6} + \frac{132^2}{6} + \frac{114^2}{6} - \frac{366^2}{18}$$

$$= 2400 + 2904 + 2166 - 7442 =$$
$$= 7470 - 7442 = 28$$

df for between varieties or n1 $= N - 1 = 3 - 1 = 2$

(3) Find sum of squares for within varieties.
Sum of squares for within varieties = Total sum of squares

$$- \text{sum of squares between varieties} = 64 - 28 = 36$$

df for within varieties or n2 $= n - N = 17 - 2 = 15$

(4) Find variances for between varieties and within varieties by dividing the respective sum of squares by corresponding degrees of freedom.

(5) Form the analysis of variance table:

Analysis of variance table

Sources of variation	Sum of squares	df	Mean square or variance	Variance ratio or F
Between varieties	28	2	14(v2)	
				v2/v1 = 14/2.4 = 5.83
Within varieties	36	15	2.4(v1)	
Total	64	17	–	–

Table value of variance ratio for n1 = 2 and n2 = 15 at a level of significance of 0.05 is 3.68.

As the calculated value 5.83 is greater than the table value 3.68 (5.83 > 3.68), therefore the differences between the means are significant and cannot be attributed to chance.

Second method

This method is based on the fact that deviations from the means are independent of the choice of origin and the value of variance ratio or F remains unaltered if origin is changed or shifted. In other words if all the figures or values are decreased (or increased) by the same constant or they are multiplied or divided by a common factor, the values obtained for three sums of squares and the value of variance ratio are unchanged. In this method, the arithmetic is simplified because the smaller numbers replace the larger ones.

In Illustration 11.1, by shifting the origin to x = 20, i.e. diminishing all the yields by 20 we may rewrite the table.

	x			x^2	
A	B	C	A	B	C
−1	3	0	1	9	0
1	0	−3	1	0	9
0	2	1	0	4	1
−2	0	−1	4	0	1
1	4	0	1	16	0
1	3	−3	1	9	9
0	12	−6	8	38	20

$$\Sigma x = 0 + 12 - 6 = +6 \qquad \Sigma x^2 = 8 + 38 + 20 = 66$$
$$n = 18$$

(1) Total sum of squares $= \Sigma x^2 - \dfrac{(\Sigma x)^2}{n}$

$$= 66 - \frac{6^2}{36} = 66 - 2 = 64$$

$$df = n - 1 = 18 - 1 = 17$$

(2) Sum of squares between varieties =

$$= \Sigma\left[\frac{X^2}{V}\right] - \frac{(\Sigma x)^2}{n}$$

$$= \frac{0^2}{6} + \frac{12^2}{6} + \frac{(-6)^2}{6} - \frac{6^2}{18}$$

$$= 30 - 2 = 28$$

$$df = N - 1 = 3 - 1 = 2$$

(3) Sum of squares within varieties = 64 − 28 = 36

$$df = n - N = 17 - 2 = 15$$

The rest of the procedure is the same.

One way classification with unequal number of observations in each class

Although it is desirable to have equal number of observations in each class, yet it may not be possible due to lack of design or loss of part of the data or due to a greater emphasis on certain aspects. The number of observations in the various classes in such cases will be unequal.

Illustration 11.2 The data related to the polypropylene plates compression strength (in 10 lb load at first failure) made on 6 separate days. Set up a table of analysis of variance and find the variance ratio.

Test whether there is any significant difference between mean compression strength on various days.

Box compression strengths

Days										
1	58	62	66	45	58	65	52	62	51	72	10
2	61	59	57	55							4
3	73	67	69	67.5	61.5	70.5	64	69.5	57.9		9
4	40	63.5	67.5	58	56.5	5				
5	56	54	66	3						
6	72	68	64.5	62	56	77.5	68.5			

Solution: By shifting the origin to (x = 60), the data will be (subtract 60 from all values).

Days	1	2	3	4	5	6
Compression strength	−2	1	13	−20	−4	12
	2	−1	7	3.5	−6	8
	6	−3	9	7.5	6	4.5
	−15	−5	7.5	−2	2	
	−2	1.5	−3.5	−4		
	5	10.5	17.5			
	−8	4	8.5			
	2 9.5					
	−9	−2.5				
	12					

x	−9	−8	59.5	−14.5	−4	48.5
y	10	4	9	5	3	7

$$\Sigma x = -9 - 8 + 59.5 - 14.5 - 4 + 48.5 = 72.5$$
$$n = 10 + 4 + 9 + 5 + 3 + 7 = 38$$

x² (squares)						
Days	1	2	3	4	5	6
Compression	4	1	169	400	16	144
strength	4	1	49	12.25	36	64
	36	9	81	56.25	36	20.25
	225	25	56.25	4	4	
	4	2.25	12.25	16		
	25	110.25	306.25			
	64	16	72.25			
	4	90.25				
	81	6.25				
	144					
	591	36	580.25	484.75	88	626.75

$$\Sigma x^2 = 591 + 36 + 580.25 + 484.75 + 88 + 626.75 = 2406.75$$

(1) Total sum of squares $= \Sigma x^2 - \dfrac{(\Sigma x)^2}{n}$

$$= 2406.75 - \dfrac{72.5^2}{38}$$

$$= 2406.75 - \dfrac{5256.25}{38}$$

$$= 2406.75 - 138.32 = 2268.43$$

Total df $= n - 1 = 38 - 1 = 37$

(2) Sum of squares for "between days"

$$= \Sigma\left[\dfrac{X^2}{V}\right] - \dfrac{(\Sigma x)^2}{n}$$

$$= \left[\dfrac{(-9)^2}{10} + \dfrac{(-8)^2}{4} + \dfrac{59.5^2}{9} + \dfrac{(-14.5)^2}{5} + \dfrac{(-4)^2}{3} + \dfrac{48.5^2}{7}\right] - \dfrac{72.5^2}{38}$$

$= [8.1 + 16 + 393.36 + 42.05 + 5.33 + 336.04] - 138.32$
$= 800.88 - 138.32 = 662.56$

df for between days $= n - 1 = 6 - 1 = 5$

(3) Sum of squares for within days
= Total sum of squares – Sum of squares for between days
= 2268.43 – 662.56 = 1605.87

Analysis of variance

Sources of variation	Sum of squares	df	Mean square or variance	Variance ratio or F
Between days	662.56	5(n_1)	132.51 (v_2)	$\dfrac{v_2}{v_1}$ = 132.51/50.18
Within days	1605.87	32(n_2)	50.18 (v_1)	= 2.64
Total	2268.43	37	–	–

Here, $n_1 = 5$, $n_2 = 32$
The table value of F(i) at 5 percent level = 2.51
and (ii) at 1 percent level   = 3.66
The calculated value 2.64 > table value of 2.51.
Therefore, the difference between variances is significant at 5 percent level.
The calculated value 2.64 < table value of 3.66.
Therefore, the difference between variances is insignificant at 1 percent level.

Illustration 11.3 Following table gives the measurement of tearing strengths of fabric samples (A to D) with 5 replications. Carry out Anova by calculating variance between samples.

A	B	C	D
8	12	18	13
10	11	12	9
12	9	16	12
8	14	6	16
7	4	8	15

Solution:

	Sample I X$_1$	Sample II X$_2$	Sample III X$_3$	Sample IV X$_4$
	8	12	18	13
	10	11	12	9
	12	9	16	12
	8	14	6	16
	7	4	8	15
Total	45	50	60	65
Average	9	10	12	13

$\overline{X}_1$, $\overline{X}_2$, etc. represent the means of each sample and N is the number of samples.

$$\overline{X} = \frac{\overline{X}_1 + \overline{X}_2 + \overline{X}_3 + \overline{X}_4}{N}$$

where, $\overline{X}_1$, $\overline{X}_2$, etc. represent the mean of each sample and N the number of samples.

$$\overline{X} = \frac{9 + 10 + 12 + 13}{4} = \frac{44}{4} = 11$$

Variance between samples

To obtain variation between samples, calculate the square of the deviation of the various samples from the grand average. Thus we have the following table:

Sample I ($\overline{X}_1 - \overline{X}$)²	Sample II ($\overline{X}_2 - \overline{X}$)²	Sample III ($\overline{X}_3 - \overline{X}$)²	Sample IV ($\overline{X}_4 - \overline{X}$)²
4	1	1	4
4	1	1	4
4	1	1	4
4	1	1	4
4	1	1	4
20	5	5	20

Sum of the squares between the samples
$$= 20 + 5 + 5 + 20 = 50$$

Mean squares between the samples is $50 / (4 - 1) = 16.7$ (Because there are four samples and the degrees of freedom are $4 - 1 = 3$).

Variance within the samples

Here we find the sum of the squares is the deviations of various items in a sample from the mean values of respective samples.

Sample I		Sample II		Sample III		Sample IV	
X_1	$(X_1 - \overline{X}_1)^2$	X_2	$(X_2 - \overline{X}_2)^2$	X_3	$(X_3 - \overline{X}_3)^2$	X_4	$(X_4 - \overline{X}_4)^2$
8	1	12	4	18	36	13	0
10	1	11	1	12	9	9	16
12	9	9	1	16	16	12	1
8	1	14	16	6	36	16	9
7	4	4	36	8	16	15	4
$\Sigma(X_1 - \overline{X}_1)^2 = 16$		$\Sigma(X_1 - \overline{X}_1)^2 = 58$		$(\overline{X}_1 - \overline{X}_1)^2 = 104$		$\Sigma(X_1 - \overline{X}_1)^2 = 30$	

Total sum of squares within the samples $= 16 + 58 + 104 + 30 = 208$
Mean squares within the samples $= 208/(20 - 4) = 208 / 16 = 13$.

Total variation is calculated by taking the squares of the deviation of each of the items from the grand average.

Sample I		Sample II		Sample III		Sample IV	
X_1	$(X_1 - \overline{X})^2$	X_2	$(X_2 - \overline{X})^2$	X_3	$(X_3 - \overline{X})^2$	X_4	$(X_4 - \overline{X})^2$
8	9	12	1	18	49	13	4
10	1	11	0	12	1	9	4
12	1	9	4	16	25	12	1
8	9	14	8	6	25	16	25
7	16	4	49	8	9	15	16
$\Sigma(X_1 - \overline{X}_1)^2 = 36$		$\Sigma(X_1 - \overline{X}_1)^2 = 63$		$\Sigma(X_1 - \overline{X}_1)^2 = 109$		$\Sigma(X_1 - \overline{X}_1)^2 = 50$	

Total sum of squares $= 36 + 63 + 109 + 50 = 258$
Degree of freedom $= 20 - 1 = 19$

All the above results can be tabulated as follows:

Sample I		Sample II		Sample III		Sample IV	
X_1	$(X_1 - \overline{X})^2$	X_2	$(X_2 - \overline{X})^2$	X_3	$(X_3 - \overline{X})^2$	X_4	$(X_4 - \overline{X})^2$
8	9	12	1	18	49	13	4
10	1	11	0	12	1	9	4
12	1	9	4	16	25	12	1
8	9	14	8	6	25	16	25
7	16	4	49	8	9	15	16
$\Sigma(X_1 - \overline{X}_1)^2 = 36$		$\Sigma(X_1 - \overline{X}_1)^2 = 63$		$\Sigma(X_1 - \overline{X}_1)^2 = 109$		$\Sigma(X_1 - \overline{X}_1)^2 = 50$	

Hence, the difference in the mean values of the samples is not significant, i.e. the samples could have come from the same universe.

Short-cut method

The above method is time consuming. Follow the first method as explained in Illustration 11.1.

Sample I		Sample II		Sample III		Sample IV	
X_1	X_1^2	X_2	X_2^2	X_3	X_3^2	X_4	X_4^2
8	64	12	144	18	224	13	169
10	100	11	121	12	144	9	81
12	144	9	81	16	256	12	144
8	66	14	196	6	36	16	256
7	49	4	16	8	64	15	225

$\Sigma X_1 = 45$ $\Sigma X_1^2 = 421$ $\Sigma X_2 = 50$ $\Sigma X_2^2 = 558$ $\Sigma X_3 = 60$ $\Sigma X_3^2 = 824$ $\Sigma X_4 = 65$ $X_4^2 = 875$

The sum of all the items of various samples $= \Sigma X_1 + \Sigma X_2 + \Sigma X_3 + \Sigma X_4$

$$= 45 + 50 + 60 + 65 = 220$$

Correction factor

$$= \frac{T^2}{N} = \frac{220^2}{20} = 2,420$$

Total sum of squares $= \Sigma X_1^2 + \Sigma X_2^2 + \Sigma X_3^2 \Sigma X_4^2 - T^2/N$

$$= 421 + 558 + 824 + 875 - 2420$$
$$= 2678 - 2420 = 258 \text{ (as before)}$$

Sum of squares between the samples:

$$\frac{\left(\Sigma X_1\right)^2}{N} + \frac{\left(\Sigma X_1\right)^2}{N} + \frac{\left(\Sigma X_1\right)^2}{N} + \frac{\left(\Sigma X_1\right)^2}{N} = -\frac{T^2}{N}$$

$$= \frac{45^2}{5} + \frac{50^2}{5} + \frac{60^2}{5} + \frac{65^2}{5} - 2420$$

$$= \frac{2025}{5} + \frac{2500}{5} + \frac{3600}{5} + \frac{4225}{5} - 2420$$

$$= \frac{12350}{5} - 2420 = 2470 - 2420 = 50(as\ before)$$

Sum of squares within samples = Total sum of squares – Sum of squares between samples

$$= 258 - 50 = 208 \text{ (as before)}$$

By coding: Let us take 10 as common for the question taken in Illustration 11.1. The coded data are given below and the calculations are done there from:

Coded data

A	B	C	D
X_1	X_2	X_3	X_4
−2	+2	+8	+3
0	+1	+2	−1
+2	−1	+6	+2
−2	+4	−4	+6
−3	−0	−2	+5
$\Sigma X_1 = -5$	$\Sigma X_2 = 0$	$\Sigma X_3 = 10$	$\Sigma X_4 = 15$
$\overline{X} = -1$	0	2	3

$$\text{Grand mean or } \overline{\overline{X}} = \frac{\overline{X}_1 + \overline{X}_2 + \overline{X}_3 + \overline{X}_4}{4} = \frac{-1+0+2+3}{4} = 1$$

$(\overline{X}_1 - \overline{\overline{X}})^2$	$(\overline{X}_2 - \overline{\overline{X}})^2$	$(\overline{X}_3 - \overline{\overline{X}})^2$	$(\overline{X}_4 - \overline{\overline{X}})^2$
4	1	1	4
4	1	1	4
4	1	1	4
4	1	1	4
4	1	1	4
$\Sigma(\overline{X}_1 - \overline{\overline{X}})^2 = 20$	$\Sigma(\overline{X}_1 - \overline{\overline{X}})^2 = 5$	$\Sigma(\overline{X}_1 - \overline{\overline{X}})^2 = 5$	$\Sigma(\overline{X}_1 - \overline{\overline{X}})^2 = 20$

Sum of squares between samples = 20 + 5 + 5 + 20 = 50
Mean squares between samples = 50/(4 − 1) = 16.7 (as before)
Coding refers to the addition, multiplication, subtraction or division of data by a constant.

Sum of squares within samples

X_1	$(X_1 - \overline{X}_1)^2$	X_2	$(X_2 - \overline{X}_2)^2$	X_3	$(X_3 - \overline{X}_3)^2$	X_4	$(X_4 - \overline{X}_4)^2$
−1	1	+2	4	+8	36	+3	0
0	1	+1	1	+2	0	−1	16
+2	9	−1	1	+6	16	+2	1
2	1	+4	16	−4	36	+6	9
−3	4	−6	36	−2	16	+5	4
$\Sigma(\overline{X}_1 - \overline{X}_1)^2 = 16$		$\Sigma(\overline{X}_1 - \overline{X}_1)^2 = 58$		$\Sigma(\overline{X}_1 - \overline{X}_1)^2 = 104$		$\Sigma(\overline{X}_1 - \overline{X}_1)^2 = 30$	

Total sum of squares within the samples = 16 + 58 + 104 + 30 = 208
Mean squares within the samples = 208 / (20 − 4) = 13 (as before)

Illustration 11.4 The following figures relate to production in kilogram of three sorts A, B and C of fabrics produced with 2 counts:

A	14	16	18		
B	14	13	15	22	
C	18	16	19	19	20

Is there any significant difference in the production of three sorts?

Solution: Let us take the hypothesis that there is no significant difference in the production. Carry out the analysis of variance by taking 15 as common.

	A	B	C
	X1	X2	X3
	−1	−1	+3
	+1	−2	+1
	+3	0	+4
	+7	+4	+4
	+5		+5
Total	ΣX1 = 3	ΣX2 = 4	ΣX3 = 17
Mean	X̄1 = 1	X̄2 = 1	X̄3 = 3.4

$$\text{Grand mean or } \overline{X} = \frac{\overline{X}_1 + \overline{X}_2 + \overline{X}_3}{3} = \frac{1 + 1 + 3.4}{3} = \frac{5.4}{3} = 1.8$$

Sum of squares between samples

$(X_1 - \overline{X})^2$	$(X_1 - \overline{X})^2$	$(X_1 - \overline{X})^2$
0.04	0.64	2.56
0.04	0.64	2.56
0.04	0.64	2.56
	0.64	2.56
	0.64	2.56
		2.56
$\Sigma (X_1 - \overline{X})^2 = 1.92$	$\Sigma (X_1 - \overline{X})^2 = 2.56$	$\Sigma (X_1 - \overline{X})^2 = 12.80$

Sum of squares between samples = 1.92 + 2.56 + 12.80 = 17.28

Sum of squares within samples

X_1	$(X_1 - \overline{X}_1)^2$	X_2	$(X_2 - \overline{X}_2)^2$	X_3	$(X_3 - \overline{X}_3)^2$
−1	4	−1	4	+3	0.16
+1	0	−2	9	+1	5.76
+3	4	0	1	+4	0.36
		+7	36	+4	0.36
				+5	2.56
$\Sigma(X_1 - \overline{X}_1)^2 = 8$		$\Sigma(X_1 - \overline{X}_1)^2 = 50$		$\Sigma(X_1 - \overline{X}_1)^2 = 9.20$	

Sum of squares within samples = 8 + 50 + 9.2 = 67.2

Analysis of variance

Source of variation	S.S.	v	M.S.
Between samples	17.28	–	8.64
Within samples	67.20	9	7.47
Total	84.48	11	–

$F_{cal} < F_{tab}$. Hence there is no evidence to doubt the hypothesis. We, therefore, conclude that the three sorts do not differ significantly with regard to production.

Illustration 11.5 Table gives the ends/cm measured for 3 fabrics made at different periods. Carry out ANOVA.

Fabrics	Periods				
	I	II	III	IV	V
A	20	21	23	16	20
B	18	20	17	15	25
C	25	28	22	28	32

Solution: Let us take the hypothesis that there is no difference in fabrics with regard to yield. Taking 20 as origin, the given data becomes:

Fabrics	Periods					Total
	I	II	III	IV	V	
A	0	+1	+3	–4	0	0
B	–2	0	–3	–5	+5	–5
C	+5	+8	+2	+8	+12	35
Total	3	9	2	–1	17	30

Here T = 30

Correction factor = $T^2/N = 900/15 = 60$

$$\text{Sum of squares between fabrics} = \frac{0^2 + (-5)^2 + 35^2}{5} - \frac{T^2}{N}$$

$$= 250 - 60 = 190$$

$$v = 3 - 1 = 2$$

Total sum of squares $= [0^2 + (-2)^2 + 5^2 + 1^2 + 0^2 + 8^2 + 3^2 + (-3)^2 +$
$$+ 2^2 + (-4)^2 + (-5)^2 + 8^2 + 0^2 + 5^2 +$$
$$+ 12^2] - T^2/N$$

$$= [4+25+1+64+9+9+4+16+25+64+25+144] - 60$$
$$= 390 - 60 = 330$$

Sum of squares within fabrics
$$= \text{Total sum of squares} - \text{Sum of squares between strains}$$
$$= 330 - 190 = 140$$
$$v = 15 - 3 = 12$$

Analysis of variance table

Sources of variation	Degrees of freedom	Sum of squares	Mean square	F
Between fabrics	2	190	95	8.14
Within fabrics	12	140	11.67	

F_{tab} 3.88 (2,12 at 5%)

As $F_{cal} > F_{tab}$ fabric differ significantly as far as epi is concerned.

The calculated value of F is greater than the table value and hence our hypothesis is rejected. Hence it is concluded that the fabrics are significantly different with regard to epi.

Illustration 11.6 Table gives GSM of industrial fabrics.

W	X	Y
300	600	700
400	300	300
300	300	400
500	400	600
0	–	500

Perform the analysis of variance and draw your conclusions.

Solution: Let us take the hypothesis that the sales of the three salesmen are of the same size or they do not differ. In order to simplify calculations let us divide each value by 100. So the coded data are as follows:

A	B	C
3	6	7
4	3	3
3	3	4
5	4	6
0	–	5
Mean of A = 15/5 = 3;	Mean of B = 16/4 = 4;	Mean of C = 25/5 = 5

$$\text{Grand mean or } \overline{X} = \frac{3+4+5}{3} = 4$$

Variance within samples

X_1	$(X_1 - X_2)^2$	X_2	$(X_2 - \overline{X}_3)^2$	X_3	$(X_3 - \overline{X}_3)^2$
3	0	6	4	7	4
4	1	3	1	3	4
3	0	3	1	4	1
5	4	4	0	6	1
0	9	–	–	5	0
$\Sigma X_1 = 15$	$\Sigma (X_1 - X_2)^2 = 14$	$\Sigma X_2 = 16$	$(X_2 - \overline{X}_3)^2 = 6$	$\Sigma X_3 = 25$	$\Sigma (X_3 - \overline{X}_3)^2 = 10$

Total sum of squares within samples = 14 + 6 + 10 = 30

v = 3 – 1 = 2

Variance between samples

$(X_1 - \bar{X})^2$	$(X_2 - \bar{X})^2$	$(X_3 - \bar{X})^2$
1	0	1
1	0	1
1	0	1
1	0	1
1	–	1
$\Sigma(X_1 - \bar{X})^2 = 5$	$\Sigma(X_2 - \bar{X})^2 = 0$	$\Sigma(X_3 - \bar{X})^2 = 5$

Variance between samples = $5 + 0 + 5 = 10$, $v = 11$

Analysis of variance

Source of variation	Degrees of freedom	Sum of squares	Mean square	Variance ratio
Between	2	10	5	
Within	11	30	2.73	1.83
Total	13	40		

For $v_1 = 2$ and $v_2 = 11$ $F_{0.05} = 3.98$
$F_{cal} < F_{tab}$, therefore fabrics GSM is not significant.

Illustration 11.7 In a laboratory the effect of florescent agent on a hospital bed spread (sheetings) was studied. Following table gives the whiteness index values. Carry out the analysis of variance.

Florescent agents		
X	Y	Z
77	72	76
81	58	85
71	74	82
76	66	80
80	70	77
T1 =385	T2 = 340	T3 = 400

Answer:

$T_1 = 385$, $T_2 = 340$, $T_3 = 400$
$T = 1125$
$CF = T^2 / N = (1125)^2 / 15 = 84.375$
N = Total number of observations

$$SSQT = (77^2 + 81^2 + ... + 77^2) - CF$$

$$= 85{,}041 - 84{,}375 = 666$$
$$SSQT = (T_1^2 / n) + (T_2^2 / n) + (T_3^2 / n) - CF$$
$$= [385^2/5] + [340^2/5] + [400^2/5] - 84{,}375 = 390$$
$$SSQE = SSQ_T - SSQ_t = 666 - 390 = 276.$$

Anova

Source of variation	Degrees of freedom	Sum of squares	Mean sum of squares	F
Treatments (Between groups)	2	390	195	
				195 / 23 = 8.48
Error	12	276	23	
Total	14	666		

Conclusion

Since 8.48 exceeds 6.98, the value for 2 and 12 degrees of freedom, at 1% level of significance, we may conclude that the treatment differences are statistically significant at 1% level of significance. In other words the florescent agents do differ in their action.

Illustration 11.8 The following are the weight losses of a polyester staple fibre following base hydrolysis. Examine whether the base concentration has any influencing effect on weight loss percent.

Base concentration tests	2%	4%	6%
1	8	7	12
2	6	5	14
3	5	5	12
4	7	6	10
5	7	6	14

Solution: Total of each lubricants $T_1 = 33$, $T_2 = 29$, $T_3 = 62$
Grant total T = 124
$$CF = (124)^2/15 = 1025.06$$

Total sum of squares:

$$SSQ_T = 8^2 + 6^2 + \ldots +14^2 - CF$$

Treatment sum of squares (between variability)

$$SSQ_t = \frac{33^2 +29^2 +62^2}{5} = CF$$

Anova

Source of variation	df	SS	M.S.S.	F-ratio
Between groups	2	129.74	64.87	40.54
Within groups	12	19.2	1.6	
Total	14	148.94		

As calculated F is greater than F-tab value, it is concluded that the concentration of base has influenced the weight loss.

Illustration 11.9 A tarpaulin was tested on 4 different tensile testing machines for strength index.

Tester	W	X	Y	Z
Test no.				
1	200	100	600	500
2	100	400	900	300
3	300	300	600	200
4	300	500	300	500
5	100	300	100	500

Examine whether there is any difference between the instruments.

Solution: Divide each observations by 100 (By this F-ratio does not change).

Tester Test no.	W	X	Y	Z	
1	2	1	6	5	
2	1	4	9	3	
3	3	3	6	2	
4	3	5	3	5	
5	1	3	1	5	
	10	16	25	71	T = 70
	T_1	T_2	T_3	T_4	

$$CF = 71^2/20 = 252.05.$$

$$SSQ_T = 2^2 + 1^2 + \ldots\ldots +5^2 - CF$$
$$= 335 - 252.05 = 82.95$$
$$S.S. = SSQ_t$$
$$= \frac{10^2 + 16^2 + 25^2 + 20^2}{5} - CF$$
$$= 276.2 - 252.05 = 24.15$$

Within groups or error S.S. = 82.95 − 24.15 = 58.8

ANOVA

Source of variation	df	S.S.	M.S.S.	F-ratio
Between groups	3	24.15	8.05	
				2.19
Within groups	16	58.80	3.675	
Total	19	82.95		

Since F-calculated is less than F-table value at 3,16 df, it is concluded that instruments are differing in measuring the tensile strength.

Illustration 11.10 A 150 denier (250 tpm) polyester furnishing fabric was woven on different plain looms with different pick wheel. Following table gives the measurement of picks by densimeter at various parts of the cloth. Carryout anova and draw the conclusions.

Test	Looms			
	P	Q	R	S
1	70	60	60	70
2	70	80	70	90
3	60	70	80	80
4	50	60	70	80

Solution:

Divide each observation by 10

Looms	P	Q	R	S
Test				
1	6	7	6	7
2	7	8	7	9
3	6	7	8	8
4	5	6	7	8
	$T_1 = 24$	$T_2 = 28$	$T_3 = 32$	$T = 112$

C.F. $= (112)^2 / 16 = 784$

$$\text{Total sum of square} = SSQ_t = (36+49+\ldots) - CF$$

$$= 800 - 784 = 16$$

$$\text{Between looms sum of square} = \frac{24^2 + 28^2 + 28^2 + 32^2}{4} =$$

$$= 792 - 784 = 8$$

$$\text{Within loom S.S. or } SSQ_E = 16 - 8 = 8$$

Anova

Source of variability	df	SS	M.S.S	F-ratio
Between group	3	8	2.66	
				4.03
Within group	12	8	0.66	
	15	16		

As F-calculated is less than F-table value at 3, 12 df, the looms do not differ significantly.

Illustration 11.11 Following table shows the time in seconds for water to penetrate the fabrics (Actual time less 100) to shower proof.

Observations	Fabrics			
	I	II	III	IV
1	3	27	49	23
2	10	41	13	18
3	7	36	46	6
4	14	27	34	37
5	19	19	53	6

Carry out analysis of variance.

Solution: Column totals = $T_1 = 25$; $T_2 = 150$; $T_3 = 195$; $T_4 = 90$;

$$\text{Grand total} = 460$$
$$\text{Grand mean} = 460/20 = 23$$
$$\text{Mean of each column} = 5, 30, 39, 18$$
$$\text{Correction factors CF} = T^2/N = 460^2/20 = 10580$$
$$\text{Total sum of squares (SSQ}_T) = 3^2 + 10^2 + 7^2 + \ldots\ldots 6^2 - CF$$
$$= 16456 - 10580 = 5876$$

$$SSQ_t = \frac{T_1^2}{n} + \frac{T_2^2}{n} + \frac{T_3^2}{n} + \frac{T_4^2}{n} - CF$$

$$= \frac{25^2}{5} + \frac{150^2}{5} + \frac{195^2}{5} + \frac{90^2}{5} - 10580$$

$$= \frac{625 + 22500 + 38025 + 8100}{5} - 10580 = 3270$$

$$SSQ_E = SSQ_T - SSQ_t = 5876 - 3270 = 2606$$

Anova

Source of variation	Dof	SS	MSS	F
Treatment	3	3270	1090	
				6.69
Error	16	2606	162.87	

F_{tab} at 3,16 is 5.4 as $F_{cal} > F_{tab}$. Hence the fabrics differ in their effectiveness to shower proof.

Illustration 11.12 Following table gives the results of Abrasion tests (in thousands of rubs) on four fabrics.

1	2	3	4
26	24	21	20
23	22	18	19
24	24	17	17

Simplifying the data by subtracting all by 26.

1	2	3	4
0	−2	−5	−6
−3	−4	−8	−7
−2	−2	−9	−9
−5	−8	−22	−22

Total $= -57$, CF $= \dfrac{T^2}{n} = \dfrac{57^2}{12} = 270.75$

$$SSQ_T = (0 + 9 + 4 + 4 + 16 + 4 + 25 + 64 + 81 + 36 + \\ + 49 + 81) - 270.75 = 102.25$$

$$SSQ_t = \frac{T_1^2}{n} + \frac{T_2^2}{n} + \frac{T_3^2}{n} + \frac{T_4^2}{n} - CF$$

$$= \frac{25 + 64 + 484 + 484}{3} - CF = 81.5833$$

$$SSQ_E = SSQ_T - SSQ_t$$

$$= 102.25 - 81.5833 = 20.67$$

Source	Df	SS	MSS	F
Treatments	3	81.5833	27.1944	
				10.5270
Error	8	20.67	2.5833	

F_{tab} for 3,8 at 1% is 7.6.

$F_{cal} > F_{tab}$. Hence it is concluded that there is significant difference exists between fabrics.

Two-way classification

In two-way classification, the data are classified according to two different criteria or factors, i.e. data may be classified into different classes and different groups.

Usually the data are given in column and rows. If there are c columns and r rows, then the total number of items is equal to c × r = cr

Therefore the total number df = cr − 1

df for between columns = c − 1

df for between rows = r − 1

df for error or residual or remainder = cr − 1 − (c − 1) − (r − 1) − cr − 1 −
$$− c + 1 − r + 1$$
$$= cr − c − r + 1 = (c − 1)(r − 1)$$

The total sum of squares, sum of squares for 'between columns' and sum of squares for 'between rows' are obtained in the same way as before.

Error (or residual or remainder) = Total squares − squares for between columns − squares for between rows

The method has been illustrated in the following example.

Illustration 11.13 A garment company appoints four salesmen W, X, Y and Z and observes their sales in three regions A, B, C. The figures (in lakhs) are given in the following table:

Regions	Salesmen				Total
	W	X	Y	Z	
A	36	36	21	35	128
B	28	29	31	32	120
C	26	28	29	29	112
Salesmen's totals	90	93	81	96	360

Carry out an analysis of variance.

Solution: The above data are classified according to criteria (i) salesmen and (ii) regions. In order to simplify calculations we code the data by subtracting 30 from each figure. The data in the coded form are given below.

Regions	Salesmen				Total
	W	X	Y	Z	
A	+6	+6	−9	+5	+8
B	−2	−1	+1	+2	0
C	−4	−2	−1	−1	−8
0	3	−9	6		Grand total T = 0

Correction factor = $T^2/N = 0^2/12 = 0$ (number of items or N is 12)

Sum of squares between salesmen

$$= \frac{0^2}{3} + \frac{3^2}{3} + \frac{(-9)^2}{3} + \frac{6^2}{3} - \frac{T^2}{N}$$

$$= 0 + 3 + 27 + 12 + 0 = 42$$

$v = (4 - 1) = 3$

Sum of squares between seasons

$$= \frac{8^2}{4} + \frac{0^2}{4} + \frac{(-8)^2}{4} - \frac{T^2}{N} = 10 + 0 + 16 - 0 = 32$$

$v = (3 - 1) = 2$

Total sum of squares

$$= [6^2 + (-2)^2 + (-4)^2 + 6^2 + (-1)^2 + (-2)^2 + (-9)^2 + (1)^2 + (-1)^2$$
$$+ 5^2 + 2^2 + (-1)^2 - T^2/N$$

$$= 210 - 0 = 210$$

$v = (12 - 1) = 11$

The above information is presented in the following table of analysis of variance:

Source of variation	Sum of squares	df	Mean square
Between columns (salesmen)	42	3	14
Between rows (seasons)	32	2	16
Residual	136	6	22.67
	210	11	

Let us take the hypothesis that there is no difference between the sales of salesmen and of regions or, in other words, the three independent estimates of variance are the estimates of variance of a common population.

Now first compare the salesmen variance estimate with the residual variance estimate; thus

$$F = 14 / 22.67 = 0.618$$

The table value of F for $v_1 = 3$ and $v_2 = 6$ at 5% level of significance is 4.76. The calculated value is less than the table value and we conclude that the sales of different salesmen do not differ significantly.

Now let us compare the region variance estimate with the residual variance estimate; thus

$$F = 16 / 22.67 = 0.706$$

The critical value of F for $v_1 = 2$ and $v_2 = 6$ at 5% level of significance is 5.14. The calculated value is less than this and hence there is no significant difference in the regions as far as the sales are concerned.

Illustration 11.14 The following data represent production of 30^s cones by 3 workers.

Workers	Machines		
	Kamitsu A	Textool B	R.Jwinder C
X	16	64	40
Y	56	72	64
Z	12	56	28

Test (i) whether the mean productivity is the same for the different machine types, and (ii) whether the three workers differ with respect to mean productivity.

Solution: (i) Let us take the hypothesis that the mean productivity is the same for the three different machines.

(ii) The three workers do not differ with regard to mean productivity.

Workers	Machines			Total
	A	B	C	
X	16	64	40	120
Y	56	72	56	184
Z	12	56	28	96
Total	84	192	124	400
$\overline{X}$	28	64	41.33	

Common factor $= T^2/N = 400^2/9 = 17777.78$

Total sum of squares $= [16^2 + 56^2 + 12^2 + 64^2 + 72^2 + 56^2 + 40^2 +$
$$+ 56^2 + 28^2] - C.F.$$
$$= 256 + 3136 + 144 + 4096 + 5184 + 3136 +$$
$$+ 1600 + 3136 + 784] - 17777.78$$
$$= 21728 - 17777.8 = 3950.2$$

Sum of squares between columns (machines):

$$= 1/3 \ [84^2 + 192^2 + 124^2] - C.F.$$
$$= 1/3 \ [7056+36864+15376] - 17777.8$$
$$= 1/3(59296) - 17777.8 = 1974.2$$

Sum of squares between rows (workers):

$$= 1/3 \ [120^2 + 184^2 + 96^2] - \text{C.F.}$$
$$= 1/3 \ [14400 + 33856 + 9216] - 17777.8$$
$$= 19157.33 - 17777.8 = 1379.53$$

Residual or error = Total sum of squares − (sum of squares between columns + sum of squares between rows).

$$= 3950.2 - [1974.2 + 1379.53] = 3950.2 - 3353.73$$
$$= 596.47$$

Analysis of variance

Sources of variation	S.S.	n	M.S.	F
Between machines	1974.20	3 − 1 = 2	987.10	6.62
Between workers	1379.53	3 − 1 = 2	689.77	4.63
Residual	596.47	(3 − 1) (3 − 1) = 4	149.12	

(a) For $v_1 = 2$ and $v_2 = 4$, $F_{0.05} = 6.94$

   $F_{cal} < F_{tab}$

(b) For $v_1 = 2$ and $v_2 = 4$, $F_{0.05} = 6.94$.

   $F_{cal} < F_{tab}$

The hypothesis holds true. Hence the workers do not differ with regard to mean productivity.

Illustration 11.15 The following data represent the production per day (m) produced by 5 different weavers using 4 different types of autolooms.

	Autolooms			
	A	B	C	D
Weavers 1	44	38	47	36
Weavers 2	46	40	52	43
Weavers 3	34	36	44	32
Weavers 4	43	38	46	33
Weavers 5	38	42	49	39

a) Test whether the mean productivity is the same for the different looms.

b) Test whether the 5 men differ with respect to mean productivity.

Solution: Let us take the hypothesis that (a) the mean productivity in the same for four different looms and (b) the 5 men do not differ with respect to mean productivity. To simplify calculations let us divide each value by 40. The code 1 data is given below:

Workers	Machine type				Total
	A	B	C	D	
1	+4	−2	+7	−4	+5
2	+6	0	+12	+3	+21
3	−6	−4	+4	−8	−14
4	+3	−2	+6	−7	0
5	−2	+2	+9	−1	8
Total	+5	−6	+38	−17	T = 20

Correction factor = $T^2/N = 400/20 = 20$

Sum of squares between machines =

$$= \frac{5^2}{5} + \frac{(-6)^2}{5} + \frac{38^2}{5} + \frac{(-17)^2}{5} - \text{correction factor}$$

$$= (5 + 7.2 + 288.8 + 57.8) - 20$$

$$= 358.8 - 20 = 338.8$$

$v = (c - 1) = (4 - 1) = 3$

Sum of squares between workers =

$$= \frac{5^2}{4} + \frac{21^2}{4} + \frac{(-14)^2}{4} + \frac{0^2}{4} + \frac{8^2}{4} - \frac{T^2}{N}$$

$$= \frac{25}{4} + \frac{441}{4} + \frac{196}{4} + \frac{0}{4} + \frac{64}{4} - 20$$

$$= (6.25 + 110.25 + 49 + 0 + 16) - 20$$

$$= 181.5 - 20 = 161.5$$

$v = (r - 1) = (5 - 1) = 4$

Total sum of squares =

$$= [4^2 + 6^2 + (-6)^2 + 3^2 + (-2)^2 + (-2)^2 + 0^2 + (-4)^2 + (-2)^2 +$$
$$+ 2^2 + 7^2 + 12^2 + 4^2 + 6^2 + 9^2 + (-4)^2 + (3)^2 + (-8)^2 +$$
$$(-7)^2 + (-1)^2] - T^2/N$$

$$= [16 + 36 + 36 + 9 + 4 + 4 + 16 + 4 + 4 + 49 + 144 +$$
$$+ 16 + 36 + 81 + 16 + 9 + 64 + 49 + 1] - 20$$

$$= 594 - 20 = 574$$

$$\text{Residual or remainder} = \text{Total sum of squares} - (\text{Sum of}$$
$$\text{squares between machines} -$$
$$-\text{Sum of squares between workers})$$

$$= 574 - 338.8 - 161.5 = 73.7$$

$$\text{Degrees of freedom for remainder} = 19 - 3 - 4 = 12$$
$$(c - 1)(r - 1) = (3 \times 4) = 12.$$

Analysis of variance

Source of variation	S.S.	d.f.	M.S.	Variance ratio or F
Between machine types	338.8	3	112.933	112.933/6.142 = 13.387
Between workers	1615	4	40.375	40.375/6.142 = 6.574
Remainder or residual	73.7	12	6.142	
	574	19		

(a) For $v_{3, 12}$ $F_{0.05} = 3.49$; F at 3,12, 5% from tables – 3.49 conclude that the mean productivity is not same for the four different types of looms.

$F_{cal} > F_{tab}$ it is $F_{tab} = 3.26$ (at 4, 12 5%). Hence the workers differ with respect to mean productivity. $F_{cal} > F_{tab}$

Illustration 11.16 The following table gives the number of rain coats sold by 4 salesmen in three months.

Month	Salesmen			
	A	B	C	D
1	50	40	43	39
2	46	48	50	45
3	39	44	40	39

Is there a significant difference in the sales made by the four salesmen? Is there a significant difference in the sales made during different months?

Solution: Let us take the hypothesis that the sales made by the four salesmen do not differ significantly. To facilitate computations, let us deduct 40 from each given value. After deduction the values would be:

Month	Salesmen				Total
	A	B	C	D	
May	10	0	8	−1	17
June	6	8	10	5	29
July	−1	4	0	−1	2
Total	15	12	18	3	48

Correction factor, i.e., C.F. $= T^2/N = 48^2/12 = 192$

Sum of squares between salesmen

$$= \frac{(\Sigma X_1)^2}{N} + \frac{(\Sigma X_2)^2}{N} + \frac{(\Sigma X_3)^2}{N} + \frac{(\Sigma X_4)^2}{N} - C.F.$$

$$= \frac{15^2}{3} + \frac{12^2}{3} + \frac{18^2}{3} + \frac{3^2}{3} - 192$$

$$= 75 + 48 + 108 + 3 - 192 = 42$$

Sum of squares between months

$$= \frac{17^2}{4} + \frac{29^2}{4} + \frac{2^2}{4} = 192$$

$$= 72.25 + 210.25 + 1 - 192 = 91.5$$

Total sum of squares

$$= [10^2 + 6^2 + (-1)^2 + (0)^2 + 8^2 + 4^2 + 8^2 + 10^2 + 0^2 +$$
$$+ (-1)^2 + 5^2 + (-1)^2] - 192$$

$$= [100 + 36 + 1 + 64 + 16 + 64 + 100 + 1 + 25 + 1] - 192$$

$$= 408 - 192 = 216$$

Analysis of variance

Source of variation	Sum of squares	n	Mean square
Between machines	42	3	42/3 = 14.00
Between months	91.5	2	91.5/2 = 45.75
Residual	82.5	6	82.5/6 = 13.75
Total	216	11	

F (salesmen) = 14 / 13.75 = 1.018; F_{tab} = 4.76 (3,6) 5%; $F_{tab} > F_{cal}$

Hence the sales made by the four salesmen do not differ significantly.

F (months) = 45.75 / 13.75 = 3.33 F_{tab} = 5.14 (at 2,6, 5%)
$F_{cal} < F_{tab}$

Hence the sales made during different months do not differ significantly.

Illustration 11.17 The following data represent the number of units of loom crank bushes production per day turned out by five different workmen using four different types of machines.

(a) Test to see whether the mean productivity is the same for the four different machine types.

(b)   Test to see whether the five men differ with respect to mean productivity.

		Machine type			
		A	B	C	D
Workmen	1	44	38	47	36
	2	46	40	52	43
	3	34	36	44	32
	4	43	38	46	33
	5	38	42	49	39

Solution: By shifting the origin to x = 40 the data will be (subtract 40 from each value)

Machine		x			X for workmen	x²			
Workmen	A	B	C	D		A	B	C	D
1	4	-2	7	-4	5	16	4	49	16
2	6	0	12	3	21	36	0	144	9
3	-6	-4	4	-8	-14	36	16	16	64
4	3	-2	6	-7	0	9	4	36	49
5	-2	2	9	-1	8	4	4	81	1
X for machines	5	-6	38	-17	$\Sigma x = 20$	101	28	326	139
V	5	5	5	5	$\Sigma x^2 = 101 + 28 + 326 + 139 =$				
594									

Here n = c × r = 4 × 5 = 20

(1)   Total sum of squares $= \Sigma x^2 - \dfrac{(\Sigma x)^2}{n}$

$$= 594 - \frac{20^2}{20} = 574$$

Total df = cr – 1 = 20 – 1 = 19

(2)   Sum of squares for between machine types

$$= \Sigma \left[\frac{X^2}{V} \right] - \frac{(\Sigma x)^2}{n}$$

$$= \left[\frac{5^2}{5} + \frac{(-6)^2}{5} + \frac{38^2}{5} + \frac{(-17)^2}{5} \right] - \frac{20^2}{20}$$

$$= 5 + 7.2 + 288.8 + 57.8 - 20 = 388.8$$

df for between machine types = c – 1 = 4 – 1 = 3

(3)   Sum of squares for between men

$$= \Sigma \left[\frac{X^2}{V} \right] - \frac{(\Sigma x)^2}{n}$$

$$= \left[\frac{5^2}{4} + \frac{(21)^2}{4} + \frac{(-14)^2}{4} + \frac{(0)^2}{5} + \frac{8^2}{4} \right] - \frac{20^2}{20}$$

$$= 6.25 + 110.25 + 49 + 0 + 16 - 20 = 161.5$$

df for between men = r − 1 = 5 − 1 = 4

(4)   Remainder or residual = Total sum of squares − squares for between machines − squares for between men

$$= 574 - 388.8 - 161.5 = 73.7$$

df for remainder = 19 − 3 − 4 = 12

[(c − 1) (r − 1) = (4 − 1) (5 − 1) = 3 × 4 = 12].

The analysis of variance table is

Source of variation	Sum of squares	df	Mean squares or variance	Variance ratio or F
Between machine Types	338.8	3	112.93	112.93/6.14 = 18.4
Between workmen	161.5	4	40.375	40.375/6.14 = 6.58
Remainder or error	73.7	12	6.14	
Total	574	19		

a)   The value of variance ratio for machine types = 18.4. Table value of variance ratio for 3 and 12 degrees of freedom at 5 percent level significance = 3.49.

As 18.4 > 3.49

Therefore, there is significant difference between the mean productivities and mean productivity is not the same for different types.

b)   The value of variance-ratio for workmen = 6.58. Table value of variance-ratio for 4 and 12 degrees of freedom (5%) = 3.26; as 6.58 > 3.26

Therefore there is significant difference between mean productivities of workmen and the five men differ with respect to mean productivity.

Illustration 11.18 A laboratory technician measures the breaking strength of each of four kinds of sewing threads by using four different measuring instruments and obtains the following results:

Sewing threads	Instruments			
	A	B	C	D
S 1	1	1	1	3
S 2	5	6	7	5
S 3	6	3	2	4
S 4	5	1	4	6

Statistically test and state whether (i) the differences among the means obtained for the sewing threads are significant: (ii) The differences among the means obtained for the four instruments are significant.

Solution:

Instruments	A	B	C	D	Thread total	Mean
Sewing threads						
S 1	1	1	1	3	6	1.5
S 2	5	6	7	5	23	5.75
S 3	6	3	2	4	15	3.75
S 4	5	1	4	6	16	4.00
Instruments total	17	11	14	18	60	
Mean		4.25	2.75	3.5	4.5	

$C_1 = 17$, $C_2 = 11$, $C_3 = 14$, $C_4 = 18$.
$R_1 = 6$, $R_2 = 23$, $R_3 = 15$, $R_4 = 16$.
$T = C_1 + C_2 + C_3 + C_4 = 60$
$T = R_1 + R_2 + R_3 + R_4 = 60$

$$CF = T^2/N = (60)^2/16 = 225$$
$$= 290 - CF = 290 - 225 = 65$$

$$SSQ_R = R^2/C + R^2_2/C + R^2_3/C + R^2_4/C - C.F.$$
$$(C = \text{number of columns})$$
$$= 6^2/4 + 23^2/4 + 15^2/4 + 16^2/4 - CF$$
$$= 261.5 - 225 = 36.5$$
$$SSQ_C = CI^2 / r + C^2_2 / r + C^2_3 / r + C^2_4 / r - CF$$
$$SSQ_C = 17^2/4 + 11^2/4 + 14^2/4 + 18^2/4 - CF$$
$$SSQ_C = 232.5 - 225 = 7.5$$
$$SSQ_E = SSQ_T - SSQ_R - SSQ_C = 65 - 36.5 - 7.5 = 21$$

Having computed the necessary sums of squares, i.e. variabilities for different components, we can set the analysis of variance table as shown below:

Anova

Source	dd	SS	M.SS	F-ratio
Instrument	3	7.5	2.5	1.073
Sewing thread	3	36.5	12.16	5.22
Error	9	21.0	2.33	–
Total	15	65	–	–

By referring to the F-table value for 3, 9 at 1% level, F_{cal} (instruments) is less than F_{tab}. Hence it is concluded that instruments A....D do not differ significantly. On the other hand F_{tab} for 3,9 at 1% level is higher than F_{cal}; whereas F_{tab} for 3,9 at 5% level is 3.9, i.e. $F_{cal} > F_{tab}$. But the information available is insufficient as F_{tab} at 1% level and $F_{cal} > F_{tab}$ at 5% level. In short neither the instrument not the sewing threads differ significantly.

Illustration 11.19 Table given below shows the percentage area of washing shrinkage (Actual shrinkage – 7) × 10 tested on a same fabric. Set up Anova.

Tests	Treatments				
	1	2	3	4	5
1	2	6	−5	0	8
2	3	7	−4	2	11
3	13	4	−3	−1	13
4	11	7	0	9	2
5	10	11	6	4	11
6	16	10	3	8	13
7	8	19	3	6	14
8	9	17	10	11	13
9	10	2	7	15	19
10	19	15	7	11	25

Column total $C_1 = 101$, $C_2 = 117$, $C_3 = 24$, $C_4 = 65$, $C_5 = 134$

Row total R_1 = 11, $R_2 = 19$, $R_3 = 26$, $R_4 = 29$, $R_5 = 42$, $R_6 = 50$,
$R_7 = 55$, $R_8 = 60$, $R_9 = 72$, $R_{10} = 77$.

Grand total = Σ columns total = Σ row total = 441.

C.F. = $441^2/ 50 = 3889.62$

$SSQ_T = 2^2 + 3^2 + 13^2 +...........25^2 – C.F.$
= $1087 – 3889.62 = 2197.38$

$$SSQ_R = \frac{R_1^2}{C} + \frac{R_2^2}{C} ....+ \frac{R_{10}^2}{C} - CF$$

$$= \frac{11^2 + 19^2.................+ 77^2}{5} - 3889.62$$

= $4800.2 – 3889.62 = 910.58$

$$SSQ_C = \frac{C_1^2}{r} + \frac{C_2^2}{r} + \frac{C_3^2}{r} + \frac{C_4^2}{r} + \frac{C_5^2}{r} - CF$$
$$= 4664.7 - 3889.62 = 775.08$$

$$SSQ_E = SSQ_T - SSQ_R - SSQ_C = 2197.38 - 910.58 - 775.08 = 511.72$$

Source	d.f.	SS	MSS	F
Between columns	4	775.08	193.77	13.6
Between rows	9	910.58	101.18	7.1
Error	36	511.72	14.21	

$F_{cal} > F_{tab}$, hence it is concluded that the treatments are significant and also the tests.

Analysis of variance with more than one observation/cell

Illustration 11.20 Production in meters of 40s poplin woven on typical looms I, II, III in two auto sheds are given below.

Auto shed A			Auto shed B		
Loom I	Loom II	Loom III	Loom I	Loom II	Loom III
79	98	94	90	97	69
102	74	87	76	95	82
112	66	96	70	97	73
104	101	98	64	80	86
81	95	102	86	98	81
107	88	102	71	74	97
100	82	108	72	74	86
87	77	91	90	77	70
117	86	112	95	89	61
111	92	105	78	58	62
1000	859	995	792	839	787

Carry out ANOVA.

Solution:

	Subtotals			
	Loom I	Loom II	Loom III	Total of 30 observations
Auto shed A	1000	859	995	2854
Auto shed B	792	839	787	2418
Totals of 20 observations	1792	1698	1782	5772

$C_1 = 1792; C_2 = 1698; C_3 = 1782$

$R_1 = 2854, \quad R_2 = 2418$

The grand total $C_1 + C_2 + C_3 = 1792 + 1698 + 1782 = 5772$

Check: $R_1 + R_2 = 2854 + 2418 = 5772$

C.F. : $T^2/N = 5772^2 / 60$

$SSQ_t = 79^2 + 102^2 + ... + 61^2 + 82^2 - 5272^2/60$

$= 11463$

$SSQ_C = C_1^2/rn + C_2^2/rn + C_3^2/rn - c.f.$ (r = number of observations in each column and n = number of observations in each cell).

$$\frac{1792^2 + 1698^2 + 1782^2}{20} - \frac{5772^2}{60} = 463500 - 463233 = 267$$

$SSQ_R = R_1^2/cn + R_2^2/cn - c.f.$ (C = number of columns)

$$\frac{2854^2 + 2418^2}{30} = \frac{5272^2}{60} = 3168$$

Sum of squares among cell, total (SSQs)
(Table of sub totals)

$$SSQ_S = \frac{1000^2 + 859^2 + ...787^2}{10} - \frac{5272^2}{60} = 4613$$

Interaction sum of squares ($SSQ_R \times C$)

$= SSQ_S - SSQ_C - SSQ_R$

$= 4613 - 3168 - 267 = 1178$

Step 8: Error sum of squares (SSQ_E) or corrected.

Sum of squares with in groups

$SSQ_E = SSQ_T - SSQ_C - SSQ_R - SSQ_R \times C$

$= 11463 - 267 - 3168 - 1178 = 6851$

Check: $SSQ_E = SSQ_T - SSQ_S = 11463 - 4613 = 6851$

Anova

Source of variation	Df	ss	M.ss	F ratio
Between frames	1	3168	3168	3168/127 = 24.94
Between looms	2	267	133	133/127 = 1.04
Freedom × looms	2	1178	589	587/127 = 4.62
Within groups or error	54	6851	127	
Total	59	11463		

Inference:

(i) For auto sheds: $F_{cal} > F_{tab}$ for 1 and 54 d.f. at 1% level of significance. Hence the means obtained for different auto sheds is statistically significant at 1% level of significance. Whereas 2 and 54 d.f. at 5% level of significance, $F_{cal} < F_{tab}$ value. Hence the means obtained for different looms is not statistically significant at 5% level of significance. For interaction between looms and auto sheds.

$F_{cal} > F_{tab}$ value for 2 and 6 d.f. at 5% level of significance. This means that we cannot consider that the results have been drawn at random from a single population. The population means corresponding to the six samples of ten differ.

Illustration 11.21 An experiment was conducted to examine the effect of two 'treatments' on the strength of sewn joints in parachutes, and details are as follows:

Length of overlap	Stitch density			
	Low	Medium	High	Overlap totals
Short	32	41	68	
	28	38	71	
	60	79	139	278
Long	37	61	77	
	42	64	79	
	79	125	156	360
Stitch	139	204	295	638

Means of the values

Length of overlap	Stitch density		
	Low	medium	high
Short	30	39.5	69.5
Long	39.5	62.5	78.0
Mean increase in strength due to increase in overlap	9.5	23	8.5

Here are two factors: length of overlap and stitch density. The former is with 2 levels (if b = 2) and the later with 3 levels (a = 3) and n = 2.

$$C.F. = \frac{638^2}{3 \times 2 \times 2} = 33920.3$$

$$SSQ_S = \frac{60^2 + 79^2 + \ldots 156^2}{2} - C.F. = 3761.7$$

$$SSQ_C = \frac{139^2 + 20^2 + 295^2}{4} - C.F.$$

$$= 36990.5 - 33920.3 = 3070.3$$

$$SSQ_R = \frac{278^2 + 360^2}{3 \times 2} - C.F. = 34480.7 - 33920.3 = 560.4$$

Interaction sum of squares ($SSQ_{R \times C} = SSQ_S - SSQ_C - SSQ_R = 3761.7 - 3070.3 - 560.4 = 131$)

Error sum of squares (corrected sum of squares within groups)

$$SSQ_E = SSQ_T - SSQ_C - SSQ_R - SSQ_{R \times C}$$
$$= 3798 - 3070.3 - 560.4 - 131 = 36.3$$

Anova

Source of variation	Sum of squares	Dof	M.S.S.	F
Stitch densities	3070.2	2	1535.1	Very high value
Overlaps	560.4	1	560.4	High value
Interaction	131.1	2	65.55	10.99
Residual	36.0	6	6.0	

$F_{cal} >>> F_{tab}$ hence it is concluded that the interaction between the factors is highly significant. It can be said that effect of increasing overlap is dependent on which level of stitch density is used. It is advisable to consider

the last significant difference between two means $= t_{k,r} \, S \sqrt{\dfrac{2}{n}}$, where S^2 is

the residual mean square and k the associated degrees of freedom.

From the above table $S = \sqrt{6} = 2.45$, $k = 6$, referring to 5% level of significance t value is 2.45 (at 6 and for $\alpha = 0.025$). Hence least significant

difference between means of sample size 2 is $= 2.45 \times 2.45 \times \sqrt{\dfrac{2}{2}} = 6$

Referring to the table in which mean increase in strength due to increase in overlap, it is observed that the actual values are greater than 6 and hence the values are significant. Thus whatever level of stitch density is used, it is worth while increasing the overlap length, but the effect of doing so is greatest at medium overlaps.

Illustration 11.22 Five technologists measured the count of yarns produced by each of four spinning machines. Each measured two yarn specimens with the following results.

Machine	Technologists				
	A	B	C	D	E
I	9	12	6	2	−1
	5	8	9	−2	2

(Contd.)

Machine	Technologists				
	A	B	C	D	E
II	7	10	5	−3	2
	12	11	7	0	4
III	−7	−5	−8	−12	−7
	−4	−2	−9	−15	−9
IV	6	7	8	−4	0
	8	10	9	−5	−3

Carry out the analysis of variance and find the least significant difference between any two frames.

Solution:

Machine	Technologists					Machine totals
	A	B	C	D	E	
I	9	12	6	2	−1	
	5	8	9	−2	2	
	14	20	15	0	1	50
II	7	10	5	−3	2	
	12	11	7	0	4	
	19	21	12	−3	6	55
III	−7	−5	−8	−12	−7	
	−4	−2	−9	−15	−9	
	−11	−7	−17	−27	−16	−78
IV	6	7	8	−4	0	
	8	10	9	−5	−3	
	14	17	17	−9	−3	36
Technologists total	36	51	27	−39	−12	63

Mean values

Machines	Technology				
	A	B	C	D	E
I	7	10	7.5	0	0.5
II	9.5	10.5	6	−1.5	3
III	−5.5	−3.5	−8.5	−13.5	−8
IV	7	8.5	8.5	−4.5	−1.5
Change in count due to Change in machine	18	25.5	13.5	−	−

Here b = 4, n = 2, a = 5

$$CF = \frac{63^2}{4 \times 2 \times 5} = 99.225$$

SSQ$_T$ = 81 + 25 + 49 + 144 + 49 + 16 + 36 + 64 + 144 + 64 + 100 + 121
    + 25 + 4 + 49 + 100 + 36....9 − CF

$$= 2143 - 99.225 = 2043.775$$

SSQ_S = Sum of squares of sub totals.

$$=$$

$$= \frac{\begin{matrix} 14^2 + 19^2 + 11^2 + 14^2 + 20^2 + 21^2 + 7^2 + 17^2 + 15^2 + 12^2 + \\ 17^2 + 17^2 + 0^2 + 3^2 + 27^2 + 9^2 + 1^2 + 6^2 + 16^2 + 3^2 \end{matrix}}{2} - CF$$

$$= \frac{\begin{matrix} 196 + 361 + 121 + 196 + 400 + 441 + 49 + 289 + 225 + 144 + \\ 289 + 289 + 0 + 9 + 729 + 81 + 1 + 36 + 256 + 9 \end{matrix}}{2}$$

$$= 1961.275$$

SSQ_C = Sum of squares of column totals

$$= \frac{36^2 + 51^2 + 27^2 + 39^2 + 12^2}{4 \times 2} - 99.225$$

$$= 786.375 - 99.225 = 687.15$$

SSQ_R = Sum of squares of rows totals

$$= \frac{50^2 + 55^2 + 78^2 + 36^2}{5 \times 2} - C.F$$

$$= \frac{2500 + 3025 + 6084 + 1296}{10} - 99.225$$

$$= 1290.5 - 99.225 = 1191.275$$

$$SSQ_{R \times C} = SSQ_S - SSQ_C - SSQ_R$$

$$= 1961.275 - 687.15 - 1191.275 = 82.85$$

Error sum of squares or corrected sum of squares with in groups

$$SSQ_E = SSQ_T - SSQ_C - SSQ_R - SSQ_{R \times C}$$

$$= 2043.775 - 687.15 - 1191.275 - 82.85 = 82.5$$

Anova table

Source of variation	Sum of squares	Degrees of freedom	MSS	F ratio
Technologists	687.15	4	171.78	41.64
Machines	1191.275	3	397.09	96.26
Interaction	82.85	12	6.90	1.672
Residual	82.5	20	4.125	

It is clear that F_{cal} is greater than F_{tab} for both columns and rows and hence are concluded as highly significant 1% level of significance.

Second experiment

It is well known that the effects of two factors or treatments, at all combinations of the levels of the factors and the experiments of this kind are called as factorial experiments. Second experiments are those in which each factor is studied at two levels only.

Illustration 11.23 A second experiment was performed to investigate the effects of varying 4 knitting machine parameters on the dimensions of Punto-di-Roma fabrics knitted from polyester-fibre yarn. The factors are A – dial height, B – take down tension, C – Stretcher board width, D – needle timing delay. All these factors are applied at two levels which are indicated by '+' – high and '–' – low. Table given below indicates the lengths of fabric produced by 100 revolutions of a knitting machine (actual length in cm – 26) × 10

				A–		A+	
				B–	B+	B–	B+
C–			D–	0	30	20	22
			D–	2	35	9	28
C+			D–	16	25	11	19
			D+	23	24	13	17

Row no.	A	B	C	D	X	(1)	(2)	(3)	(4)	Factor effect	Factor sum of squares	Factor
1	–	–	–	–	0	20	72	143	294	18.375	–	Mean
2	+	–	–	–	20	52	71	151	–16	–2.00	16.00	A
3	–	+	–	–	30	27	74	1	106	13.25	702.25	B
4	+	+	–	–	22	44	77	–17	–40	–5.00	100.00	AB
5	–	–	+	–	16	11	12	49	2	0.25	0.25	C
6	+	–	+	–	11	63	–11	57	–40	–5.00	100.00	AC
7	–	+	+	–	25	36	0	–29	–62	–7.75	240.25	BC
8	+	+	+	–	19	41	–17	–11	44	5.5	121.00	ABC
9	–	–	–	+	2	20	32	–1	8	1.00	4.00	D
10	+	–	–	+	9	–8	17	3	–18	–2.25	20.25	AD
11	–	+	–	+	35	–5	52	–23	8	1.00	4.00	BD
12	+	+	–	+	28	–6	5	–17	18	2.25	20.25	ABD
13	–	–	+	+	23	7	–28	–15	4	0.50	1.00	CD
14	+	–	+	+	13	–7	–1	47	6	0.75	2.25	ACD
15	–	+	+	+	24	–10	–14	27	–32	–4.00	64.00	BCD
16	+	+	+	+	17	–7	3	17	–10	–1.25	6.25	ABCD

First 4 columns are headed by the letters denoting the factors. In any column the number of '–' and '+' are in alternate and similarly other columns are filled with the signs. Now referring to these signs referring the given table the columns X is filled. For example 1st row under ABCD '–' is observed, i.e., all the factors at '–' level. Referring to the table A–, B–,

C–, D– is 0 and similarly the second row +, –, –, –, the next element in the column 1 is A+, B–, C–, D– i.e. 20 and so on.

Column 1 is obtained by adding two elements in the previous column which are one below the other. For example 1st element in column 1 is 20 i.e., (0 + 20), 2nd element is 52 i.e. (30 + 22) and so on. In other words first 8 elements of column 1 is filled and the remaining 8 elements are obtained by subtracting the top element from the bottom one in the groups of two selected above i.e. 9th element in 1st column is 20 – 0 = 20, 10th element is 22 – 30= –8 and so on. Like this the 16th element will be 17 – 24= –7.

Columns 2, 3, 4 are obtained one by one with the procedure explained above.

Factors affect column. The first entry is obtained by dividing by n and the remaining entries by 2^{n-1} i.e. referring to the 4th column. 294 is divided by 2^n is 16 (as n = 4 in this example) to get 18.375, second entry is given by –16/8 (i.e. all other entries are divided by 2^{n-1} is $2^3 = 8$) = –2 and so on.

Factors sum of squares column

The entries in this column are obtained by (Column 4)^2/2^n. First entry in this column will not be available as it represents the mean but the second entry is $(-16)^2/16 = 16$, 3rd entry is $(106)^2/16 = 702.25$ and so on.

Factor column

The entries in this column is done depending on the '+' sign in each row and the respective factor under which this '+' is observed is written. For example 1st row all are '–' hence it indicates the 'mean'. Second row '+' is seen under 'A' hence the factor is A. Similarly 4th row '+' is seen under A and B and hence the factor is AB and so on.

Anova

Source	Sum of squares	Dof	MSS	F
A	16	1	16	0.374
B	702.25	1	702.25	16.4
C	0.25	1	0.25	0.006
D	4.00	1	4.00	0.094
AB	100.00	1	100.00	2.34
AC	100.00	1	100.00	2.34
AD	20.25	1	20.25	0.474
BC	240.25	1	240.25	5.61
BD	4.00	1	4.00	0.094
CD	1.00	1	1.00	0.023
ABC	121.00 ⎫	1 ⎫		
ACD	20.25 ⎪	1 ⎪		
BCD	2.25 ⎬ 5	1 ⎬ 5		
BCD	64.00 ⎪	1 ⎪		
ABCD	6.25 ⎭	1 ⎭		

In the Anova table the interaction of 3 factors are grouped on the lines that higher orders of interactions are difficult to interpret and are used to give experimental error.

It is to be noted that all the factors are used at two levels and hence the degrees of freedom is one. From the Anova table it is clear that factor 'B' effect is highly significant at 1% level.

Factorial replication

It can be understood that in 2^n experiments, as 'n' becomes larger, there increase the number of factor combinations. The designs obtained by studying the interactions between the main effects and two factors is called fractional replication.

Illustration 11.24 An experiment was conducted in which 3 deliveries were chosen at random, four cases were randomly selected from each delivery and 5 random cones were selected from each case. The linear density measured from each cone and the results are as follows:

Delivery case		1				2				3		
	1	2	3	4	1	2	3	4	1	2	3	4
Cone												
1	0	8	2	5	8	16	1	22	20	12	20	8
2	9	5	5	16	1	12	5	5	12	1	8	0
3	1	12	12	8	8	5	16	8	20	8	12	8
4	9	8	1	12	0	16	0	24	28	16	4	12
5	5	1	5	5	5	23	5	5	12	5	2	1

Carry out Anova.

Solution: Case totals = (24,34,25,46) (22,72,27,64) (92,42,56,29)
Delivery totals = 129, 185, 219
Grand total = 533

S_1 = Sum of squares of individual observations

$= 0^2 + 9^2 + 1^2 \ldots \ldots 12^2 + 1^2 = 7447$

$$S_2 = \frac{\text{Sum of squares of case totals}}{n}$$

$$= \frac{24^2 + 34^2 \ldots 56^2 + 29^2}{5} = 5834.2$$

$$S_3 = \frac{\text{Sum of squares of delivery totals}}{cn}$$

$$= \frac{129^2 + 185^2 + 219^2}{4 \times 5} = 4941.35$$

$$S_4 = \frac{(\text{Grand total})^2}{d\,cn}$$

$$= \frac{533^2}{3 \times 4 \times 5} = 4734.82$$

Anova

Source of variation	Sum of squares	Dof	MSSQ	Expected values of mean Squares
Between deliveries	$S_3 - S_4$	$d - 1$	M_d	$\sigma^2 + n\sigma_c^2 + cn\sigma_d^2$
Between cases Within deliveries	$S_2 - S_3$	$d(c - 1)$	M_c	$\sigma^2 + n\sigma_c^2$
Between cones Within cases	$S_1 - S_2$	$cd(n - 1)$	Mo	σ_2
Total	$S_1 - S_4$	$(dn - 1)$		

Source of variation	Sum of squares	Dof	MSSQ	Expected values of mean squares
Between deliveries	206.53	2	103.3	$\sigma^2 + 5\sigma_c^2 + 20\sigma_d^2$
Between cases Within deliveries	892.85	9	99.2	$\sigma^2 + 5\sigma_c^2$
Between cones Within cases	1612.80	48	33.6	σ^2
Total	2712.18	59		

$$S^2 = 33.6, \quad S_c^2 = \frac{99.2 - 33.6}{5} = 13.1$$

$$S_d^2 = \frac{103.3 - 99.2}{20} = 0.205$$

where σ^2 = variance due to random variation between cones
σ_c^2 = variance due to random variation between cases
σ_d^2 = variance due to random variation between deliveries

σ^2 is estimated by M_o, $\sigma_c^2 = \dfrac{M_c - M_0}{n}$

$$\sigma_d^2 = (M_d - M_c)/cn$$

11.5   Other designs – three-way classification – latin square

Sometimes the data are classified according to three different criteria, i.e. according to columns, rows and varieties. In that case we require a three-dimensional generalization. The values are arranged according to the different criteria in a square known as Latin square. Suppose the data are classified according to rows, columns and varieties being represented by the letters A, B, C,... etc. Then a latin square is an arrangement of the letter (i.e. Varieties) in a square in such a way that each letter (variety) occurs once and only once in each row and each column. A latin square, of m order, is an arrangement of m symbols or letters in square such that each symbol occurs once and only once in each row and each column. There will be m rows, m columns and m varieties. Every symbol will appear m times in a latin square. By various permutations and combinations, letters or symbols can be arranged in several different ways and thus several different latin squares can be constructed but each symbol or variety appears once and only once in each column and each row. Varieties, rows and columns are all equal. For example in a 5 by 5 (5 × 5) latin square, where data may be classified according to rows, columns and varieties being represented by letters A, B, C, D, E the arrangement may be as below.

		(1)							(2)			
	1	2	3	4	5			1	2	3	4	5
1	E	A	C	B	D		1	A	B	C	D	E
2	B	C	E	D	A		2	B	E	A	C	D
3	A	B	D	E	C	Rows	3	C	D	B	E	A
4	C	D	B	A	E		4	D	C	E	A	B
5	D	E	A	C	B		5	E	A	D	B	C

		(3) Columns				
		1	2	3	4	5
	1	A	B	C	D	E
	2	B	C	E	A	D
Rows	3	C	E	D	B	A
	4	D	A	B	E	C
	5	E	D	A	C	B

Standard latin square. In a standard latin square, the first and the first column contain the letters in their natural order. Latin squares numbered (2) and (3) above are standard 5 × 5 latin squares. While constructing the latin squares for use in experimental arrangements, a randomization procedure is used.

The procedure or analysis of variance of data arranged in a latin square has been illustrated in the following example.

The analysis of data is based on the assumption that interactions are zero.

Illustration 11.25 The following table gives cotton yields for five fertilizer treatments of plots arranged in a latin square. Test for significance of column, row and treatment effects at 1 percent level.

Rows	Columns				
	1	2	3	4	5
1	34(C)	21(A)	52(E)	24(B)	40(D)
2	33(B)	45(E)	47(D)	26(C)	25(A)
3	31(A)	38(C)	34(B)	39(D)	38(E)
4	44(E)	41(D)	32(C)	17(A)	39(B)
5	33(D)	35(B)	26(A)	46(E)	35(C)

Solution: It is a (5×5) latin s quare. By shifting the origin to $x = 35$ (subtract 35 from each value), the table is as follows:

	Columns					X for	Squares				
	1	2	3	4	5	rows	1	2	3	4	5
Rows											
1	−1	−14	17	−11	5	−4	1	196	289	121	25
2	−2	10	12	−9	10	1	4	100	144	81	100
3	−4	3	−1	4	3	5	16	9	1	16	9
4	9	6	−3	−18	4	−2	81	36	9	324	16
5	−2	0	−9	11	0	0	4	0	81	121	0
X for Columns	0	5	16	− 23	2	0	106	341	524	663	150

$$\Sigma\, x^2 = 106 + 341 + 524 + 663 + 150 = 1784$$

Treatment	1	2	3	4	5	X for treatments
A	−4	−14	−9	−18	−10	−55
B	−2	0	−1	−11	4	−10
C	−1	3	−3	−9	0	−10
D	−2	6	12	4	5	25
E	9	10	17	11	3	50

Here n = number of items = 25 (It is 5 × 5 latin square).

(1) Total sum of squares $= \Sigma\, x^2 - \dfrac{(\Sigma x)^2}{n}$

$$= 1784 - \frac{0^2}{25} = 1784$$

Total df $= n - 1 = 25 - 1 = 24$.

(2) Sum of squares for "between columns"

$$= \Sigma \left[\frac{X^2}{V} \right] - \frac{(\Sigma x)^2}{n}$$

$$= \left[\frac{0^2}{5} + \frac{5^2}{5} + \frac{16^2}{5} + \frac{(-23)^2}{5} + \frac{2^2}{5} - 0 \right]$$

$$= 0 + 5 + 51.2 + 105.8 + 0.8 = 162.8$$

df for between columns = c − 1 = 5 −1 = 4

(3) Sum of squares for "between rows"

$$= \Sigma \left[\frac{X^2}{V} \right] - \frac{(\Sigma x)^2}{n}$$

$$= \left[\frac{(-4)^2}{5} + \frac{1^2}{5} + \frac{5^2}{5} + \frac{(-2)^2}{5} + \frac{0^2}{5} \right] - 0$$

$$= 3.2 + 0.2 + 5 + 0.8 + 0 = 9.2$$

(4) Sum of squares for "between treatments"

$$= \Sigma \left[\frac{X^2}{V} \right] - \frac{(\Sigma x)^2}{n}$$

$$= \left[\frac{(-55)^2}{5} + \frac{(-10)^2}{5} + \frac{(-10)^2}{5} + \frac{(25)^2}{5} + \frac{50^2}{5} \right] - 0$$

$$= 605 + 20 + 20 + 125 + 500 = 1270$$

df for between treatments = t − 1 = 5 − 1 = 4

(5) Residual error or remainder

$$= 1784 - 162.8 - 9.2 - 1270 = 342$$

df = 24 − 4 − 4 − 4 = 12

The variance table is

Source of variation	Sum of squares	df	Mean square or variance	Variance ratio or F
Between columns	162.8	4	40.7	40.7/28.5 = 1.428
Between rows	9.2	4	2.3	2.3/28.5 = 0.08
Between treatments	1270	4	317.5	317.5/28.5 = 11.1
Error	342	12	28.5	
Total	1784	24	–	–

Table value of variance ratio at 1 percent level for 4 and 12 degrees of freedom = 5.41

(a) For column effect 1.428 < 5.41, so column effect is non-significant.
(b) For row effect 0.8 < 5.41, so row effect is also non-significant.
(c) For treatment effect 11.1 > 5.41, so treatment effect is highly significant.

Samples within samples – nested samples or hierarchical classifications
In a hierarchical classification, each sample is divided into subsamples which may be further divided into subgroups. In nested samples, there is repeated grouping and sub-grouping. The method of analysis of variance in case of hierarchical classification (i.e. samples within samples) consists of resolving the total variation into the following parts:

(i)   Between the levels of first criterion
(ii) Between the levels of second criterion, within each level of first criterion
(iii) Interaction in case of two-way classification
(iv) Residual

The method is illustrated in the following examples:

Samples within samples – Equal size (balanced hierarchical classification)

Illustration 11.26 Carry out an analysis of variance on the following data:

Sample	Machine A			Machine B		
	Making			Making		
	1	2	3	1	2	3
1	26	33	18	32	40	20
2	10	30	24	61	48	39
3	15	19	12	22	27	36
4	21	36	26	54	60	40
5	18	25	33	33	42	31

Solution: This is a case of hierarchical classification.

(1) Find total sum of squares.
(2) Find sum of squares for makings. The sum of squares for makings can be split up into two parts.
    (a)   Sum of squares for between machines
    (b)   Sum of squares for between makings, within machines
(3) Find the residual.

Sample	Machine A			Machine B		
	Making			Making		
	1	2	3	1	2	3
1	26	33	18	32	40	20
2	10	30	24	61	48	39
3	15	19	12	22	27	36
4	21	36	26	54	60	40
5	18	25	33	33	42	31
X for makings	90	143	113	202	217	166
V	5	5	5	5	5	5
X for Machines	90 + 143 + 113 = 346			202 + 217 + 166 = 585		
V	15			15		

(1) Total sum of squares

Squares					
Machine A			Machine B		
676	1089	324	1024	1600	400
100	900	576	3724	2304	1521
225	361	144	484	729	1296
441	1296	676	2916	3600	1600
324	625	1089	1089	1764	961
1766	4271	2809	9234	9997	5778

$\Sigma x^2 = 1766 + 4271 + 2809 + 9234 + 9997 + 5778 = 33855$
$\Sigma x = 346 + 585 = 931$

Total sum of squares $= \Sigma x^2 - \dfrac{(\Sigma x)^2}{n}$

$$= 33855 - \frac{931^2}{30} = 33855 - 28892 = 4963$$

df $= n - 1 = 30 - 1 = 29$

(2) Total sum of squares for makings $= \Sigma\left(\dfrac{X^2}{V}\right) - \dfrac{(\Sigma x)^2}{n}$

$$= \left(\frac{90^2}{5} + \frac{143^2}{5} + \frac{113^2}{5} + \frac{202^2}{5} + \frac{217^2}{5} + \frac{166^2}{5}\right) - \frac{931^2}{30}$$

$$= 1620 + 4089.8 + 2553.8 + 8160.8 + 9417.8 + 5511.2 - 28892$$

$$= 2461.4$$

df $= 6 - 1 = 5$

(a) Sum of squares for between machines

$$= \Sigma\left(\frac{X^2}{V}\right) - \frac{(\Sigma x)^2}{n}$$

$$= \left(\frac{346^2}{15} + \frac{585^2}{15}\right) - \frac{931^2}{30}$$

$$= 7981 + 22815 - 28892 = 1904$$

df for between machines $= N - 1 = 2 - 1 = 1$

(b) Sum of squares for between makings, within machines

$=$ Total sum of squares for makings – sum of squares for between machines.

$$= 2461.4 - 1904 = 557.4$$

df $= 5 - 1 = 4$

(3) Residual $= 4963 - 1904 - 557.4 = 2501.6$

df $= 29 - 1 - 4 = 24$

Analysis of variance table

Source of variation	Sum of squares	df	Mean square or variance	Variance ratio or F
Between machines	1904	1	1904	1904/139.35 = 13.67
Between makings,	557.4	4	139.35	
Within machines residual	2501.6	24	104.2	139.35/104.2 = 1.34
Total	4963	29		

* F for between machines = Variance for between machines / Variance for making within machines

Table value of F for 1 and 4 df at 5% level = 7.71

As 13.67 > 7.71, so it is significant.

At 1% level, it is not significant.

F for between makings = Variance for makings within machines/Residual with machines

Table value of F for $n_1 = 4$ $n_2 = 24$ at 5% level = 2.78

Therefore it is not significant.

Samples within samples – Unequal size (unbalanced hierarchical classification)

Illustration 11.27 Set up an analysis of variance table and analyse the results.

Percentage stretch in the warp direction

Stenter A Sorts					Stenter B Sorts		
1	2	4	3	5	1	2	3
3.0	3.4	3.6	3.4	2.7	2.5	2.9	3.1
3.4	3.2	3.4	3.5	2.9	3.0	2.9	3.3
3.0	3.1	3.2	3.4		3.1	2.7	3.0
3.0						2.9	
3.1						2.9	
5	3	3	3	2	3	5	3

Solution: By shifting the origin to x = 3, the table is

	Stenter A					Stenter B		
	1	2	3	4	5	1	2	3
	0	0.4	0.6	0.4	−0.3	−0.5	−0.1	0.1
	0.4	0.2	0.4	0.5	−0.1	0	−0.1	0.3
	0	0.1	0.2	0.4		0.1	−0.3	0
	0						−0.1	
	0.1						−0.1	
X for Sorts	0.5	0.7	1.2	1.3	−0.4	−0.4	−0.7	0.4
V	5	3	3	3	2	3	5	3
X for years	0.5 + 0.7 + 1.2 + 1.3 − 0.4 = 3.3					−0.4 − 0.7 + 0.4 = −0.7		
V			16				11	

	Squares							
	Stenter A					Stenter B		
1	2	3	4	5	1	2	3
0	0.16	0.36	0.16	0.09	0.25	0.01	0.01
0.16	0.04	0.16	0.25	0.01	0	0.01	0.09

(Contd.)

				Squares			
		Stenter A				Stenter B	
1	2	3	4	5	1	2	3
0	0.01	0.04	0.16	0.01	0.09	0	
0	0.01						
0.01	0.01						
0.17	0.21	0.56	0.57	0.10	0.26	0.13	0.10

$\Sigma x^2 = 0.17 + 0.21 + 0.56 + 0.57 + 0.10 + 0.26 + 0.13 + 0.10 = 2.10$

$\Sigma x = 3.3 - 0.7 = 2.6$

(1) Total sum of squares $= \Sigma x^2 - \dfrac{(\Sigma x)^2}{n}$

$$= 2.10 - \frac{2.6^2}{27} = 2.10 - 0.25 = 1.85$$

Total df $= n - 1 = 27 - 1 = 26$

(2) Sum of squares for sorts $= \Sigma \left(\dfrac{X^2}{V} \right) - \dfrac{(\Sigma x)^2}{n}$

$$= \left(\begin{array}{l} \dfrac{0.5^2}{5} + \dfrac{0.7^2}{5} + \dfrac{1.2^2}{5} + \dfrac{1.3^2}{5} + \dfrac{(-0.4)^2}{5} + \dfrac{(-0.4)^2}{5} + \\[2ex] \qquad\qquad\qquad + \dfrac{(-0.7)^2}{5} + \dfrac{(-0.4)^2}{3} \end{array} \right) - \dfrac{2.6^2}{27}$$

$= 0.050 + 0.163 + 0.480 + 0.563 + 0.080 + 0.053 + 0.098 +$
$\qquad\qquad\qquad\qquad\qquad\qquad\qquad\qquad + 0.053 - 0.250$

$= 1.290$

Total df for sorts $= N - 1 = 8 - 1 = 7$

The sum of squares for consignments can be split up into the following two parts.

a) Sum of squares for between the stenters

$$= \Sigma \left[\frac{X^2}{V} \right] - \frac{(\Sigma x)^2}{n}$$

$$= \Sigma \left[\frac{3.3^2}{16} + \frac{-(0.7)^2}{11} \right] - \frac{2.6^2}{27}$$

$= 0.681 + 0.045 - 0.250 = 0.476$

df for between years $= 2 - 1 = 1$

b)   **Sum of squares for sorts within stenters**

= Squares for sorts – squares between stenters

= 1.290 – 0.476 = 0.814

(3)   Residual = 1.85 – 0.476 – 0.814 = 0.560
df = 26 – 1 – 6 = 19

Analysis of variance table

Source of variation	Sum of squares	df	Mean square or Variance	Variance ratio or F
Between years	0.476	1	0.476	0.476/0.136 = 3.5
Between sorts within stenters	0.814	6	0.136	0.136/0.029 = 4.6
Residual	0.560	19	0.029	
Total	1.850	26		

Table value of F for 1 and 6 degrees of freedom at 5% level = 5.99
3.5 < 5.99
So it is not significant.

Table value of F for 6 and 19 degrees of freedom at 5% level = 2.63
4.60 > 2.63
Therefore it is significant.

Illustration 11.28 Analyse the variance and asses the effects of adding nitrogen and phosphate and any possible interactions.

Growth of grass: Grams of grass per square meter

	Nitrogen treatment		
	1	2	3
Phosphate treatment			
1 ⟶	22.8	25.8	27.6
	24.0	26.1	28.2
2 ⟶	26.6	28.8	30.2
	24.5	24.1	29.5
3 ⟶	26.1	29.3	32.4
	25.8	27.3	30.9

Solution: Shift the origin to x = 25

	Nitrogen treatment			
	1	2	3	X or P
Phosphate treatment				
1 $\longrightarrow$	$\begin{cases} -2.2 \\ -1.0 \end{cases}$	0.8 1.1	$\begin{cases} 2.6 \\ 3.2 \end{cases}$ 4.5	6
2 $\longrightarrow$	$\begin{cases} 1.6 \\ -0.5 \end{cases}$	3.8 -0.9	$\begin{cases} 5.2 \\ 4.5 \end{cases}$ 13.7	6
3 $\longrightarrow$	$\begin{cases} 1.1 \\ 0.8 \end{cases}$	4.3 2.3	$\begin{cases} 7.4 \\ 5.9 \end{cases}$ 21.8	6
X for N-treatment	-0.2	11.4	28.8 40	
V	6	6	6	

Sample-wise total

		N-treatment		
		1	2	3
P-treatment	1	-3.2	1.9	5.8
	2	1.1	2.9	9.7
	3	1.9	6.6	13.3

V for each treatment = 2

	Squares	[N-treatment]		
		1	2	3
P treatment	1	$\begin{cases} 4.84 \\ 1.00 \end{cases}$	0.64 1.21	6.76 10.24
	2	$\begin{cases} 2.56 \\ 0.25 \end{cases}$	14.44 0.81	27.04 20.25
	3	$\begin{cases} 1.21 \\ 0.64 \end{cases}$	18.49 5.29	54.76 34.81
		10.50	40.88	153.86

$\Sigma x^2 = 205.24$

(1)   Total sum of squares

$$= \Sigma x^2 - \frac{(\Sigma x)^2}{n}$$

$$= 205.24 - \frac{40^2}{18} = 205.24 - 88.89 = 116.35$$

$$df = n - 1 = 18 - 1 = 17$$

(2)   Total sum of squares for samples

$$= \Sigma \left[\frac{X^2}{V} \right] - \frac{(\Sigma x)^2}{n}$$

$$= \Sigma \left[\frac{(-3.2)^2}{2} + \frac{(1.1)^2}{2} + \frac{(1.9)^2}{2} + \frac{(1.9)^2}{2} + \frac{(2.9)^2}{2} + \frac{(6.6)^2}{2} + \right. \\ \left. \frac{(5.8)^2}{2} + \frac{(9.7)^2}{2} + \frac{(13.3)^2}{2} \right] - \frac{40^2}{18}$$

$$= 5.12 + 0.605 + 1.805 + 1.805 + 4.205 + 21.78 + 16.82 + \\ 47.045 + 88.445 - 88.89 = 98.74$$

Total df for samples = 9 − 1 = 8

a)   Sum of squares for between N-treatments.

$$= \Sigma \left[\frac{X^2}{V} \right] - \frac{(\Sigma x)^2}{n}$$

$$= \Sigma \left[\frac{(-0.2)^2}{6} + \frac{(11.4)^2}{6} + \frac{(28.8)^2}{6} \right] - \frac{40^2}{18}$$

$$= 0.006 + 21.66 + 138.24 - 88.89 = 71.016$$

df = 3 − 1 = 2

b)   Sum of squares for between P-treatments.

$$= \Sigma \left[\frac{X^2}{V} \right] - \frac{(\Sigma x)^2}{n}$$

$$= \Sigma \left[\frac{(4.5)^2}{6} + \frac{(13.7)^2}{6} + \frac{(21.8)^2}{6} \right] - \frac{40^2}{18}$$

$$= 3.375 + 31.281 + 79.206 - 88.890 = 24.972$$

df = 3 − 1 = 2

c)   Interaction between N × P
    = 98.74 − 71.016 − 24.972 = 2.752
    df = 8 − 2 − 2 = 4

Note: *Interaction* − The numerical value of total variation for samples exceeds the sum of variations due to between N-treatments and between P-treatments. This difference is the variation due to interaction between the treatments.

(3)   Residual: = 116.35 − 71.016 − 24.972 − 2.752 = 17.61
     df = 17 − 2 − 2 − 4 = 9

Analysis of variance table

Source of variation	Sum of squares	df	Mean square	F
Between N-treatments	71.016	2	35.508	35.508/1.956 = 18.15
Between P-treatments	24.972	2	12.486	12.486/1.956 = 6.38
Interaction	2.752	4	0.688	0.688/1.956 = 0.35
Residual or error	17.610	9	1.956	
Total	116.350	17	–	

Table value of F for 2, 9 degrees of freedom at 5% level = 4.26
Between N levels, F is significant.
Between P levels, F is significant.
Table value of F for 4, 9 degrees of freedom at 5% percent level = 3.63
For N × P interaction, F is not significant.

Problems for practice

Problem: Table gives the strength of 100 leas, 20 each from five machines. The problem is to test whether the yarn produced on these machines differ in lea strength from one another.

Breaking strength (kg) of Leas from yarns of different machines

	A	B	C	D	E
	23	26	34	26	36
	30	33	36	30	25
	21	22	32	25	38
	24	31	24	33	24
	31	29	30	24	35
	24	33	29	27	26
	25	29	25	32	31
	25	33	25	29	25
	28	26	29	24	37
	25	25	32	25	28
	31	34	27	31	38
	30	31	32	32	25
	28	36	31	23	36
	23	32	33	28	30
	29	23	24	26	32
	24	35	27	30	36
	30	35	33	26	25
	22	25	30	32	33
	25	37	27	23	29
	23	26	31	30	23
Total Mean	521	601	591	556	612
	26.05	30.05	29.55	27.8	30.6

Problem: Given the following data carry out ANOVA

Days	Total	Mean	Days	Total	Mean	Days	Total	Mean
1	145	29	8	137	27.4	15	134	26.8
2	154	30.8	9	144	28.8	16	152	30.4
3	138	27.6	10	135	27	17	149	29.8
4	136	27.2	11	161	32.2	18	142	28.4
5	149	29.8	12	150	30	19	141	28.2
6	139	27.8	13	154	30.8	20	133	26.6
7	142	28.4	14	146	29.2			
						Total	2881	28.81

Problem: Five treatments were used on four types of fabrics and the linear shrinkage percent assessed in each case. For each type of fabric and treatment, three samples have been tested and the results are given table. Carry out Anova.

Linear shrinkage percent of fabric

Treatment	Fabric			
	1	2	3	4
1	5.8	6.0	6.1	6.6
	6.1	6.6	6.3	6.8
	5.7	7.0	6.0	6.4
2	6.4	6.8	6.6	6.9
	6.7	7.0	6.7	6.6
3	6.0	6.8	5.5	5.5
	5.8	6.2	5.9	5.8
	5.4	6.0	5.7	5.9
4	5.6	6.9	6.0	5.9
	5.6	6.5	5.5	6.2
	5.8	6.7	5.6	5.6
5	6.0	5.9	5.8	5.4
	5.6	6.3	5.8	5.6
	5.8	6.6	6.2	5.5

Table A Giving area of the normal curve to the left of the standardized deviate (X)

X	Area	X	Area	X	Area	X	Area
0.00	0.5000	1.00	0.8413	2.00	0.9772	3.00	0.9987
0.05	0.5199	1.05	0.8531	2.05	0.9798	3.05	0.9989
0.10	0.5398	1.10	0.8643	2.10	0.9821	3.10	0.9990
0.15	0.5596	1.15	0.8749	2.15	0.9842	3.15	0.9992
0.20	0.5793	1.20	0.8849	2.20	0.9861	3.20	0.9993
0.25	0.5987	1.25	0.8943	2.25	0.9878	3.25	0.9994
0.30	0.6179	1.30	0.9032	2.30	0.9893	3.30	0.9995
0.35	0.6368	1.35	0.9115	2.35	0.9906	3.35	0.9996
0.40	0.6554	1.40	0.9192	2.40	0.9918	3.40	0.9997
0.45	0.6736	1.45	0.9265	2.45	0.9929	3.45	0.9997
0.50	0.6915	1.50	0.9332	2.50	0.9938	3.50	0.9998
0.55	0.7088	1.55	0.9394	2.55	0.9946	3.55	0.9998
0.60	0.7257	1.60	0.9452	2.60	0.9953	3.60	0.9998
0.65	0.7421	1.65	0.9505	2.65	0.9960	3.65	0.9999
0.70	0.7580	1.70	0.9554	2.70	0.9965	3.70	0.9999
0.75	0.7734	1.75	0.9599	2.75	0.9970		
0.80	0.7881	1.80	0.9641	2.80	0.9974		
0.85	0.8023	1.85	0.6780	2.85	0.9974		
0.90	0.8159	1.90	0.9713	2.90	0.9981		
0.95	0.8289	1.95	0.9744	2.95	0.9984		

Table B Percent points of 't' distribution

Degree of freedom	Single tail		Two tails	
	5%	1%	5%	1%
1	6.31	31.82	12.71	63.66
2	2.92	6.96	4.30	9.92
3	2.35	4.54	3.18	5.84
4	2.13	3.75	2.78	4.60
5	2.02	3.36	2.57	4.83
6	1.94	3.14	2.45	3.71
7	1.90	3.00	2.36	3.50
8	1.86	2.90	2.31	3.36
9	1.83	2.82	2.26	3.25
10	1.81	2.76	2.22	3.17
11	1.80	2.72	2.20	3.11
12	1.78	2.68	2.18	3.06
13	1.77	2.65	2.16	3.01
14	1.76	2.62	2.14	2.98
15	1.75	2.60	2.13	2.95
16	1.75	2.58	2.12	2.92
17	1.74	2.57	2.11	2.90
18	1.73	2.55	2.10	2.88
19	1.73	2.54	2.09	2.86
20	1.72	2.53	2.09	2.84
21	1.72	2.52	2.08	2.83
22	1.72	2.51	2.07	2.82
23	1.71	2.50	2.07	2.81
24	1.71	2.49	2.06	2.80
25	1.71	2.48	2.06	2.79
26	1.71	2.48	2.06	2.78
27	1.70	2.47	2.05	2.77
28	1.70	2.47	2.05	2.76
29	1.70	2.46	2.04	2.76
30	1.70	2.46	2.04	2.75
40	1.68	2.42	2.02	2.70
60	1.67	2.39	2.00	2.66
120	1.66	2.35	1.98	2.62
∞	1.64	2.33	1.96	2.53

Table C Percent points of χ² distribution – one tail test

Degrees of freedom	Lower tail		Upper tail	
	5%	1%	5%	1%
1	0.0002	0.004	6.63	3.84
2	0.02	0.10	9.21	5.99
3	0.11	0.35	11.34	7.81
4	0.30	0.71	13.28	9.49
5	0.55	1.15	15.09	11.07
6	0.87	1.64	16.81	12.59
7	1.24	2.17	18.48	14.07
8	2.73	1.65	20.09	15.51
9	2.09	3.33	21.67	16.92
10	2.56	3.94	23.21	18.31
11	3.05	4.57	24.72	19.88
12	3.57	5.23	26.22	21.03
13	4.11	5.89	27.69	22.36
14	4.66	6.57	29.14	23.68
15	5.23	9.26	30.58	25.00
16	5.18	7.96	32.00	26.30
17	6.41	8.67	33.41	27.59
18	7.01	9.39	34.81	28.87
19	7.63	10.12	30.14	36.19
20	8.26	10.85	37.57	31.41
21	8.90	11.59	38.93	32.60
22	9.54	12.34	40.29	33.92
23	10.20	13.09	41.64	35.17
24	10.86	13.85	42.98	36.42
25	11.52	14.61	44.31	37.65
26	12.20	15.38	45.64	38.89
27	12.88	16.15	46.96	40.11
28	13.56	16.93	48.28	41.34
29	14.26	17.71	49.59	42.56
30	14.95	18.49	59.89	43.77
40	22.16	26.51	63.69	55.76
60	37.48	43.19	88.38	99.08

Table C (contd...) Percent points of χ^2 distribution – two tail test

Degree of freedom	5% Interval		1% Interval	
1	0.003	7.82	0.0001	11.35
2	0.08	9.53	0.02	13.29
3	0.30	11.19	0.10	15.13
4	0.61	12.80	0.26	16.90
5	0.99	14.37	0.50	18.63
6	1.43	15.90	0.79	20.30
7	1.90	17.39	1.12	21.93
8	2.41	18.86	1.50	23.53
9	2.95	20.31	1.91	25.11
10	3.52	21.73	2.34	26.65
11	4.10	23.13	2.81	28.18
12	4.70	24.52	3.29	29.68
13	5.32	25.90	3.79	31.17
14	5.95	27.26	4.32	32.64
15	6.59	28.61	4.85	34.10
16	7.25	29.96	5.40	35.54
17	7.91	31.29	5.97	36.97
18	8.58	32.61	6.54	38.39
19	9.27	33.92	7.13	39.80
20	9.96	35.23	7.73	41.20
21	10.66	36.52	8.34	42.59
22	11.36	37.82	8.95	43.97
23	12.07	39.10	9.58	45.34
24	12.79	40.38	10.21	46.71
25	13.51	41.66	10.85	48.06
26	14.24	42.93	11.49	49.42
27	14.98	44.19	12.14	50.76
28	15.72	45.45	12.80	52.10
29	16.46	46.71	13.47	53.43
30	17.21	47.96	14.14	54.76
40	24.88	60.27	21.09	67.79
60	40.97	84.18	35.97	92.91

Table D Upper 5% points of the F distribution

n_1/n_2	1	2	3	4	5	6	7	8	9	10
1	161.40	199.50	215.70	224.60	230.20	234.00	236.80	238.90	240.50	241.90
2	18.51	19.00	19.16	19.25	19.30	19.33	19.35	19.37	19.38	19.40
3	10.13	9.55	9.28	9.12	9.01	8.94	8.89	8.85	8.81	8.79
4	7.70	6.94	6.59	6.39	6.26	6.16	6.09	6.04	6.00	5.96
5	6.61	5.79	5.41	5.19	5.05	4.95	4.88	4.82	4.77	4.47
6	5.99	5.14	4.76	4.53	4.39	4.28	4.21	4.15	4.10	4.06
7	5.59	4.74	4.35	4.12	3.97	3.87	3.79	3.73	3.68	3.64
8	5.32	4.46	4.07	3.84	3.69	3.59	3.50	3.44	3.39	3.35
9	5.12	4.26	3.86	3.63	3.48	3.37	3.29	3.23	3.18	3.14
10	4.96	4.10	3.71	3.48	3.33	3.22	3.14	3.07	3.02	2.98
11	4.84	3.98	3.59	3.36	3.20	3.09	3.01	2.95	2.90	2.84
12	4.75	3.89	3.49	3.26	3.11	3.00	2.91	2.85	2.80	2.75
13	4.67	4.81	3.41	3.18	3.03	2.92	2.83	2.77	2.71	2.67
14	4.60	3.74	3.34	3.11	2.96	2.85	2.76	2.70	2.65	2.60
15	4.54	3.68	3.29	3.06	2.90	2.79	2.71	2.64	2.59	2.54
16	4.49	3.63	3.24	3.01	2.85	2.74	2.66	2.59	2.54	2.49
17	4.45	3.59	3.20	2.96	2.81	17.70	2.61	2.55	2.49	2.45
18	4.41	3.55	3.16	2.93	2.77	2.63	2.58	2.51	2.46	2.42
19	4.38	3.52	3.13	2.90	2.74	2.63	2.54	2.48	2.42	2.38
20	4.35	3.49	3.10	2.87	2.71	2.60	2.51	2.45	2.39	2.35
21	4.32	3.47	3.07	2.84	2.68	2.57	2.49	2.42	2.37	2.32
22	4.30	3.44	3.05	2.82	2.66	2.55	2.46	2.40	2.34	2.30
23	4.28	3.42	3.03	2.80	2.64	2.53	2.44	2.37	2.32	2.27
24	4.26	3.40	3.01	2.78	2.62	2.51	2.42	2.36	2.20	2.25
25	4.24	3.39	2.99	2.76	2.60	2.49	2.40	2.34	2.28	2.24
26	4.23	3.37	2.98	2.74	2.59	2.47	2.39	2.32	2.27	2.23
27	4.21	3.35	2.96	2.73	2.57	2.46	2.37	2.31	2.25	2.22
28	4.20	3.34	2.95	2.71	2.56	2.45	2.36	2.29	2.24	2.21
29	4.18	3.33	2.93	2.70	2.55	2.43	2.35	2.28	2.22	2.20
30	4.17	3.32	2.92	2.69	2.53	2.42	2.33	2.27	2.21	2.16
40	4.08	3.23	2.84	2.61	2.45	2.34	2.25	2.18	2.12	2.08
60	4.00	3.15	2.76	2.53	2.37	2.25	2.17	2.10	2.04	1.99
120	3.92	3.01	2.68	2.45	2.27	2.17	2.09	2.02	1.96	1.90
∞	3.84	3.00	2.60	2.37	2.21	2.10	2.01	1.94	1.88	1.83

Table D (cont...) Upper 5% points of the F distribution

n₁/n₂	12	15	20	24	30	40	60	120	∞
1	243.90	247.90	248.00	249.10	250.00	251.10	252.20	253.00	254.00
2	19.41	19.43	19.44	19.45	19.46	19.47	19.48	19.49	19.00
3	8.74	8.70	8.66	8.64	8.62	8.60	8.57	8.55	8.50
4	5.91	5.86	5.80	5.77	5.74	5.71	5.69	5.66	5.60
5	4.68	4.62	4.56	4.53	4.50	4.46	4.43	4.40	4.30
6	4.00	3.94	3.87	3.84	3.81	3.77	3.74	3.70	3.60
7	3.57	3.51	3.44	3.41	3.38	3.34	3.30	3.27	3.23
8	3.28	3.22	3.15	3.12	3.08	3.05	3.01	2.97	2.93
9	3.07	3.01	2.93	2.90	2.86	2.82	2.79	2.75	2.71
10	2.91	2.85	2.77	2.74	2.70	2.67	2.62	2.58	2.54
11	2.79	2.72	2.65	2.61	2.57	2.53	2.49	2.44	2.41
12	2.69	2.62	2.54	2.51	2.46	2.42	2.38	2.34	2.30
13	2.60	2.53	2.46	2.42	2.38	2.34	2.32	2.26	2.20
14	2.53	2.46	2.39	2.35	2.31	2.27	2.22	2.18	2.10
15	2.48	2.40	2.33	2.29	2.25	2.21	2.16	2.12	2.00
16	2.42	2.35	2.28	2.24	2.20	2.16	2.11	2.06	2.00
17	2.38	2.31	2.23	2.19	2.15	2.11	2.06	2.75	2.60
18	2.34	2.27	2.19	2.15	2.11	2.07	2.02	1.97	1.92
19	2.31	2.23	2.15	2.11	2.07	2.02	1.98	1.93	1.80
20	2.28	2.20	2.12	2.08	2.04	1.99	1.95	1.89	1.80
21	2.25	2.18	2.09	2.05	2.00	1.96	1.92	1.86	1.81
22	2.23	2.15	2.07	2.03	1.98	1.93	1.89	1.83	1.70
23	2.20	2.13	2.04	2.01	1.96	1.91	1.86	1.81	1.70
24	2.18	2.11	20.02	1.98	1.94	1.89	1.84	1.79	1.70
25	2.16	2.09	2.00	1.96	1.92	1.87	1.82	1.76	1.70
30	2.09	2.01	1.93	1.89	1.84	1.79	1.74	1.68	1.62
40	2.00	1.92	1.84	1.79	1.74	1.69	1.64	1.58	1.50
60	1.92	1.84	1.75	1.70	1.65	1.59	1.53	1.47	1.30
120	1.83	1.75	1.66	1.61	1.55	1.49	1.43	1.35	1.25
∞	1.75	1.67	1.57	1.52	1.46	1.44	1.42	1.23	1.00

Appendix Table D (*contd...*) Upper 2.5% points of the F distribution

n_1/n_2	5	6	7	8	9	12	15	20	24	30	40	60	120	∞
5	7.15	6.98	6.85	6.76	6.68	6.52	6.43	6.33	6.28	6.23	6.18	6.12	6.07	6.02
6	5.99	5.82	5.70	5.60	5.52	5.37	5.27	5.17	5.12	5.07	5.01	4.96	4.90	4.85
7	5.29	5.12	4.99	4.90	4.82	4.67	4.57	4.47	4.42	4.36	4.31	4.25	4.20	4.14
8	4.82	4.65	4.53	4.43	4.36	4.20	4.10	4.00	3.95	3.89	3.84	3.78	3.73	3.67
9	4.48	4.32	4.20	4.10	4.03	3.87	3.77	3.67	3.61	3.56	3.51	3.45	3.39	3.33
10	4.24	4.07	3.95	3.85	3.78	3.62	3.52	3.42	3.37	3.31	3.26	3.20	3.14	3.08
11	4.04	3.88	3.76	3.66	3.59	3.43	3.33	3.23	3.27	3.12	3.06	3.00	2.94	2.83
12	3.89	3.73	3.61	3.51	3.44	3.28	3.18	3.07	3.02	2.96	2.91	2.85	2.79	2.72
13	3.77	3.60	3.48	3.39	3.31	3.15	3.05	2.95	2.89	2.84	2.78	2.72	2.66	2.60
14	3.66	3.50	3.38	3.29	3.21	3.05	2.95	2.84	2.79	2.73	2.67	2.61	2.55	2.49
15	3.58	3.41	3.29	3.20	3.12	2.96	2.86	2.76	2.70	2.64	2.58	2.52	2.46	2.40
16	3.50	3.34	3.22	3.12	3.05	2.89	2.79	2.68	2.63	2.57	2.51	2.45	2.38	2.32
17	3.44	3.28	3.16	3.06	2.98	2.82	2.72	2.62	2.56	2.50	2.44	2.38	2.32	2.25
18	3.38	3.22	3.10	3.01	2.93	2.77	2.67	2.56	2.50	2.44	2.38	2.32	2.26	2.19
19	3.33	3.17	3.05	2.96	2.88	2.72	2.62	2.51	2.45	2.39	2.30	3.27	2.20	2.13
20	3.29	3.13	3.01	2.91	2.84	2.68	2.57	2.46	2.41	2.35	2.29	2.22	2.16	2.09
25	3.13	2.97	2.85	2.75	2.68	2.51	2.41	2.30	2.24	2.18	2.12	2.05	1.98	191.00
30	3.03	2.87	2.75	2.65	2.57	2.41	2.31	2.20	2.14	2.07	2.01	1.94	1.87	1.79
40	2.90	2.74	2.62	2.53	2.45	2.29	2.18	2.07	2.01	1.94	1.88	1.80	1.72	1.64
60	2.79	2.63	2.51	2.41	2.33	2.17	2.06	1.94	1.88	1.82	1.74	1.67	1.58	1.48
120	2.67	2.39	2.39	2.30	2.22	2.16	1.94	1.82	1.76	1.69	1.61	1.63	1.43	1.31
∞	2.57	2.21	2.21	2.19	2.11	2.05	1.83	1.71	1.64	1.57	1.48	1.39	1.27	1.00